USC DEPARTMENT OF CHEMISTRY

PJStephens
Seaver 724

MOLECULAR SYMMETRY

An Introduction to Group Theory and its Uses in Chemistry

Molecular Symmetry

AN INTRODUCTION TO GROUP THEORY
AND ITS USES IN CHEMISTRY

DAVID S. SCHONLAND

Senior Lecturer in Mathematics
University of Southampton

VAN NOSTRAND REINHOLD COMPANY
LONDON

NEW YORK   CINCINNATI   TORONTO   MELBOURNE

VAN NOSTRAND REINHOLD COMPANY LTD
Windsor House, 46 Victoria Street, London S.W.1

INTERNATIONAL OFFICES
New York   Cincinnati   Toronto   Melbourne

Library of Congress Catalog Card No. 65–20161

Reprinted 1971

PRINTED IN GREAT BRITAIN BY
THE GARDEN CITY PRESS LIMITED
LETCHWORTH, HERTFORDSHIRE, SG6 1JS

' Mathematics is the art of giving the same name to different things.' — H. POINCARÉ.

TO MY
MOTHER AND FATHER

PREFACE

This book is addressed to those students of chemistry who, without calling themselves theoreticians, wish to make practical use of the powerful mathematical tool for the study of molecules that is provided by group theory. I have supposed that the reader will possess the general knowledge of mathematics and of quantum mechanics that any graduate student may be presumed to have acquired but the book is otherwise self-contained and, in particular, the mathematical concepts that are involved in group theory are developed from first principles.

The theory is undeniably abstract but I have tried to avoid presenting it as a long chain of definitions and theorems; rather I have attempted to show how abstract concepts arise as generalizations of familiar mathematical ideas. I have illustrated these concepts at each stage by examples worked out in a fair amount of detail with the hope that the reader who is prepared to follow them through will thereby acquire a fairly painless grasp of the theory. In this kind of theory, manipulative skill is of relatively minor importance; what is essential is an appreciation of the purpose of each new definition and an understanding of the relations between the concept that it embodies and concepts that have previously been established.

This remark applies particularly to Chapters 3, 4 and 5 which are concerned to set out the mathematical ideas that form the background to Chapters 6 and 7. These two chapters contain all the results that are needed in practical applications and I have appended to them some problems intended to familiarize the reader with the varied uses of the group character tables. The remaining chapters, to which problems are also attached, sketch out some major fields of application of the theory. A selection of the topics to be included in an introductory text of this kind was inevitable and I have chosen to explain a few things in fair detail, with an emphasis on the qualitative uses of the theory, rather than to attempt a wide coverage of the whole range of applications. The Bibliography at the end of the book, to which the occasional numbered references in the text refer, contains suggestions for further reading in more specialized books. It also includes references to some original papers that are milestones in the history of the application of group theory to molecular problems.

  The idea of writing this book stemmed from lectures given to graduate students at the University of Southampton. I am particularly grateful to Mr. E. Cartmell and to Professor E. T. Davies for encouraging me in the project.

D.S.S.

CONTENTS

CHAPTER 9: MOLECULAR ORBITALS

CHAPTER 10: ELECTRONIC SPECTRA

APPENDIXES

Chapter 1

INTRODUCTION

The most important single fact about the collection of electrons and atomic nuclei that constitutes a molecule is that the positions of the atomic nuclei relative to each other define an almost rigid framework which gives a firm geometrical structure to the molecule. Thus one can describe methane as a regular tetrahedron with protons at its vertices and a carbon nucleus at its centre or one can talk about the hexagonal ring structure of benzene, and one can even give fairly precise figures for the distances between the nuclei in these molecules.

It is one of the fundamental facts of chemistry that such descriptions are meaningful, even though one knows that the nuclei are not rigidly fixed in relation to each other. It is this fact which underlies the *Born–Oppenheimer approximation* that is the point of departure for the theoretical study of molecules. This approximation divides the problem of the dynamics of the particles that constitute a molecule into three distinct parts: translations and rotations of the molecular framework as a whole, vibrations of the nuclei about their equilibrium positions in the framework, and the motions of the electrons relative to the molecular framework. Such a clear separation of the total motion of a molecule into independent parts is, of course, an approximation; the vibrations of the nuclei must influence, and be influenced by, the motions of the electrons and they must also influence, and be influenced by, the rotational motion of the molecule as a whole. The fact remains that the Born–Oppenheimer approximation is, in most respects, a very good approximation and that it leads to an understanding of many molecular properties in quantitative detail.

When this simplification of the problem has been made, however, a quantitative discussion of the electronic or vibrational states of even the simplest molecules presents formidable mathematical difficulties and it is essential to find easily applied approximate and qualitative methods which will enable us to interpret experimental measurements of the spectra and other physical properties of a molecule and to make inferences about the molecule from these measurements.

It is here that group theory plays a vital part. The separate descriptions of the electronic and vibrational motions of a molecule both take the framework formed by the atomic nuclei in their equilibrium positions as a starting point, and the symmetry of this equilibrium framework determines in considerable detail the qualitative nature of the possible vibrational and electronic states and the transitions that may occur between them. Group theory provides us with a systematic way of describing this symmetry and of analyzing its implications; it gives the experimentalist a tool with which to interpret and explain his data and the theoretician an indispensable guide through the complexities of his problem of relating the experimental results to the structure of a molecule.

The mathematical theory of groups is a highly developed and abstract subject and it is unfortunately true that a fair degree of familiarity with its purely mathematical ideas is required before their applicability to concrete physical problems becomes apparent. Nevertheless, although the basic mathematical ideas are abstract, they are not difficult, and the actual mathematical techniques that are required in order to apply the theory are almost ludicrously simple, requiring little more than the addition and multiplication of integers.

The main outcome of the theory is a systematic method of *classifying* the ground and excited vibrational and electronic states of a molecule and of finding the *selection rules* that operate for transitions between them. These results are exact within the limits of the Born–Oppenheimer approximation and they do not require a knowledge of the actual wave functions of a molecule. The information derived from a study of symmetry alone, just because it is independent of the quantitative details of the particular wave functions of particular molecules, is necessarily *qualitative*. The theory can, for example, tell us precisely how many strong bands should be observed in the infra-red spectrum of a molecule of a certain type but it has nothing at all to say about the intensities or the wavelengths of the bands that will be found in the spectrum of any particular molecule of this type. This at any rate is the situation if one takes a rather purist view of the theory. There are many examples in practice where semi-quantitative results can be obtained if a few general principles, based on experience of what is likely to happen in a particular case, are mixed in with the pure theory of symmetry.

Indeed, if group theory offered nothing more than a means of obtaining the selection rules or the rules for classifying the states of a molecule it would be an unnecessary study for chemists, since these rules can be obtained by more familiar, if also more complicated, mathematical methods. The great usefulness of group theory in the study of molecules is in some ways analogous to the uses of the periodic system in classifying and relating the chemical properties of the elements. The theory provides a background of concepts against which the detailed connection between the properties of a molecule and its symmetry can be clearly seen; it also enables us to understand the coherent pattern which underlies the sometimes very different properties of molecules of the same type. An early example of this use of group theory was its application to the study of molecular vibrations; a more modern example is the understanding of the electronic structure and spectra of transition-metal complexes that has now been achieved.

The fruitfulness of group theory as it is applied to the study of molecules is a consequence of an interplay between two quite different sets of mathematical concepts. On the one hand, there is the given geometrical structure of a molecule with its symmetry properties; this is the subject of Chapter 2, where it is shown that the symmetry of any molecule can be described and classified by introducing the notion of the *point group* of the molecule. On the other hand, there is the whole complex of ideas embodied in the fact that the physical properties of a molecule can ultimately be expressed in terms of its wave function, which is a function of the coordinates of all the particles of the molecule as they move relative to each other in three-dimensional physical space. Chapter 3, which establishes the general concept of a *vector space*, is concerned with the way in which ideas that are familiar to us when applied to ordinary space can be extended to deal with the coordinates of all the particles taken together and with the wave functions which describe the motions of these particles.

The applications of group theory are born of the union of the idea of a group with that of a vector space; this gives rise to the *theory of group representations* which is discussed in Chapters 4, 5 and 6. Chapter 6, in particular, contains the specific results that are applied in practice; the preceding chapters are concerned to establish the general background of concepts which give meaning to these results.

The general connection between representation theory and quantum mechanics is described in Chapter 7 and the remaining chapters deal with some particular applications: Chapter 8 with the theory of molecular vibrations and Chapters 9 and 10 with problems of electronic structure and spectra. The last two chapters can be read independently of Chapter 8. No attempt is made in these chapters to give a full survey of the whole field concerned; the intention has been rather to discuss a few general topics in some detail with the hope that the reader will thereby acquire a 'feel' for the way in which the theory can be applied.

Chapter 2

SYMMETRY OPERATIONS AND GROUPS

2.1 Symmetry Operations

The starting point for the discussion of the symmetry of a molecule is the geometrical framework formed by its atomic nuclei which we think of as occupying positions fixed in space. The molecule may contain a number of identical nuclei occupying physically equivalent positions in the framework; in the theory of molecular symmetry we consider the rearrangements of such identical and physically equivalent nuclei that can be achieved by a rotation of the molecular framework as a whole about an axis, by a reflection of the molecular framework as a whole in a plane so as to produce a mirror image, or by a combination of rotations and reflections.

Such operations of rotation and reflection are called *symmetry operations*: a symmetry operation applied to a molecule results in a movement of the molecular framework to a new position which coincides exactly with the original position and is physically indistinguishable from it. A symmetry operation can have no effect on any physical property of the molecule and all the applications of the theory of symmetry to molecules are based on this fact and the consequences that follow from it.

Our first task is to describe the different types of symmetry operations that a molecule may possess. There are altogether five different kinds of symmetry operations; these are discussed under the headings (*a*) to (*e*) below.

(*a*) The identical operation

This is the symmetry operation which changes nothing and leaves all the nuclei in their original positions. It is denoted by the symbol E.

(*b*) A rotation about an axis of symmetry

This is denoted by $C(\alpha)$ where α is the angle of rotation. If the molecular framework is brought into coincidence with itself by a rotation through an angle α about some axis, then a rotation about the same axis through an angle

$n\alpha$, where n is any integer, will also move the framework into coincidence with itself and will be a symmetry operation which can be regarded as the result of applying the operation $C(\alpha)$ n times in succession. Further, if α is the smallest angle of rotation about the axis which gives rise to a symmetry operation then by successive applications of $C(\alpha)$ to the molecular framework we must eventually bring all its nuclei back to their original positions after rotating the molecule through an angle 2π. It follows that there must be some integer n for which $n\alpha = 2\pi$ and $\alpha = 2\pi/n$. We denote the symmetry operation $C(2\pi/n)$ by C_n and say that the corresponding axis of rotation is an *n-fold symmetry axis*.

The one exception to this argument is the special case of a linear molecule since any rotation about the axis of a linear molecule is a symmetry operation and there are an infinite number of rotations to be considered. This particular case will be ignored for the moment and will be treated separately in Section 2.7.

We can consistently denote the result of k applications of the rotation C_n, which will be a rotation about the symmetry axis through a total angle of $2\pi k/n$, by $C_n{}^k$. The fact that a rotation through an angle $2\pi k/n$ about an axis followed by a rotation through an angle $2\pi l/n$ about the same axis is equivalent to a single rotation about the axis through an angle $2\pi(l+k)/n$ is expressed in this notation of 'raising C_n to the power k' by the relation

$$C_n{}^l C_n{}^k = C_n{}^{l+k},$$

consistent with the rules for combining indices in ordinary algebra. The significance of negative values of the index in this notation is discussed below in Section 2.3.

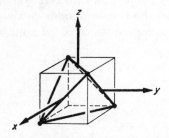

2.1 A tetrahedron inscribed in a cube.

The result of applying C_n exactly n times is to bring the molecule back into its original position after a rotation through 2π about the symmetry axis. This is equivalent to applying the identical operation E, and we therefore write

$$C_n{}^n = E.$$

As an example of rotations as symmetry operations, consider the regular tetrahedron formed by the methane molecule shown in Fig. 2.1. We can place the four protons at four of the corners of a cube whose centre is the carbon nucleus and take x, y, z axes perpendicular to the faces of the cube with the origin at the carbon nucleus. Then a rotation C_2 through $180° = 2\pi/2$ about the x or the y or the z axis will move all the protons into equivalent positions; these three axes are twofold symmetry axes. Also a rotation through $120° = 2\pi/3$ about any of the four CH bonds will be a symmetry operation which leaves one proton fixed and moves the other three, so that there are altogether four threefold symmetry axes with corresponding symmetry operations C_3 and $C_3{}^2$, this latter operation being a rotation through $240°$.

(c) A reflection in a plane of symmetry

The operation of reflecting the molecule in a plane of symmetry is called σ. We remark that the effect of reflecting the molecule twice in the same plane is to bring it back to its original position and write

$$\sigma^2 = E.$$

A glance at Fig. 2.1 shows that for methane any plane passing through a pair of protons and the carbon nucleus, i.e. though a pair of opposite edges of the cube, is a plane of symmetry for the tetrahedron and that the corresponding operation σ leaves two of the protons in their original positions and interchanges the other two. There are altogether six such planes of symmetry and so methane possesses six different symmetry operations of type σ.

(d) A rotary reflection or improper rotation

As an example of this type of operation we look again at Fig. 2.1 and note that, although neither a rotation through $90° = 2\pi/4$ about the z axis nor a reflection in the xy plane are themselves symmetry operations of the tetrahedron, nevertheless, the two operations combined together do result in a genuine symmetry operation which is the same whether we first apply

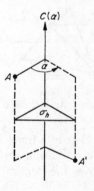

2.2 An improper rotation of A to A'.

the rotation and follow it by the reflection or whether we do the operations in the reverse order.

A combined operation of this kind is called a *rotary reflection* or an *improper rotation* and is denoted by the symbol S_n standing for the combination of a rotation through an angle $2\pi/n$ about some axis (the *rotary reflection* or *alternating axis*) and a reflection in a plane perpendicular to this axis. This operation is illustrated in Fig. 2.2 from which it will be seen that the order in which the rotation and the reflection are performed is immaterial. If we use the symbol σ_h to denote the reflection in the plane perpendicular to the rotary reflection axis we can write

$$S_n = \sigma_h C_n.$$

By applying S_n twice we do two rotations C_n and two reflections σ_h; since the double reflection is equivalent to the identical operation E the result is a simple rotation through the angle $2(2\pi/n)$. We may, therefore, write

$$S_n{}^2 = C_n{}^2.$$

In general, k applications of S_n will give

$$S_n{}^k = \sigma_h C_n{}^k \text{ if } k \text{ is odd} \quad \text{and} \quad S_n{}^k = C_n{}^k \text{ if } k \text{ is even.}$$

Thus if n is odd,

$$S_n{}^n = \sigma_h C_n{}^n = \sigma_h,$$

and a simple reflection in the plane must be a symmetry operation. Also

$$S_n{}^{n+1} = \sigma_h{}^2 C_n = C_n,$$

and a simple rotation about the C_n axis is a symmetry operation. In this case the σ_h plane is a symmetry plane in its own right and the axis of rotation is an ordinary n-fold axis. If n is even, however,

$$S_n{}^n = C_n{}^n = E,$$

and the reflection plane and rotation axis are not necessarily independent of each other; it may be, as in the case of the tetrahedron, that only the combined operation $S_n = \sigma_h C_n$ is a symmetry operation of the molecule.

Returning to the example of methane we see that the x, y and z axes are all fourfold rotary reflection axes with improper rotations S_4 and $S_4{}^3$ for each axis, but that for each axis the operation $S_4{}^2 = C_4{}^2 = C_2$ is one of the proper rotations of the molecule discussed in (b) above.

(e) Inversion in a centre of symmetry

This operation, denoted by i, is illustrated in Fig. 2.3. If O is the centre of symmetry then the effect of i is to move any point A of the molecule to a point A' on the line AO produced such that $OA' = OA$. It can readily be seen that i is a special case of an improper rotation where the angle of rotation is 180°;

$$i = S_2 = \sigma_h C_2.$$

The effect of inverting twice in the same centre of symmetry is to return the molecule to its original position, so that we can write

$$i^2 = E.$$

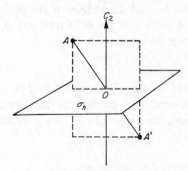

2.3 Inversion: $i = \sigma_h C_2$.

The tetrahedron that we have been discussing so far does not possess a centre of symmetry. Examples where inversion is a symmetry operation are (i) a molecule, such as SF_6, which forms a regular octahedron and (ii) any molecule, such as benzene, which has a symmetry axis of even order, so that C_2 is one of its symmetry operations, and a plane of symmetry at right angles to this axis.

This concludes the description of the different types of symmetry operation. To summarize the results we have found for the tetrahedral molecule CH_4 we can say that it possesses altogether twenty-four distinct symmetry operations which are: the identical operation E; three rotations C_2 about the x, y and z axes; two rotations C_3 and $C_3{}^2$ about each of the four CH bonds; six reflections σ in the six planes containing a pair of protons and the carbon nucleus; and two improper rotations S_4 and $S_4{}^3$ about each of the x, y and z axes.

In a similar fashion one can write down a list of all the symmetry operations belonging to any given molecule. This set of symmetry operations forms the *symmetry group* of the molecule and must conform to one or other of a limited number of types. Before this matter can be discussed, however, it is necessary to develop an 'algebra of symmetry operations' which will enable us to handle algebraically the relations that exist between the symmetry operations of a molecule.

2.2 Products of Symmetry Operations

In the preceding section we used algebraic symbols to denote the various symmetry operations and were able to express some of their properties in the form of equations such as, for example, $S_4{}^2 = C_2$. In this equation the left-hand side stands for the result of two successive applications of the improper rotation S_4 and the equation is an expression of the fact that this double symmetry operation has the same effect on the molecule as the single symmetry operation C_2. We now proceed to show how this kind of algebraic symbolism can be extended to apply to general combinations of symmetry operations.

Suppose that P and Q are symbols standing for any two of the symmetry operations of a molecule. The effect of P on the molecule is to move the molecular framework into coincidence with itself; if we apply Q to this new position of the molecule we shall again move the framework into itself so that the result of first applying P and following it by Q will be some symmetry operation of the molecule, say R. The relation between P, Q and R can be expressed by the equation

$$QP = R,$$

on the understanding that the *product QP of two symmetry operations P and Q means the symmetry operation that is the result of first applying P to the molecule and following it by Q*. It is most important to note the convention that is adopted in this definition of the product of two symmetry operations: the factors in the product must be read from right to left; P is the first operation and Q is the second. This is important because in general the result of applying two symmetry operations will depend on the order in which they are performed and QP is not necessarily the same thing as PQ. If, as may be the case for some symmetry operations, $PQ = QP$ we say that the operations P and Q *commute*.

Thus, for example, two successive rotations about the same axis will commute since they result in a rotation about the same axis through an angle which is the sum of the two separate angles of rotation. The result of two successive rotations about different axes, however, does depend on the order in which they are performed; rotations about different axes do not commute. This is illustrated in Fig. 2.4.

EXAMPLE

As an example of the way in which one can form products of symmetry operations consider the ammonia molecule in which the three protons are situated at the vertices of an equilateral triangle and the nitrogen nucleus is vertically above the centre of this triangle. The triangle is shown in Fig. 2.5; the fixed positions in space occupied by the three protons are labelled A, B and C and the protons occupying these positions are given distinguishing marks so that one can follow the effect of a symmetry operation upon them. Apart from the identical operation E, the symmetry operations of the molecule are three reflections, which we call $\sigma_a, \sigma_b, \sigma_c$, in planes of symmetry passing through the points A, B and C respectively, and two rotations C_3 and $C_3{}^2$ through angles of 120° and 240° about the threefold

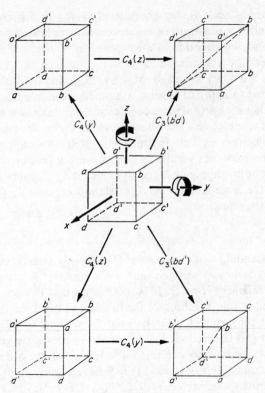

2.4 Non-commuting rotations.

$$C_4(z)C_4(y) = C_3(b'd); \quad C_4(y)C_4(z) = C_3(bd').$$

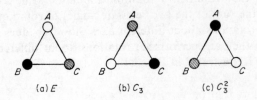

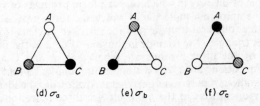

2.5 Symmetry operations for ammonia.

symmetry axis passing through the nitrogen nucleus and the centre of the triangle. The effects of these symmetry operations on the positions of the three protons are shown in Figs. 2.5(a)–(f): 2.5(a) represents the initial positions of the protons and 2.5(b)–(f) show how these are changed by the various symmetry operations.

Consider the product $\sigma_b\sigma_a$. The application of σ_a to Fig. 2.5(a) produces Fig. 2.5(d) and the application of σ_b to *this* figure turns it into Fig. 2.5(c); thus the effect of the product operation $\sigma_b\sigma_a$ is the same as the effect of the single operation C_3^2. On the other hand, the application of σ_b to Fig. 2.5(a) gives Fig. 2.5(e) and σ_a turns this figure into Fig. 2.5(b); thus the product $\sigma_a\sigma_b$ is equivalent to the single operation C_3. The 'multiplication rules' for σ_a and σ_b are, therefore

$$\sigma_a\sigma_b = C_3; \qquad \sigma_b\sigma_a = C_3^2.$$

Figures representing all the possible products of pairs of the symmetry operations of ammonia can be found in the same way and used to identify the resultant single operations to which these products correspond. A complete list of all the products is

$$\sigma_a\sigma_b = \sigma_b\sigma_c = \sigma_c\sigma_a = C_3, \qquad \sigma_b\sigma_a = \sigma_c\sigma_b = \sigma_a\sigma_c = C_3^2, \qquad (2.1a)$$

$$\left.\begin{array}{l} C_3\sigma_b = \sigma_bC_3^2 = C_3^2\sigma_c = \sigma_cC_3 = \sigma_a, \\ C_3\sigma_c = \sigma_cC_3^2 = C_3^2\sigma_a = \sigma_aC_3 = \sigma_b, \\ C_3\sigma_a = \sigma_aC_3^2 = C_3^2\sigma_b = \sigma_bC_3 = \sigma_c, \end{array}\right\} \qquad (2.1b)$$

to which should be added the relations

$$\sigma_a^2 = \sigma_b^2 = \sigma_c^2 = C_3C_3^2 = C_3^2C_3 = E, \qquad (2.1c)$$

and the obvious relation

$$ER = RE = R,$$

where R stands for any one of the symmetry operations. It will be seen that E commutes with every symmetry operation, that C_3 and C_3^2 commute with each other but with none of the reflections, and that none of the reflections commute with each other.

It is easy to see that we can extend the definition of the product to include more than two factors. For if $R = QP$, and if T is some other symmetry operation, the product TR is yet another symmetry operation which, because of the nature of R, is that operation which results from applying first P, then Q and then T; we can simply write

$$TR = T(QP).$$

The final result can only depend on the nature of P, Q and T and the order in which they are applied and must be independent of whether we imagine P and Q to be combined together into a single operation which we follow by T, or whether we imagine P to be applied first and follow it by the single operation TQ. We can express this formally by writing

$$(TQ)P = T(QP) = TQP, \qquad (2.2)$$

where the final form implies that the product of these three factors is un-ambiguously determined without any necessity for inserting brackets. The only essential is that the correct order of operations must be maintained. The content of (2.2) is expressed in technical language by saying that the product of symmetry operations is *associative*. This associative property enables us to write down a product $T \ldots QP$ containing any number of factors without any ambiguity or need for bracketing pairs of factors together; alternatively if we wish we may bracket neighbouring factors together in any way we like.

EXAMPLES

These results may be illustrated by some examples taken from equations (2.1).

(i) Consider the product $\sigma_a C_3 \sigma_c$. Using (2.1) we can write

$$\sigma_a(C_3\sigma_c) = \sigma_a\sigma_b = C_3,$$

and also

$$(\sigma_a C_3)\sigma_c = \sigma_b\sigma_c = C_3,$$

thus verifying the associative nature of the products in this example.

(ii) Multiplying the equation $C_3 = \sigma_a\sigma_b$ (taken from (2.1a)) on the left by σ_a (note that it is essential to specify the correct order of the factors on the two sides of the equation) we obtain

$$\sigma_a C_3 = \sigma_a(\sigma_a\sigma_b) = (\sigma_a\sigma_a)\sigma_b = E\sigma_b = \sigma_b,$$

which is one of the relations given in (2.1b). In the same way the reader may verify that all of the equations in (2.1b) can be deduced from those given in (2.1a) with the help of (2.1c).

(iii) Consider the pair of equations

$$\sigma_a\sigma_b = C_3, \qquad \sigma_b\sigma_a = C_3{}^2.$$

Since $E = C_3 C_3{}^2$ we must for consistency require $(\sigma_a\sigma_b)(\sigma_b\sigma_a) = E$. That this is indeed the case may be seen by invoking the associative property and writing

$$(\sigma_a\sigma_b)(\sigma_b\sigma_a) = \sigma_a(\sigma_b\sigma_b)\sigma_a = \sigma_a E\sigma_a = \sigma_a\sigma_a = E.$$

We have seen that it is possible to introduce the idea of 'multiplying' two symmetry operations together in a natural and sensible way. We now go on to show that it is possible also to introduce something resembling division into our algebra of symmetry operations.

2.3 Inverse Operations

The notion of the inverse of a symmetry operation is the nearest approach we can make to the idea of the division of one symmetry operation by another. From the nature of a symmetry operation one can see that for every symmetry operation R which moves the nuclei of a molecule from one position to another there must be some symmetry operation T which reverses the effect of R and moves the nuclei back to their original positions. The relation between R and T will be symmetric in the sense that if T is the operation which reverses the effect of R, then R will be the operation which reverses the effect of T. We can express this algebraically by saying that for each symmetry operation R there is another symmetry operation T such that

$$TR = RT = E.$$

We call T the inverse operation to R and write $T = R^{-1}$. Similarly R is the inverse of T and $R = T^{-1}$. In this notation for the inverse, the symmetry operation R^{-1} is that operation for which

$$RR^{-1} = R^{-1}R = E. \tag{2.3}$$

Since R is also the inverse of R^{-1} we have the relation

$$(R^{-1})^{-1} = R.$$

The inverse R^{-1} of a symmetry operation R is itself an ordinary symmetry operation and can be incorporated into products of these operations on an equal footing with the other factors; the associative law still applies. Thus if P and Q are two symmetry operations we have

$$(PQ)(Q^{-1}P^{-1}) = P(QQ^{-1})P^{-1} = PEP^{-1} = PP^{-1} = E,$$

and similarly

$$(Q^{-1}P^{-1})(PQ) = E.$$

Hence it follows from the definition (2.3) of the inverse that the inverse of the product PQ is

$$(PQ)^{-1} = Q^{-1}P^{-1}. \tag{2.4}$$

Due regard must be paid to the non-commuting properties of symmetry operations when using the inverse. For example if

$$PR = QR,$$

we can multiply both sides of this equation *on the right* by R^{-1} and, using the fact that $RR^{-1} = E$, deduce that $P = Q$. If instead, however, the relation between P, Q and R were

$$PR = RQ,$$

the most that can be said is that $P = RQR^{-1}$, which will only be equal to Q if Q and R happen to commute. Thus we may never speak simply of 'dividing an equation by R'; we can only 'multiply by R^{-1} on the left' or 'on the right'.

The operations which are inverse to the fundamental symmetry operations are easily found.

(*a*) **Reflection and inversion**

From the relations

$$\sigma^2 = E, \qquad i^2 = E,$$

which express the fact that two successive reflections in the same plane, or two successive inversions in a centre of symmetry, take a molecule back to its original position, it follows that σ and i are their own inverses;

$$\sigma^{-1} = \sigma; \qquad i^{-1} = i.$$

(b) Rotations

In order to accommodate the idea of an inverse rotation we extend our notation for rotations in a fairly obvious way to allow for negative indices.

To describe a rotation completely it is necessary to give the axis of rotation a direction and to define a positive sense for a rotation about this direction, for example a right-handed screw sense. A rotation in the opposite sense is then described as a rotation through a negative angle and the inverse to the rotation C_n^k through the positive angle $2\pi k/n$ will be a rotation through the negative angle $-(2\pi k/n)$ which we can denote by C_n^{-k}; i.e. we write $(C_n^k)^{-1} = C_n^{-k}$. This is consistent with our general notation for rotations and the rule for combining indices, for then we should write

$$C_n^k C_n^{-k} = C_n^{k-k} = C_n^0 = E,$$

since a rotation through zero angle is the identical operation. This notation implies that

$$C_n^{n-k} = C_n^n C_n^{-k} = E C_n^{-k} = C_n^{-k},$$

which is consistent since a positive rotation through the angle $2\pi(n-k)/n = 2\pi - 2\pi k/n$ is the same thing as a negative rotation through the angle $-(2\pi k/n)$. The situation is illustrated in Fig. 2.6.

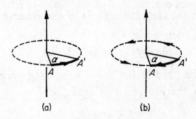

(a)   (b)

2.6 Inverse rotations.
(a) positive rotation through angle α.
(b) negative rotation through $-\alpha$ or positive rotation through $2\pi - \alpha$.

(c) Improper rotations

The operation S_n^k differs from C_n^k only when k is odd; then $S_n^k = \sigma_h C_n^k$ and the inverse operation is $S_n^{-k} = \sigma_h C_n^{-k}$. One may express S_n^{-k} in terms of S_n by noting that, for even n, $S_n^n = E$ so that $S_n^{-k} = S_n^{n-k}$, while for odd n, $S_n^{2n} = E$ so that $S_n^{-k} = S_n^{2n-k}$. For example, $S_4^{-1} = S_4^3$ whereas $S_3^{-1} = S_3^5$.

2.4 The Point Group of a Molecule

We now consider the set of all the symmetry operations belonging to a given molecule. Typical symmetry operations belonging to this set are denoted by $P, Q, R, \ldots$ and we call these operations the *elements* of the set.

Thus for example ammonia has a set of six symmetry operations and the elements of this set are E, C_3, $C_3{}^2$, σ_a, σ_b, σ_c, (Fig. 2.5). Similarly the set of symmetry operations belonging to methane has twenty-four elements which are listed at the end of Section 2.1.

The set of symmetry operations belonging to a given molecule has the following four properties:

(i) The product QP of two elements P and Q of the set is an element of the set (i.e. the product, as we have defined it, of two symmetry operations of the molecule is also a symmetry operation of the molecule).

(ii) The product is associative; $R(QP) = (RQ)P$.

(iii) The set contains an element E with the property

$$RE = ER = R,$$

where R is any element of the set. This element is called the *unit element* of the set; it is, of course, just the identical operation which leaves the molecule unchanged.

(iv) Each element R of the set has an inverse R^{-1} which is also an element of the set and satisfies

$$RR^{-1} = R^{-1}R = E.$$

These four properties are the defining properties of a *group*: a group is a set of elements of whatever kind for which we can define the product of a pair of elements and which has the properties (i)–(iv) above. Hence it follows that the set of all the symmetry operations belonging to a molecule forms a group, the *symmetry group* of the molecule, and that the methods of group theory can be used to discuss the symmetry of a molecule.

Group theory is not concerned with the nature of the group elements; it deals only with the formal structure of the group defined by the multiplication rules for the group elements. For example we have used the geometrical shape of the ammonia molecule to obtain its symmetry operations and have found the results of multiplying each pair of symmetry operations together; these results are summarized in equations (2.1). Any other molecule with the same basic symmetry, for example PCl_3 or CH_3Cl, will have the same set of symmetry operations, i.e. the same symmetry group, with the same relations (2.1) between them and all molecules like this are treated alike from the point of view of group theory.

In this theory we abstract from the molecule its system of axes and planes of symmetry with their corresponding symmetry operations. The structure and properties of the symmetry group of the molecule depend only on the relations between its elements, the symmetry operations, and these relations are completely determined by the spatial relations between the axes and planes of symmetry. Any two molecules, no matter how different in form or complexity, which have the same system of axes and planes of symmetry will have the same symmetry group and those of their properties which depend on symmetry will be the same.

This is one of the reasons for the power and generality of group theoretical methods in discussing the properties of molecules; for although the number of different imaginable molecules is unbounded, this is not true of their possible systems of axes and planes of symmetry. These are severely restricted by geometrical considerations and it is possible to write down a list of all the molecular symmetry groups that can exist and to discuss their properties once and for all. To apply the results of the theory to a particular molecule, all that is necessary is to identify its symmetry group and then to use standard methods to extract the desired information from the known properties of this group.

Before going on to discuss the molecular symmetry groups in more detail we note one feature that they all possess. A symmetry operation which rotates or reflects a molecule into itself must leave the centre of mass (centre of gravity) of the molecule unmoved: if the molecule has a plane or axis of symmetry, the centre of mass must lie on this plane or axis. It follows that all the axes and planes of symmetry of a molecule must intersect in at least one common point and that at least one point remains fixed under all the symmetry operations of the molecule. For this reason the symmetry group of a molecule is generally referred to as its *point group* and we shall use this name, which is taken over from crystallography, from now on.

2.5 Classes of Conjugate Elements

For our purposes one of the most important concepts in group theory is that of the division of the elements of a group into classes of conjugate elements. Two elements P and Q of a group are said to be conjugate to each other if there is some element R of the group which is such that

$$P = R^{-1}QR. \tag{2.5}$$

This relation between P and Q is symmetric for it follows from (2.5) that

$$Q = RPR^{-1},$$

and this is a relation of exactly the same form as (2.5) with R replaced by R^{-1} which is of course some element of the group.

It also follows from (2.5) that if P and Q are both conjugate to the same element W of the group then P and Q are conjugate to each other. For if

$$P = S^{-1}WS \quad \text{and} \quad Q = TWT^{-1} \tag{2.6}$$

where S and T and consequently S^{-1} and T^{-1} are elements of the group, then from the second equation of (2.6) it follows that $W = T^{-1}QT$. If this expression for W is substituted into the first equation of (2.6), one obtains

$$P = S^{-1}(T^{-1}QT)S = (S^{-1}T^{-1})Q(TS),$$

where the associative property of the product of the group elements has been invoked. Equation (2.4) then shows that

$$P = (TS)^{-1}Q(TS). \tag{2.7}$$

This result shows that P is conjugate to Q since, by the group property (i), TS must be some element of the group and (2.7) is therefore a relation of the same form as (2.5).

Thus given any particular element W of a group we can pick out a subset of the group elements all of which are conjugate to W and therefore to each other, by forming all the possible products of the form $R^{-1}WR$ where R runs successively over all the group elements. This subset is called a *class of conjugate elements* and the elements of the group can in this way be divided into a number of mutually exclusive classes. For suppose that W_1 and W_2 belong to different classes and that there is some element P which is common to both classes. Then the group must contain elements R_1 and R_2 such that

$$P = R_1^{-1}W_1R_1 = R_2W_2R_2^{-1}.$$

From this it would follow that

$$W_1 = R_1R_2W_2R_2^{-1}R_1^{-1} = (R_1R_2)W_2(R_1R_2)^{-1}$$

and therefore that W_1 belongs to the same class as W_2 which contradicts the supposition.

It should be noted that if a group contains an element Q which commutes with every other group element R then $R^{-1}QR = Q$ for every R and Q is in a class by itself. Thus in any group the unit element E is always in a class by itself. Further if every element of the group commutes with every other element each element is in a class by itself. In general, however, a group will contain some non-commuting elements and some of its classes will contain more than one element.

EXAMPLE

The division of a group into classes can be illustrated from the relations (2.1) between the elements of the point group of ammonia. From these relations it follows that

$$E\sigma_a E = \sigma_a,$$

$$C_3^{-1}\sigma_a C_3 = C_3^2(\sigma_a C_3) = C_3^2\sigma_b = \sigma_c,$$

$$C_3\sigma_a C_3^{-1} = (C_3\sigma_a)C_3^2 = \sigma_c C_3^2 = \sigma_b,$$

$$\sigma_a^{-1}\sigma_a\sigma_a = \sigma_a,$$

$$\sigma_b^{-1}\sigma_a\sigma_b = \sigma_b(\sigma_a\sigma_b) = \sigma_b C_3 = \sigma_c,$$

$$\sigma_c^{-1}\sigma_a\sigma_c = \sigma_c(\sigma_a\sigma_c) = \sigma_c C_3^2 = \sigma_b.$$

Hence σ_a, σ_b and σ_c are three mutually conjugate elements forming one class of the group. Similarly one finds that C_3 and $C_3^{-1} = C_3^2$ both belong to the same class so that this group of six elements can be divided into the three classes E; $\sigma_a, \sigma_b, \sigma_c$; C_3, C_3^{-1}.

This example suggests that the division of the point group of a molecule into classes of conjugate elements, based on the rather abstract definition of a class given above, in fact represents a natural sub-division of the group elements into sets of geometrically similar operations; in our example these are the identical operation, the three reflections, and the two rotations. This is indeed the case. There is no need to start from the detailed multiplication rules of the group elements and to work out all the products of the form $R^{-1}WR$ as we did above. The simple rules for dividing the elements of a molecular point group into its classes are:

(i) A rotation C_n^k about an axis of symmetry and its inverse C_n^{-k} belong to the same class (a different class for each value of $k=1,\ldots,n-1$) if the molecule has a plane of symmetry containing the axis or if there is a twofold symmetry axis which intersects the n-fold axis at right angles; if not, C_n^k and C_n^{-k} are in classes by themselves. The same is true for improper rotations.

Thus in the above example the rotations C_3 and C_3^{-1} belong to the same class since there are in fact three planes of symmetry containing the threefold axis.

(ii) Two reflections belong to the same class if the group contains a symmetry operation which moves all the points on one of the planes of symmetry into corresponding positions on the other.

This rule shows that for ammonia the three reflections $\sigma_a, \sigma_b, \sigma_c$ belong to the same class since successive applications of the rotation C_3 move the reflection planes into each other.

(iii) Two rotations C_n^k, $C_n'^k$ (or two improper rotations S_n^k, $S_n'^k$) about different n-fold symmetry axes belong to the same class if the group contains a symmetry operation which moves all the points on one of the axes of rotation into corresponding positions on the other.

(iv) If the point group of a molecule contains the inversion i in a centre of symmetry, this is always in a class by itself, since it commutes with every other symmetry operation.

These rules are sufficient for the purpose of dividing the elements of any of the molecular point groups into their classes. They are proved in Appendix A. As an example of the application of these rules the reader may verify that the symmetry operations of the tetrahedral CH_4 molecule are divided into classes in the manner indicated in the list of these operations given at the end of Section 2.1.

2.6 The Molecular Point Groups

We are now in a position to describe and classify the various molecular point groups. We shall use what is called the *Schoenflies notation* which is fairly standard in the chemical literature. In this notation, each point group is designated by a symbol, such as $\mathscr{C}_{3v}$ or $\mathscr{T}_d$, which is roughly descriptive of the symmetry of the group. There is another notation, widely used in crystallography, which is described at the end of this chapter.

The point groups can be classified into three broad divisions. There are, firstly, two simple groups $\mathscr{C}_s$ and $\mathscr{C}_i$ which arise when a molecule possesses just one plane of symmetry or just a centre of symmetry. Secondly, there is a sequence of groups which are distinguished by possessing a single main n-fold axis of symmetry: these are the groups designated by the symbols $\mathscr{C}_n$, $\mathscr{S}_{2n}$, $\mathscr{C}_{nh}$, $\mathscr{C}_{nv}$, $\mathscr{D}_n$, $\mathscr{D}_{nh}$, $\mathscr{D}_{nd}$. Finally, there are groups, with more than one main n-fold symmetry axis, which are related to the symmetry of the regular solids, in particular the tetrahedron and the octahedron. We shall discuss these groups in order of increasing complexity.

I. The groups $\mathscr{C}_s$ and $\mathscr{C}_i$

A molecule may possess just a single plane of symmetry, so that its only symmetry operations are E and the reflection σ in the plane of symmetry. This group of two elements is called $\mathscr{C}_s$.

Again the molecule may possess just a centre of symmetry, so that its only symmetry operations are E and the inversion i. This group of two elements is called $\mathscr{C}_i$.

II. Groups with one main axis of symmetry

If a molecule possesses one main n-fold axis of symmetry all its symmetry operations must leave the main symmetry axis unaltered or, at most, reverse its direction. Apart from rotations or improper rotations about the main axis the only other symmetry operations which satisfy this condition are: a reflection in a plane perpendicular to the main axis (such a plane is called a *horizontal* plane and the reflection operation is denoted by σ_h); a reflection in a plane containing the main axis (such a plane is called a *vertical* plane and the reflection operation is denoted by σ_v); or a rotation through 180° about a twofold axis perpendicular to the main axis (such a rotation is denoted by C_2'). These operations may be combined in various ways; using the results derived in Appendix A we obtain the following enumeration of groups with one main axis of symmetry.

(a) Group $\mathscr{C}_n$

This has a single n-fold symmetry axis, and the elements of $\mathscr{C}_n$ are the n rotations $C_n, C_n{}^2, \ldots, C_n{}^n = E$. These operations all commute with each other and each element of the group is in a class by itself. Figure 2.7(a) illustrates the symmetry associated with $\mathscr{C}_4$.

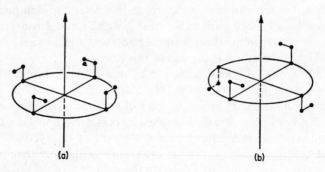

2.7 (a) $\mathscr{C}_4$: Elements E, C_4, C_2, $C_4{}^{-1}$.   (b) $\mathscr{S}_4$: Elements E, S_4, $S_4{}^2 = C_2$, $S_4{}^{-1}$.

(b) Group $\mathscr{S}_{2n}$

This has a single alternating axis of *even* order $2n$ and the group elements are the improper rotations S_{2n}, $S_{2n}{}^2 = C_n$, $S_{2n}{}^3, \ldots, S_{2n}{}^{2n} = E$. They all commute with each other and each element is in a class by itself.

The simplest group of this type is $\mathscr{S}_2$ which has the two elements E and $S_2 = i$; it is the same as the group $\mathscr{C}_i$ mentioned above. Figure 2.7(b) illustrates the symmetry associated with $\mathscr{S}_4$.

(c) Group $\mathscr{C}_{nh}$

This group is obtained from $\mathscr{C}_n$ by adding a horizontal symmetry plane perpendicular to the axis of rotation. Apart from the n rotations of $\mathscr{C}_n$, this group contains the n improper rotations $\sigma_h C_n{}^k$ including the pure reflection $\sigma_h C_n{}^n$. All these elements commute and each is in a class by itself.

EXAMPLES

(i) The simplest group of this type is $\mathscr{C}_{1h}$ with the two elements E and σ_h. It is identical with the group $\mathscr{C}_s$ mentioned above.

(ii) The next simplest group is $\mathscr{C}_{2h}$ with elements E, C_2, σ_h and $\sigma_h C_2 = i$. This is the point group of molecules like *trans*-$C_2H_2Cl_2$ (Fig. 2.8(a)).

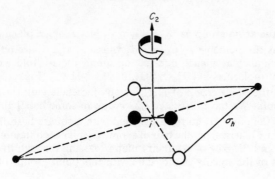

2.8 (a) $\mathscr{C}_{2h}$: *trans*-$C_2H_2Cl_2$.

(d) *Group* $\mathscr{C}_{nv}$

If we add to $\mathscr{C}_n$ a vertical symmetry plane containing the axis of rotation, the results of Appendix A(i) show that there will be altogether n such planes intersecting at angles π/n. The elements of $\mathscr{C}_{nv}$ are the n rotations of $\mathscr{C}_n$ and the n reflections σ_v in these vertical planes.

By rule (i) for dividing a group into its classes we see that for each k the rotation $C_n{}^k$ and its inverse $C_n{}^{-k}$ form a class of two elements. (If n is even one of these classes will contain just the rotation C_2 which is its own inverse.)

The division of the n reflections σ_v into classes depends on whether n is even or odd. The operation C_n, a rotation through $2\pi/n$, moves each plane of symmetry into the next plane but one. Thus if n is odd we can move any particular plane of symmetry into the position of any other plane by successive applications of C_n, and from rule (ii) it follows that all the reflections σ_v are in the same class. If n is even, however, there will be two independent sets of alternate planes which can never be mixed by any of the rotations or by any of the reflections; correspondingly, the reflections σ_v are divided into two distinct classes.

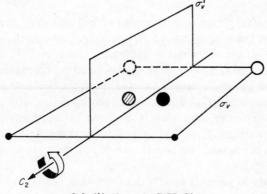

2.8 (b) $\mathscr{C}_{2v}$: *cis*-$C_2H_2Cl_2$.

EXAMPLES

(i) $\mathscr{C}_{1v}$ is the same group as $\mathscr{C}_{1h} = \mathscr{C}_s$, with just a single plane of symmetry.

(ii) $\mathscr{C}_{2v}$ has the elements E, C_2, σ_v, σ_v', where σ_v and σ_v' are reflections in two mutually perpendicular planes intersecting along the twofold axis. This is the point group of molecules like H_2O, SO_2, or cis-$C_2H_2Cl_2$ (Fig. 2.8(b)).

(iii) $\mathscr{C}_{3v}$ is the point group of NH_3, or any molecule with the symmetry of a trigonal pyramid. We have discussed this group in some detail already.

(iv) $\mathscr{C}_{4v}$ is the point group for a pyramid with a square base. The two classes of reflections in $\mathscr{C}_{4v}$ arise from the pair of symmetry planes containing the diagonals of the square and the pair of symmetry planes passing through the mid-points of opposite sides of the square. A molecule with this point group is SF_5Cl.

(e) Group $\mathscr{D}_n$

We return now to the group $\mathscr{C}_n$ of rotations about the main axis and add a twofold symmetry axis perpendicular to the main axis. Appendix A(ii) shows that there will be altogether n such twofold axes intersecting at a point on the main axis. The angle between two adjacent twofold axes is π/n. The n rotations of $\mathscr{C}_n$ and the n rotations C_2' about these twofold axes together form the group $\mathscr{D}_n$. By similar arguments to those used for $\mathscr{C}_{nv}$, we find that in $\mathscr{D}_n$ each rotation $C_n{}^k$ and its inverse $C_n{}^{-k}$ form a class of two elements; if n is odd, all the rotations about the twofold axes belong to the same class, but if n is even they divide into two distinct classes of rotations about two sets of alternate axes.

EXAMPLES

(i) The group $\mathscr{D}_2$ is that of rotations through 180° about three mutually perpendicular axes. It is sometimes denoted by $\mathscr{V}$ (German *Vierergruppe*).

(ii) If the two CH_3 groups in C_2H_6 are in arbitrarily rotated positions, neither 'eclipsed' nor 'staggered', the molecule has the point group $\mathscr{D}_3$.

(f) Group $\mathscr{D}_{nh}$

If the horizontal plane containing the twofold axes of $\mathscr{D}_n$ is also a plane of symmetry, then special case of Appendix A(i) shows that the n vertical planes containing the main axis of symmetry and a twofold axis are necessarily also planes of symmetry. This system of axes and planes of symmetry gives rise to the group $\mathscr{D}_{nh}$ which, in addition to the elements of $\mathscr{D}_n$, contains n improper rotations $\sigma_h C_n{}^k$, and n reflections $\sigma_v = \sigma_h C_2'$. The pure rotations of $\mathscr{D}_{nh}$ divide into the same classes as those of $\mathscr{D}_n$; correspondingly the improper rotations $\sigma_h C_n{}^k$, $\sigma_h C_n{}^{-k}$ pair off into classes, and the reflections σ_v form one class if n is odd and two classes of reflections in alternate planes if n is even.

Another way of looking at $\mathscr{D}_{nh}$ is to say that it arises from $\mathscr{C}_{nv}$ by the addition of a horizontal plane of symmetry perpendicular to the main axis.

Note also that if n is even $\mathscr{D}_{nh}$ contains the inversion $i = \sigma_h C_2$ and there will be a centre of symmetry.

EXAMPLES

(i) $\mathscr{D}_{2h}$, also called $\mathscr{V}_h$, has three mutually perpendicular twofold axes. If these are the x, y, z axes, and we regard the z axis as the main axis, the elements of $\mathscr{D}_{2h}$ are: E; C_2 about the z axis; C_2' about the x axis; C_2'' about the y axis; σ_h, reflection in the xy plane; $\sigma_v' = \sigma_h C_2'$, reflection in the xz plane; $\sigma_v'' = \sigma_h C_2''$, reflection in the yz plane; and $i = \sigma_h C_2 = \sigma_v' C_2'' = \sigma_v'' C_2'$, inversion in the origin. These elements all commute and each is in a separate class. An example of this point group is afforded by C_2H_4 (Fig. 2.9).

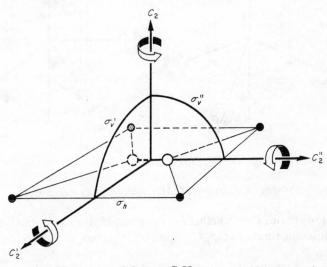

2.9 $\mathscr{D}_{2h}$: C_2H_4.

(ii) $\mathscr{D}_{3h}$ is the point group of any molecule with the complete symmetry of an equilateral triangle, e.g. $CO_3{}^{2-}$, $C(NH_2)_3{}^+$, PF_3Cl_2, *eclipsed*-C_2H_6 (Fig. 2.10(a)).

(iii) $\mathscr{D}_{4h}$ is the point group of any molecule with the complete symmetry of a square, e.g. $PtCl_4^{2-}$; phthalocyanine; octahedrally coordinated MX_4Y_2 where the X ligands are at the corners of a square.

(iv) $\mathscr{D}_{6h}$ has benzene as its best known example.

(g) Group $\mathscr{D}_{nd}$

Starting again from the system of axes of $\mathscr{D}_n$ one can add n vertical symmetry planes which contain the main axis and which *bisect* the angles between adjacent twofold axes. We denote a reflection in such a plane by σ_d. This system of planes and axes gives the group $\mathscr{D}_{nd}$ whose elements are the elements of $\mathscr{D}_n$ and in addition n reflections σ_d and n elements of the form $\sigma_d C_2'$. These are shown in Appendix A(iii) to be in fact improper rotations about the n-fold axis of the form S_{2n}^{2k+1}, $k = 0, 1, 2, \ldots, n-1$.

By suitable reflections σ_d we can move any one of the twofold axes into the position of any other, and similarly any symmetry plane can be moved into the position of any other by suitable rotations C_2'. Thus the reflections

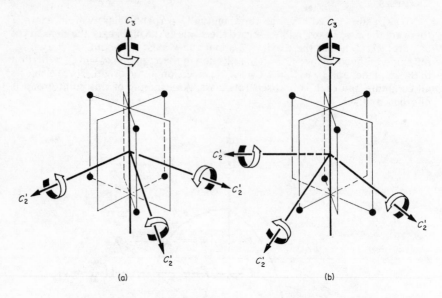

2.10 (a) $\mathscr{D}_{3h}$: eclipsed C_2H_6. (b) $\mathscr{D}_{3d}$: staggered C_2H_6.

σ_d all belong to one class whether n is even or odd; the rotations C_2' all belong to one class; the rotations $C_n{}^k$, $C_n{}^{-k}$ pair off in classes, as also do the improper rotations.

We may note that if n is odd, each of the twofold axes is perpendicular to one of the symmetry planes and the corresponding operation $\sigma_d C_2'$ is the inversion i.

EXAMPLES

(i) The 'staggered' form of C_2H_6 has the point group $\mathscr{D}_{3d}$ (Fig. 2.10(b)). The elements of this group are the elements of $\mathscr{D}_3$, namely E, the two rotations C_3 and $C_3{}^{-1}$ about the threefold axis, and three rotations C_2' about the three twofold axes. In addition there are six elements obtained by multiplying the elements of $\mathscr{D}_3$ by the inversion i. These are i, $S_6 = iC_3{}^{-1}$, $S_6{}^{-1} = iC_3$, and the three reflections $\sigma_d = iC_2'$.

(ii) The allene molecule, $CH_2=C=CH_2$, in which the planes of the two CH_2 groups are perpendicular, has point group $\mathscr{D}_{2d}$, also called $\mathscr{V}_d$.

III. Groups with more than one main axis of symmetry

If a molecule has several n-fold symmetry axes, these must intersect at a point and their spatial arrangement must be such that a rotation C_n about one of the axes results in an interchange of the other axes. This condition severely limits the number of possible groups containing more than one n-fold axis. We shall discuss the various values of n successively below.

(a) $n = 2$: groups $\mathscr{D}_2$, $\mathscr{D}_{2h}$, $\mathscr{D}_{2d}$

If we have a set of intersecting twofold axes, there must be three of them, mutually perpendicular to each other. This is the set of axes of the group $\mathscr{D}_2$ described above. There are only two different ways of adding planes of symmetry to this set of axes; these give rise to the groups $\mathscr{D}_{2h}$ and $\mathscr{D}_{2d}$.

(b) $n = 3$: groups $\mathscr{T}$, $\mathscr{T}_d$, $\mathscr{T}_h$

If we have a set of intersecting threefold axes it seems obvious (and can be rigorously proved) that there must be four such axes whose directions are those of the body diagonals of a cube, or, what is the same thing, whose directions lie along the lines joining the centre of a regular tetrahedron to its vertices (Fig. 2.1). The product of successive rotations C_3 about two of these threefold axes may be found by drawing diagrams similar to those of Fig. 2.4; it is found that the product is either another rotation C_3 or a rotation C_2 about a line joining the mid-points of opposite faces of the cube. There are altogether three such lines (the x, y, z axes of Fig. 2.1) so that the existence of the four threefold axes necessarily implies the existence of these three mutually perpendicular twofold axes. This set of threefold and twofold axes is complete: all the rotations associated with them together form a group called $\mathscr{T}$, the group of rotations which move a regular tetrahedron into itself.

There are just two ways of enlarging this group by adding planes of symmetry (any such plane must, of course, reflect a threefold axis into a threefold axis and a twofold axis into a twofold axis). The first way is to introduce reflection planes which contain two of the threefold axes and one of the twofold axes and which bisect the angle between the other twofold axes. These are the six planes which pass through pairs of opposite edges of the cube of Fig. 2.1 and this system of axes and planes of symmetry gives rise to the complete point group of a regular tetrahedron which is described at the end of Section 2.1. This group is called $\mathscr{T}_d$.

The second way of adding planes of symmetry is to take three planes each of which contains two of the twofold axes and is perpendicular to the third twofold axis. This introduces inversion as a symmetry operation and gives rise to a group called $\mathscr{T}_h$ which does not appear to be of interest in chemistry and which we shall not discuss further.

It might seem possible to extend the group still further by having both sets of symmetry planes simultaneously present. In this case, however, one would have a set of planes intersecting along the C_2 axes at angles of 45°. The product of two reflections in adjacent planes would be a rotation C_4 about their line of intersection (Appendix A(i)) which would therefore be a symmetry axis with $n=4$ and would belong to the next case to be described.

(c) $n=4$: groups $\mathcal{O}$, $\mathcal{O}_h$

If we have intersecting fourfold axes it seems obvious (and can be rigorously proved) that there must be three such axes, mutually perpendicular to each other. If one imagines these to be the axes passing through the mid-points of opposite faces of a cube, Fig. 2.4 shows that the product of two rotations C_4 about different axes is a rotation C_3 about a body diagonal of the cube. There are four such diagonals and the existence of the three fourfold axes thus necessarily implies the existence of four threefold axes like those of $\mathcal{T}$. Again, the reader may verify by adding a further rotation C_4 to the diagrams of Fig. 2.4, that a rotation C_4 about one of the fourfold axes, followed by a rotation $C_4{}^2 = C_2$ about another, is a rotation C_2 about a line joining the mid-points of a pair of opposite edges of the cube. Thus the existence of the fourfold axes necessarily implies the existence of six twofold axes of this kind. The set of three fourfold axes, four threefold axes and six twofold axes is complete: all the rotations associated with them together form a group which is called $\mathcal{O}$. It is the group of rotations that move a cube into itself. Since a regular octahedron can be symmetrically inscribed into a cube, with its vertices at the centre of the cube faces, $\mathcal{O}$ is also the group of rotations that move a regular octahedron into itself.

The only consistent way of adding planes of symmetry to the set of axes of $\mathcal{O}$ is simultaneously to introduce both the sets of planes described above for the case $n=3$. The centre of the cube then becomes a centre of symmetry and one obtains the complete point group of a cube or a regular octahedron. It is called $\mathcal{O}_h$.

(d) $n=5$: groups $\mathcal{I}$, $\mathcal{I}_h$

These groups contain twelve fivefold axes, twenty threefold axes and fifteen twofold axes. They are related to the symmetry of the icosahedron (a regular solid with twenty equilateral triangular faces) and the pentagonal dodecahedron (a regular solid with twelve regular pentagonal faces). They do not appear to have much chemical interest and we shall say nothing more about them.

There are no point groups with intersecting axes for which n is greater than five. This is related to the fact that there are only five regular solids, the tetrahedron, the cube, the octahedron, the dodecahedron and the icosahedron.

The most important of the groups of type III are $\mathcal{T}_d$ and $\mathcal{O}_h$. Their properties are summarized below.

$\mathscr{T}_d$, the point group of the regular tetrahedron

If the tetrahedron is inscribed with its vertices in alternate corners of a cube (Fig. 2.1) there are three twofold axes joining mid-points of opposite faces of the cube; four threefold axes along the body diagonals of the cube; six symmetry planes through pairs of opposite edges of the cube.

The twenty-four elements of $\mathscr{T}_d$, divided into their classes are:

E; three rotations C_2 about the twofold axes; eight rotations C_3, C_3^{-1} about the body diagonals. This set of rotations by itself forms the group $\mathscr{T}$.

The remaining twelve elements of $\mathscr{T}_d$ are a class of six reflections in the six symmetry planes and a class of six improper rotations S_4, S_4^{-1} about the twofold axes.

$\mathcal{O}_h$, the point group of the regular octahedron or the cube

An octahedron may be inscribed into a cube with the vertices of the octahedron at the centres of the cube faces. There are three fourfold axes joining the mid-points of opposite faces of the cube; four threefold axes along the body diagonals; six twofold axes joining the mid-points of pairs of opposite edges; six symmetry planes through pairs of opposite edges; three symmetry planes though the centre of the cube parallel to its faces; a centre of inversion at the centre of the cube.

The forty-eight elements of $\mathcal{O}_h$ divided into their classes are:

E; six rotations C_4, C_4^{-1} about the fourfold axes; three rotations $C_4^2 = C_2$ about the fourfold axes; eight rotations C_3, C_3^{-1} about the threefold axes; six rotations C_2' about the twofold axes. This set of twenty-four rotations by itself forms the group $\mathcal{O}$.

The remaining twenty-four elements of $\mathcal{O}_h$ are obtained by multiplying each element of $\mathcal{O}$ by the inversion i. They are i itself; six improper rotations S_4, S_4^{-1} about the fourfold axes; three reflections σ_h in the planes parallel to the cube faces; eight improper rotations S_6, S_6^{-1} about the body diagonals; six reflections σ_d in the planes through opposite edges.

The systems of planes and axes of symmetry of the point groups are summarized in Table 2.1. The problem of finding the point group of a given molecule is one that must be solved by inspection and by trying to identify all the axes and planes and symmetry. The groups $\mathcal{O}_h$ and $\mathscr{T}_d$ are generally easy to recognize. If a molecule does not belong to these one should look for a main axis of symmetry. If one can be found and if, further, there is a twofold axis perpendicular to it the point group will be of the $\mathscr{D}$ type. If there are no twofold axes perpendicular to the main axis the point group will be of the $\mathscr{C}$ type. The final decision then rests on the identification of planes of symmetry. The reader will be well advised to examine models of molecules from this point of view and to work out the point groups of molecules, both planar and non-planar with which he is familiar. It is instructive also to consider the effect of substitution on the point group of a molecule as in the following sequences:

Octahedral coordination: MX_6 $(\mathcal{O}_h)$, MX_5Y $(\mathscr{C}_{4v})$,
trans-MX_4Y_2 $(\mathscr{D}_{4h})$,   *cis*-MX_4Y_2 $(\mathscr{C}_{2v})$.

Tetrahedral coordination: MX_4 $(\mathscr{T}_d)$, MX_3Y $(\mathscr{C}_{3v})$, MX_2Y_2 $(\mathscr{C}_{2v})$.

TABLE 2.1. *Molecular point groups*

Group	Axes and planes of symmetry
$\mathscr{C}_s$	plane of symmetry
$\mathscr{C}_i$	centre of symmetry
$\mathscr{C}_n$	n-fold axis
$\mathscr{S}_{2n}$	$2n$-fold alternating axis
$\mathscr{C}_{nh}$	n-fold axis; horizontal plane
$\mathscr{C}_{nv}$	n-fold axis; n vertical planes
$\mathscr{D}_n$	n-fold axis; n horizontal twofold axes
$\mathscr{D}_{nh}$	rotations as for $\mathscr{D}_n$; one horizontal plane; n vertical planes containing the horizontal axes
$\mathscr{D}_{nd}$	rotations as for $\mathscr{D}_n$; n vertical planes bisecting angles between the horizontal axes
$\mathscr{T}_d$	tetrahedron
$\mathscr{O}_h$	octahedron or cube

Our description of symmetry operations and point groups has been based on the assumption that the nuclei of a molecule define a fixed rigid framework. This assumption is adequate for the description of the symmetry of most molecules but it breaks down for molecules which contain distinct groups of atoms that can rotate relative to each other. Consider, for example, a molecule like CH_3BF_2. The CH_3 group has $\mathscr{C}_{3v}$ symmetry, the BF_2 group has $\mathscr{C}_{2v}$ symmetry, but when these two groups are in arbitrarily rotated positions the molecule as a whole has no symmetry at all on our definition of a symmetry operation. A generalization of the idea of a symmetry operation to cover such molecules as these has been given by Longuet–Higgins [3] and the interested reader is referred to this paper for further details. (The paper requires a knowledge of the contents of Chapters 3 to 7 for its understanding.)

2.7 Linear Molecules and Atoms

The groups we have discussed so far contain a finite number of elements. A linear molecule, however, has an infinite number of symmetry operations since any rotation about its axis or a reflection in any plane containing its axis will be a symmetry operation. Nevertheless we can still speak of the point group of the molecule since these rotations and reflections will satisfy the group postulates (i)–(iv) of Section 2.4. In fact the point group of a linear molecule can be thought of as the limiting case of a point group with one main n-fold axis of symmetry as n becomes infinite and the basic angle of rotation $2\pi/n$ tends to zero. The two possible groups that can arise are:

(a) $\mathscr{C}_{\infty v}$, the limiting case of $\mathscr{C}_{nv}$. This is the point group of a linear molecule which is not symmetric about its central point. Its rotations pair off into an infinite number of classes, one for each value ϕ of the angle of rotation, containing the rotation $C(\phi)$ and its inverse $C(-\phi)$. All the reflections σ_v in planes through the axis belong to one class.

(b) $\mathscr{D}_{\infty h}$, the limiting case of $\mathscr{D}_{nh}$. This is the point group of a linear molecule which is symmetric about its central point; it contains all the elements of $\mathscr{C}_{\infty v}$ and also a corresponding set of elements obtained by multiplying each element of $\mathscr{C}_{\infty v}$ by the inversion i in the centre of symmetry of the molecule.

Finally we should mention the point group of a single atom. This is an infinite group which contains all the possible rotations about all the possible axes of rotation passing through the nucleus (these form the *three-dimensional rotation group*) and inversion in the nucleus as a centre of symmetry. In the three-dimensional rotation group all rotations through the same angle, irrespective of the axis of rotation, belong to the same class.

2.8 Crystal Symmetry

We conclude the discussion of symmetry operations with a brief description of the way in which the ideas we have developed are applied to crystals. A crystal consists of a regular repetition in space of a basic unit, the *unit cell*, which contains a number of atoms with a definite spatial arrangement. All the unit cells are identical and they have identical orientations in space so that an ideal crystal, which is imagined to extend to infinity in all directions, looks exactly the same when it is viewed from corresponding points in different unit cells.

The atoms contained in a unit cell will have a definite point group of the kind we have discussed. We choose in each unit cell a point which is left unmoved by the operations of this point group, the points in all the unit cells being chosen in exactly the same way. Then the arrangement of these points in space defines the *crystal lattice* which gives an overall picture of the way in which the unit cells are packed together to form the crystal.

The regularity of the crystal structure demands that a plane or axis of symmetry of any unit cell should be a plane or axis of symmetry for the crystal as a whole. In particular, if the point group of a unit cell contains an n-fold axis of symmetry, a rotation C_n or an improper rotation S_n about this axis must move the whole infinite crystal into itself. One can show that this condition implies that the only values of n that can occur in a crystal are $n = 1, 2, 3, 4, 6$; $n = 5$ and $n > 6$ are not possible. The reason for this restriction on possible values of n is related to the fact that it is possible to cover a plane area by fitting identical regular polygons together without leaving any gaps only if the polygons are equilateral triangles, squares or hexagons. (The value $n = 1$ is included to cover the point groups which have no axis of symmetry. These are $\mathscr{C}_s$, $\mathscr{C}$ and the trivial point group $\mathscr{C}_1$ which contains only the identical operation and which describes a unit cell which has no symmetry at all.)

There are only thirty-two point groups which have proper or improper axes of symmetry with these values of n. These crystallographic point groups, often called the thirty-two *crystal classes*, are listed in Table 2.2. This table gives two alternative notations for the point groups; the crystallographic notation is explained in Section 2.9.

The possible arrangements of points in a crystal lattice are determined by the symmetry of the point group and the various possible lattices can be divided into the seven *crystal systems* listed in Table 2.2. The symmetry of the cubic system, for example, is governed by the requirement that four three-

TABLE 2.2. *The crystal classes and the crystal systems*

System	Essential symmetry	Point groups or crystal classes
Triclinic	No planes or axes	$\mathscr{C}_1$　$\mathscr{C}_i(\mathscr{S}_2)$ 1　$\bar{1}$
Monoclinic	One twofold axis or one plane	$\mathscr{C}_2$　$\mathscr{C}_s$　$\mathscr{C}_{2h}$ 2　m　$2/m$
Orthorhombic	Three mutually perpendicular twofold axes or two perpendicular planes	$\mathscr{D}_2(\mathscr{V})$　$\mathscr{D}_{2h}(\mathscr{V}_h)$　$\mathscr{C}_{2v}$ 222　mmm　$2mm$
Trigonal and Hexagonal	One threefold or one sixfold axis	$\mathscr{C}_3$ $\mathscr{C}_{3v}$ $\mathscr{C}_{3h}$ $\mathscr{D}_3$ $\mathscr{D}_{3h}$ $\mathscr{D}_{3d}$ 3 $3m$ $\bar{6}$ 32 $\bar{6}m2$ $\bar{3}m$ $\mathscr{C}_6$ $\mathscr{C}_{6v}$ $\mathscr{C}_{6h}$ $\mathscr{D}_6$ $\mathscr{D}_{6h}$ $\mathscr{S}_6$ 6 $6mm$ $6/m$ 622 $6/mmm$ $\bar{3}$
Tetragonal	One fourfold axis	$\mathscr{S}_4$ $\mathscr{C}_4$ $\mathscr{C}_{4v}$ $\mathscr{C}_{4h}$ $\mathscr{D}_4$ $\mathscr{D}_{4h}$ $\mathscr{D}_{2d}$ $\bar{4}$ 4 $4mm$ $4/m$ 422 $4/mmm$ $\bar{4}2m$
Cubic	Four threefold axes	$\mathscr{T}$ $\mathscr{T}_d$ $\mathscr{T}_h$ $\mathscr{O}$ $\mathscr{O}_h$ 23 $\bar{4}3m$ $m3$ 432 $m3m$

fold axes of symmetry (the threefold axes of $\mathscr{T}$ or $\mathscr{O}$) should pass through each lattice point. There are just three different arrangements of lattice points which meet this requirement; they are (i) the simple cubic lattice in which the lattice points are obtained by repeating the pattern formed by the corners of a cube, (ii) the body-centred cubic lattice which is obtained from the simple cubic lattice by placing an additional lattice point at the centre of each cube and (iii) the face-centred cubic lattice which is obtained from the simple cubic lattice by placing additional lattice points at the centres of the cube faces.

The regular arrangement of the unit cells in a crystal permits of other symmetry operations besides the point group operations we have considered so far. In any crystal there will be a number of translations through certain distances in definite directions which, when they are applied to the infinite crystal as a whole, will move each unit cell into the position of another unit cell. These translations have no effect on the crystal; they are symmetry operations and all the translations taken together form a group, the *translation group* of the crystal, which describes the structure of the crystal lattice.

The symmetry operations of a crystal consist of point group operations, translations, and operations of mixed type obtained by combining point group operations with translations. One can show that these mixed operations can be expressed in terms of two distinct kinds of operation:

(i) *Screw rotation:* a rotation about an axis accompanied by a translation along the axis;

(ii) *Glide plane reflection:* a reflection in a plane accompanied by a translation along a line lying in the plane.

Note that, in general, neither the rotation (or reflection) nor the translation that are involved in an operation of this type are by themselves symmetry operations of the crystal; it is only the combined rotation–translation or reflection–translation that is a symmetry operation.

The complete set of symmetry operations for a crystal, rotations, reflections, translations, screw rotations, and glide plane reflections, forms a group, the *space group* of the crystal. This group contains in itself information about the symmetry of a unit cell (point group) and the symmetry of the crystal lattice (translation group) but in addition its screw axes and glide planes give information about the way in which the positions of the atoms in a unit cell are related to the atomic positions in neighbouring unit cells. Each point group (crystal class) has associated with it a limited number of translation groups (lattices). These can be combined in various ways to give a limited number of space groups; it can be shown that there are precisely 230 different possible space groups, distinguished from each other by their lattice type, their crystal class and the arrangement of their glide planes and screw axes. For further information the reader is referred to specialized texts on crystallography, for instance [4] or [5].

2.9 Notation

Besides the Schoenflies notation for the point groups, there is another notation, the Hermann–Mauguin or international notation, which is widely used by crystallographers. Both notations are given in Table 2.2 and it will be seen that in the international notation each point group is specified by a number of symbols strung together. These symbols describe the systems of axes and planes of symmetry of the point groups according to the following rules.

The presence of a n-fold axis of symmetry is signified by writing down the number n so that, for example, the group $\mathscr{C}_4$, which has a single fourfold axis of symmetry and no other planes or axes of symmetry, is simply written as 4 in the international notation. If there are several axes of symmetry, the appropriate n for each kind of axis is written down. Thus $\mathscr{D}_4$, with one four-fold axis and two distinct classes of twofold axes, is written 422; the octahedral group $\mathscr{O}$, with sets of fourfold, threefold and twofold axes, is written 432.

The existence of planes of symmetry is indicated by the symbol m (standing for *mirror plane*) and if there is a mirror plane perpendicular to an n-fold axis, this is indicated by n/m. Thus the international symbol for $\mathscr{C}_{4h}$ is $4/m$, while $\mathscr{C}_{4v}$ is denoted by $4mm$ since here there are two classes of vertical symmetry planes.

In this notation one might write $\mathscr{C}_{3h}$ as $3/m$, but here a different convention comes into force. The elements of $\mathscr{C}_{3h}$ are C_3, C_3^2, $C_3^3 = E$ and $\sigma_h C_3$, $\sigma_h C_3^2$, $\sigma_h C_3^3 = \sigma_h$. One can introduce the inversion $i = \sigma_h C_2 = \sigma_h C_6^3$ and write $\sigma_h = iC_6^3$. It will then be seen that all the elements of $\mathscr{C}_{3h}$ are simply powers of the basic combination iC_6. This situation is indicated in the international notation by the symbol $\bar{6}$. In general, $\bar{n}$ has associated with it the operation iC_n.

In writing down the international symbol for a group one usually includes just sufficient information for the group to be identified; it is not always necessary to specify every kind of symmetry axis or mirror plane. Thus, while $\mathscr{D}_4$ should be written as 422 since it contains two classes of twofold axes, it is often written simply as 42. Again, $\mathscr{O}$ in the full notation is 432, but this may be shortened to 43 without ambiguity.

Chapter 3

VECTOR SPACES

3.1 Vector Spaces

In Chapter 2 we were concerned with the geometrical framework of a molecule and the description of its symmetry. In this chapter we show how one can talk about such things as the wave function of a molecule in the language of what are called *vector spaces*. This provides a general background against which one can discuss the ways in which the symmetry of a molecule influences its vibrational or electronic wave functions and determines the selection rules which operate for transitions between its various states.

The idea of a vector space arises from a consideration of the properties of ordinary three-dimensional physical space, and we begin with a discussion of these properties, putting them into a form which is capable of generalization.

We can locate the position of a point P in space relative to some origin O and a fixed frame of reference by drawing a directed line from O to P. The position of P is known when the length of this line and its direction relative to the frame of reference are given. We call the directed line OP the *position vector* of P and denote it by the symbol **p**; this symbol stands for both the length and the direction of the line. To each point of space there corresponds a position vector **p** and we can think interchangeably of a point and the position vector which describes its location.

We now proceed to define certain operations which we can perform on the symbols **p**, **q**, **r**, **s**, ... denoting position vectors and which enable us to represent *geometrical* relations between position vectors by *algebraic* equations.

(*a*) *Equality:* An obvious relation between the position vectors of two points is that they are equal both in length and direction if and only if the two points coincide with each other. We express this coincidence of the two points by the = sign and say that the equation

$$\mathbf{r} = \mathbf{s}$$

means that **r** and **s** have equal lengths and the same direction.

(b) *Addition:* Suppose that **p** and **q** are the position vectors of the two points P and Q shown in Fig. 3.1. Complete the parallelogram $OPRQ$ by drawing PR parallel to OQ and QR parallel to OP. The position vector, say **r**, of the point R found in this way is the diagonal of the parallelogram. We express the geometrical relation between **r**, **p** and **q** defined by the parallelogram of Fig. 3.1 by means of the algebraic equation

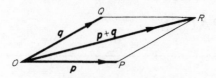

3.1 Addition of position vectors.

$$\mathbf{r} = \mathbf{p} + \mathbf{q}$$

and say that **r** is the vector sum of **p** and **q**. The order in which we write the terms on the right-hand side is irrelevant and

$$\mathbf{p} + \mathbf{q} = \mathbf{q} + \mathbf{p}. \tag{3.1}$$

This definition of vector addition can be extended to any number of terms. Thus Fig. 3.2 shows the result of adding the three vectors **r**, **s** and **t**. From

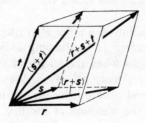

3.2 $(\mathbf{r} + \mathbf{s}) + \mathbf{t} = \mathbf{r} + (\mathbf{s} + \mathbf{t})$.

this figure it is evident that the result is independent of whether we perform the additions in the order $(\mathbf{r} + \mathbf{s}) + \mathbf{t}$ or $(\mathbf{r} + \mathbf{t}) + \mathbf{s}$ or $(\mathbf{s} + \mathbf{t}) + \mathbf{r}$; vector addition is associative and

$$(\mathbf{r} + \mathbf{s}) + \mathbf{t} = \mathbf{r} + (\mathbf{s} + \mathbf{t}) = \mathbf{r} + \mathbf{s} + \mathbf{t}, \tag{3.2}$$

where the final form on the right-hand side implies that the result is uniquely determined without any need for inserting brackets to show which pair of vectors is to be added together first.

(c) *The zero vector and subtraction:* The position vector of the origin O itself is a vector of zero length and its direction is therefore irrelevant. We denote it by **0**; from the parallelogram law for addition we see that it has the property of the zero in ordinary algebra that

$$\mathbf{r} + \mathbf{0} = \mathbf{r} \qquad (3.3)$$

for any **r**.

We now define the vector $-\mathbf{r}$ to be that vector which when added to **r** gives the zero vector; i.e. we say $\mathbf{s} = -\mathbf{r}$ if $\mathbf{r} + \mathbf{s} = \mathbf{0}$. From the parallelogram law it follows that $-\mathbf{r}$ is the vector whose length is equal to that of **r** and whose direction is exactly opposite to the direction of **r**. From this definition it follows that

$$-(-\mathbf{r}) = \mathbf{r},$$

and also that (Fig. 3.3) the equation $\mathbf{t} = \mathbf{r} + \mathbf{s}$ implies $\mathbf{r} = \mathbf{t} - \mathbf{s}$.

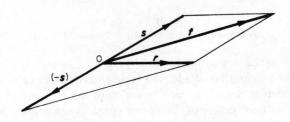

3.3 If $\mathbf{t} = \mathbf{r} + \mathbf{s}$ then $\mathbf{r} = \mathbf{t} - \mathbf{s}$.

(*d*) *Multiplication by a number:* If a is a positive real number and **r** is a position vector whose length is r we define the product $a\mathbf{r}$ to be the position vector whose length is ar and whose direction is the same as that of **r**. We can extend this definition to negative values of a as in (*c*) by saying that the negative sign reverses the direction; $-a\mathbf{r}$ is the vector equal and opposite to $a\mathbf{r}$. This definition has the obvious properties that multiplication by a number should have: for any **r**

$$a(b\mathbf{r}) = (ab)\mathbf{r},$$
$$(a+b)\mathbf{r} = a\mathbf{r} + b\mathbf{r}, \qquad (3.4)$$

and for the particular values $a = 0, 1$

$$0 \cdot \mathbf{r} = \mathbf{0}, \qquad 1 \cdot \mathbf{r} = \mathbf{r}.$$

Furthermore, if **r** and **s** are any two position vectors,

$$a(\mathbf{r} + \mathbf{s}) = a\mathbf{r} + a\mathbf{s}. \qquad (3.5)$$

The geometrical meaning of this equation is illustrated in Fig. 3.4.

To sum up these results, we have been able to define an algebra of position vectors with operations of 'addition', 'subtraction' and 'multiplication by a number' which possess all the properties listed in (3.1) to (3.5) that these operations have in ordinary algebra. These definitions and their properties refer to the set of position vectors of all points in ordinary physical space. We now proceed to define a general *vector space* as a set of entities of whatever kind for which we can define similar operations. The entities which form a vector space are called the vectors of this space, although they may be completely different in their nature from the position vectors we have discussed so far.

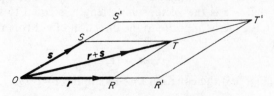

3.4 $a(\mathbf{r}+\mathbf{s}) = a\mathbf{r} + a\mathbf{s}$.
If $OR' = a \cdot OR$ and $OS' = a \cdot OS$ then $OT' = a \cdot OT$.

A vector space is a set of 'vectors' $\mathbf{p}, \mathbf{q}, \mathbf{r}, \ldots$ which can 'add' together according to a definition of addition which satisfies (3.1) and (3.2). The set must in particular contain a 'zero vector' with the property (3.3). The result of adding any two vectors of the vector space together must be to produce some other vector of the space. Further we must be able to define the 'multiplication' of a vector of the space by a number. This definition of multiplication must have the properties (3.4) and (3.5) and the result of multiplying a vector of the space by an arbitrary number must be to produce some other vector of the space.

3.2 Function Spaces

One type of vector space which is particularly important in quantum mechanics is a *function space* whose 'vectors' are a set of functions which have some property or properties in common.

Suppose that $f, g, h, \ldots$ are functions of a variable x. Then we can in an obvious way define the addition of two functions to produce a third by saying that the equation

$$h = f + g$$

means that h is that function of x which for every value of x satisfies

$$h(x) = f(x) + g(x).$$

We can define a 'zero function' which takes the value zero for every value of x and use this to define the function $-f$. Also we can define the multiplication of a function f by an arbitrary number a by saying that af is that function of x which for each value of x has the value $af(x)$ in the ordinary sense of multiplication. These definitions of addition and multiplication have all the required properties and can be extended to functions of any number of variables.

The set of functions then forms a vector space if for any two members f and g of the set the function $(f+g)$ belongs to the set and if for any member f of the set and an arbitrary number a the function af belongs to the set.

EXAMPLE

Consider the equation

$$\frac{d^2y}{dx^2} = -y. \tag{3.6}$$

If f and g are any two functions of x and a is an arbitrary number we know that

$$\frac{d^2}{dx^2}(f+g) = \frac{d^2f}{dx^2} + \frac{d^2g}{dx^2},$$

and that

$$\frac{d^2}{dx^2}(af) = a\frac{d^2f}{dx^2}.$$

It follows by substitution into (3.6) that if f is any solution of this equation so is the function af for arbitrary a and that if g is any other solution then so is the function $f+g$. Hence the set of all the functions which are solutions of (3.6) forms a vector space.

The functions we are mostly concerned with in quantum mechanics are the wave functions representing the state of an atom or molecule. A wave function ψ of a system of particles in a state with energy E is a solution of the Schrödinger equation

$$H\psi = E\psi, \tag{3.7}$$

where H is the Hamiltonian operator. If the particles have coordinates (x_1, y_1, z_1), (x_2, y_2, z_2), ..., (x_n, y_n, z_n) and their masses are m_1, m_2, ..., m_n then H is given by

$$H = -\sum_{k=1}^{n}(h^2/8\pi^2m_k)\nabla_k^2 + V,$$

where $\nabla_k^2 = \partial^2/\partial x_k^2 + \partial^2/\partial y_k^2 + \partial^2/\partial z_k^2$ and V is the potential energy of the particles.

The Hamiltonian is what is called a *linear operator*, i.e. if ϕ and ψ are any two functions of the variables appearing in H and a is any number then

$$H(a\phi) = a(H\phi) \quad \text{and} \quad H(\phi+\psi) = H\phi+H\psi.$$

(In this respect H is exactly similar to the operator d^2/dx^2 appearing in (3.6).) Hence if ϕ and ψ are any two solutions of (3.7) with the same energy E_0 so that

$$H\phi = E_0\phi, \qquad H\psi = E_0\psi,$$

it follows that for any a

$$H(a\phi) = a(H\phi) = aE_0\phi = E_0(a\phi),$$

and that

$$H(\phi+\psi) = H\phi+H\psi = E_0\phi+E_0\psi = E_0(\phi+\psi).$$

Thus the functions $a\phi$ and $(\phi+\psi)$ are also solutions of (3.7) with the same energy E_0 as ϕ and ψ. We conclude that the set of all possible wave functions of a system which have the same energy forms a vector space.

3.3 Base Vectors and Coordinate Systems

Let us return now to the physical space of position vectors. Suppose that $\mathbf{a}_1$ is the position vector of a point A_1. Then the set of vectors of the form $\alpha_1\mathbf{a}_1$, as the number α_1 ranges from $-\infty$ to ∞, defines all the points on the line OA_1; to each point on this line corresponds a vector $\alpha_1\mathbf{a}_1$ with a definite value of α_1, and no point which lies off this line has a position vector of this form.

Next suppose that $\mathbf{a}_2$ is the position vector of a point A_2 which does not lie on the line of $\mathbf{a}_1$. Then the set of all possible vectors of the form $\alpha_1\mathbf{a}_1+\alpha_2\mathbf{a}_2$, as the numbers α_1 and α_2 vary independently from $-\infty$ to ∞, defines all the points in the plane OA_1A_2; the position vector of a given point in this plane

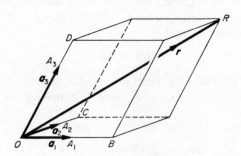

3.5 Resolution into components: $\mathbf{r}=\alpha_1\mathbf{a}_1+\alpha_2\mathbf{a}_2+\alpha_3\mathbf{a}_3$.
$OB=\alpha_1OA_1, \ OC=\alpha_2OA_2, \ OD=\alpha_3OA_3.$

can be written in the form $\alpha_1\mathbf{a}_1+\alpha_2\mathbf{a}_2$ with a definite pair of values of α_1 and α_2 characteristic of the point, and no point which does not lie in the plane has a position vector of this form.

Finally suppose that $\mathbf{a}_3$ is the position vector of a point A_3 which does not lie in the plane of $\mathbf{a}_1$ and $\mathbf{a}_2$ and consider vectors of the form

$$\mathbf{r} = \alpha_1\mathbf{a}_1+\alpha_2\mathbf{a}_2+\alpha_3\mathbf{a}_3. \tag{3.8}$$

The vectors $\mathbf{a}_1, \mathbf{a}_2, \mathbf{a}_3$ are represented in Fig. 3.5 which also shows the position vector **r** of a general point R. From the construction indicated in the figure we can see that whatever the position of the point R it is possible to write its position vector in the form (3.8) where the coefficients α_1, α_2, α_3 are uniquely determined when **r** is given. Conversely, given any set of values of these coefficients, (3.8) defines the position of some point of space.

Thus for any three given non-coplanar vectors $\mathbf{a}_1$, $\mathbf{a}_2$, $\mathbf{a}_3$ equation (3.8) represents a unique correspondence between the position vector of a point of space and the set of three numbers (α_1, α_2, α_3) which characterizes it. By choosing three definite non-coplanar vectors we have set up a *coordinate system*; $\mathbf{a}_1$, $\mathbf{a}_2$, $\mathbf{a}_3$ are the *base vectors* of this coordinate system and the *coordinates* of a point in space, or the *components* of its position vector, are the three numbers (α_1, α_2, α_3) defined by (3.8).

The condition that $\mathbf{a}_1$, $\mathbf{a}_2$, $\mathbf{a}_3$ are non-coplanar vectors can be expressed algebraically by saying that they are such that the only possible solution of the equation

$$\alpha_1 \mathbf{a}_1 + \alpha_2 \mathbf{a}_2 + \alpha_3 \mathbf{a}_3 = \mathbf{0}$$

is $\alpha_1 = \alpha_2 = \alpha_3 = 0$; no other non-zero set of values for α_1, α_2, α_3 can satisfy this equation, for suppose that it has a solution with $\alpha_3 \neq 0$. Then dividing through by α_3 would give

$$\mathbf{a}_3 = -(\alpha_1/\alpha_3)\mathbf{a}_1 - (\alpha_2/\alpha_3)\mathbf{a}_2$$

which is impossible since $\mathbf{a}_3$ does not lie in the plane of $\mathbf{a}_1$ and $\mathbf{a}_2$. Hence $\alpha_3 = 0$ and similarly $\alpha_1 = 0$ and $\alpha_2 = 0$. We say that the vectors $\mathbf{a}_1$, $\mathbf{a}_2$, $\mathbf{a}_3$ are *linearly independent*. The discussion above shows that we can find three linearly independent position vectors (and that in an infinite number of ways) but no more than three, and we express this by saying that the physical space of the position vectors has three dimensions.

Now consider a general vector space. Choose one of its vectors $\mathbf{a}_1(\neq \mathbf{0})$. Then either all the vectors of the space can be written in the form $\alpha_1 \mathbf{a}_1$ (in which case it is a space of one dimension) or they cannot. If not, we can find a vector $\mathbf{a}_2(\neq \mathbf{0})$ such that $\mathbf{a}_1$ and $\mathbf{a}_2$ are linearly independent, i.e. the equation $\alpha_1 \mathbf{a}_1 + \alpha_2 \mathbf{a}_2 = 0$ implies uniquely that $\alpha_1 = \alpha_2 = 0$. Either all the vectors of the space can be written in the form $\alpha_1 \mathbf{a}_1 + \alpha_2 \mathbf{a}_2$ (in which case it is a space of two dimensions) or they cannot. If not, we can find a third linearly independent vector $\mathbf{a}_3$ and test to see whether all the vectors of the space can be written in the form $\alpha_1 \mathbf{a}_1 + \alpha_2 \mathbf{a}_2 + \alpha_3 \mathbf{a}_3$. If not, we can go on to find a fourth linearly independent vector and we can continue in this way, if necessary, producing a sequence of linearly independent vectors. In a vector space with a finite number n of dimensions, and all the vector spaces with which we shall be concerned do have a finite number of dimensions, this process will cease when we have found n linearly independent vectors $\mathbf{a}_1$, $\mathbf{a}_2$, ..., $\mathbf{a}_n$. These form the basis of a coordinate system for our space; any vector $\mathbf{r}$ of the space can be written in the form

$$\mathbf{r} = \alpha_1\mathbf{a}_1 + \alpha_2\mathbf{a}_2 + \cdots + \alpha_n\mathbf{a}_n, \tag{3.9}$$

and is characterized by the set of n numbers $(\alpha_1, \alpha_2, \ldots, \alpha_n)$ which are its components relative to the chosen base vectors.

EXAMPLE

Consider the function space which consists of all the solutions of the differential equation (3.6). We know that the general solution of this equation is

$$y = \alpha_1 \cos x + \alpha_2 \sin x$$

where α_1 and α_2 are two arbitrary constants. The functions $f_1 = \cos x$ and $f_2 = \sin x$ are themselves solutions of (3.6) and they are linearly independent since it is impossible to satisfy the equation

$$\alpha_1 \cos x + \alpha_2 \sin x = 0,$$

with fixed non-zero values of the constants α_1 and α_2, for every value of x in any range of values of x. Thus every solution of (3.6) can be written in the form

$$y = \alpha_1 f_1 + \alpha_2 f_2$$

which is an equation of the form of (3.9). We conclude that the space of the functions which are the solutions of (3.6) is two-dimensional. The particular linearly independent solutions f_1 and f_2 of the equation are the 'base vectors' of a coordinate system in this function space and any general function y of the space is characterized by the pair of numbers α_1, α_2 which are its 'components' relative to this basis.

In the same way the function space formed by the solutions of the Schrödinger equation which belong to a particular energy level will have a dimension n, where n is some integer, and it will be possible to find n linearly independent wave functions $\psi_1, \psi_2, \ldots, \psi_n$ such that every solution of the equation with this energy can be written as

$$\psi = \alpha_1\psi_1 + \alpha_2\psi_2 + \cdots + \alpha_n\psi_n.$$

We then say that the energy level concerned has an n-fold *degeneracy*.

Once we have chosen a set of linearly independent base vectors in a general vector space, the operations of addition and of multiplication by a number are very simply expressed in terms of the components of the vectors. If $\mathbf{r}$ is a vector with components $(\alpha_1, \alpha_2, \ldots, \alpha_n)$ and $\mathbf{r}'$ is a vector with components $(\alpha_1', \alpha_2', \ldots, \alpha_n')$ then it follows from (3.9), (3.4) and (3.5) that $(\mathbf{r}+\mathbf{r}')$ is the vector with components $(\alpha_1 + \alpha_1', \alpha_2 + \alpha_2', \ldots, \alpha_n + \alpha_n')$ and that $a\mathbf{r}$ where a is any number is the vector whose components are $(a\alpha_1, a\alpha_2, \ldots, a\alpha_n)$.

3.4 Orthogonal Coordinate Systems

In the three-dimensional physical space of position vectors any three non-coplanar vectors will serve as the basis of a coordinate system; the directions of the base vectors define the directions of the three coordinate axes and their respective lengths define a unit of length for measurement along each axis.

The most generally useful way of choosing the base vectors in ordinary space is to take three vectors of unit length which are mutually perpendicular to each other. We denote three such base vectors by e_1, e_2, e_3 and say that the position vector of a point has components (or that the point itself has coordinates) x_1, x_2 and x_3 with respect to this basis so that (Fig. 3.6)

$$\mathbf{r} = x_1\mathbf{e}_1 + x_2\mathbf{e}_2 + x_3\mathbf{e}_3.$$

In normal usage one would say that the vectors e_1, e_2, e_3 define the directions of the x, y, z axes and one would use the labels (x, y, z) instead of (x_1, x_2, x_3) for the coordinates of a point. We shall often later on revert to this more

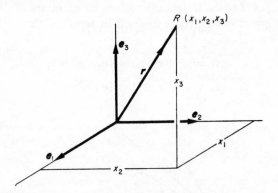

3.6 Orthogonal coordinates.

usual notation but for our present purposes it is more convenient to number the symbols standing for the different coordinates rather than to give them different letters.

We now wish to introduce into our algebraic symbolism for dealing with vectors the geometrical notion of two vectors being perpendicular to each other. We do this by defining a new operation, that of forming the *scalar product* $(\mathbf{r}, \mathbf{s})$ of two vectors $\mathbf{r}$ and $\mathbf{s}$. This is a way of combining two *vectors* together to produce a single *number*. If the lengths of $\mathbf{r}$ and $\mathbf{s}$ are r and s respectively and the angle between $\mathbf{r}$ and $\mathbf{s}$ is θ, we define the scalar product $(\mathbf{r}, \mathbf{s})$ to be the product of the lengths of $\mathbf{r}$ and $\mathbf{s}$ multiplied by the cosine of the angle between them:

$$(\mathbf{r}, \mathbf{s}) = rs \cos \theta. \tag{3.10}$$

The order in which we write the factors in the product makes no difference and

$$(\mathbf{r}, \mathbf{s}) = (\mathbf{s}, \mathbf{r}). \tag{3.11}$$

(In vector algebra the scalar product is generally denoted by **r.s**; the bracket notation is, however, more convenient for later generalization to function spaces.)

Two particular cases of (3.10) are:

(i) If **r** = **s** we obtain the scalar product of a vector with itself. In this case, $\theta = 0$ and $\cos \theta = 1$ so that

$$(\mathbf{r}, \mathbf{r}) = r^2,$$

the square of the length of **r**.

(ii) If **s** is perpendicular to **r** then $\theta = 90°$ and $\cos \theta = 0$ so that the scalar product $(\mathbf{r}, \mathbf{s})$ vanishes. Conversely, if $(\mathbf{r}, \mathbf{s}) = 0$ and neither **r** nor **s** is the zero vector then **r** and **s** are perpendicular.

Thus the fact that the three base vectors $\mathbf{e}_1$, $\mathbf{e}_2$, $\mathbf{e}_3$ are of unit length and are mutually perpendicular, is expressed in terms of their scalar products by the equations

$$(\mathbf{e}_1, \mathbf{e}_1) = (\mathbf{e}_2, \mathbf{e}_2) = (\mathbf{e}_3, \mathbf{e}_3) = 1,$$

$$(\mathbf{e}_1, \mathbf{e}_2) = (\mathbf{e}_2, \mathbf{e}_3) = (\mathbf{e}_3, \mathbf{e}_1) = 0.$$

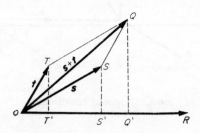

3.7 $(\mathbf{r}, \mathbf{s} + \mathbf{t}) = (\mathbf{r}, \mathbf{s}) + (\mathbf{r}, \mathbf{t})$.

The projections of **s**, **t**, **s** + **t** on **r** = OR are OS', OT', OQ'; and $OT' = S'Q'$. Then $(\mathbf{r}, \mathbf{s}) = OR \cdot OS'$, $(\mathbf{r}, \mathbf{t}) = OR \cdot OT' = OR \cdot S'Q'$, and $(\mathbf{r}, \mathbf{s} + \mathbf{t}) = OR \cdot OQ' = OR \cdot OS' + OR \cdot S'Q' = (\mathbf{r}, \mathbf{s}) + (\mathbf{r}, \mathbf{t})$.

We summarize these equations by writing

$$(\mathbf{e}_i, \mathbf{e}_j) = \delta_{ij} \quad (i = 1, 2, 3; j = 1, 2, 3) \tag{3.12}$$

where δ_{ij} is the 'Kronecker delta' defined by

$$\delta_{ij} = \begin{cases} 1 & \text{if} \quad i = j, \\ 0 & \text{if} \quad i \neq j. \end{cases} \tag{3.13}$$

(We shall often come across this symbol δ_{ij} in the course of this book.)

Two important properties of the scalar product defined in (3.10) are

$$(\mathbf{r}, b\mathbf{s}) = b(\mathbf{r}, \mathbf{s}), \tag{3.14}$$

where b is any number, and

$$(\mathbf{r}, \mathbf{s}+\mathbf{t}) = (\mathbf{r}, \mathbf{s})+(\mathbf{r}, \mathbf{t}), \qquad (3.15)$$

where $\mathbf{r}$, $\mathbf{s}$, $\mathbf{t}$ are any three vectors. Equation (3.14) is obvious from (3.10) and the definition of $b\mathbf{s}$; the proof of (3.15) is illustrated in Fig. 3.7. These properties justify us in calling the particular combination of the lengths and directions of two vectors defined by (3.10) their 'product' and allow us to manipulate the scalar product just as if it were an ordinary algebraic product. Thus if the vectors $\mathbf{r}$ and $\mathbf{r}'$ have components (x_1, x_2, x_3) and (x_1', x_2', x_3') repectively their scalar product is

$$(\mathbf{r}, \mathbf{r}') = (x_1\mathbf{e}_1+x_2\mathbf{e}_2+x_3\mathbf{e}_3, x_1'\mathbf{e}_1+x_2'\mathbf{e}_2+x_3'\mathbf{e}_3).$$

Equation (3.15) allows us to multiply this out term by term. Then by invoking (3.14) and also (3.11) we can take the numbers x_i and x_j' outside the individual brackets in which they appear and obtain

$$(\mathbf{r}, \mathbf{r}') = x_1x_1'(\mathbf{e}_1, \mathbf{e}_1)+x_2x_2'(\mathbf{e}_2, \mathbf{e}_2)+x_3x_3'(\mathbf{e}_3, \mathbf{e}_3)+(x_1x_2'+x_2x_1')(\mathbf{e}_1, \mathbf{e}_2)$$
$$+(x_2x_3'+x_3x_2')(\mathbf{e}_2, \mathbf{e}_3)+(x_3x_1'+x_1x_3')(\mathbf{e}_3, \mathbf{e}_1).$$

Then the properties (3.12) of the base vectors $\mathbf{e}_1$, $\mathbf{e}_2$, $\mathbf{e}_3$ give the simple result

$$(\mathbf{r}, \mathbf{r}') = x_1x_1'+x_2x_2'+x_3x_3'. \qquad (3.16)$$

As special cases of (3.16) we have

$$r^2 = (\mathbf{r}, \mathbf{r}) = x_1{}^2+x_2{}^2+x_3{}^2,$$

an expression for the length of $\mathbf{r}$ which is geometrically obvious from Fig. 3.6; also $(\mathbf{r}, \mathbf{r}')=0$ and $\mathbf{r}$ and $\mathbf{r}'$ are perpendicular if

$$x_1x_1'+x_2x_2'+x_3x_3' = 0.$$

The concepts of the length of a vector and of two vectors being perpendicular may appear peculiar to position vectors in ordinary space. Nevertheless we can generalize these concepts and apply them to any vector space if we can find a consistent way of defining the 'scalar product' $(\mathbf{r}, \mathbf{s})$ of two 'vectors' of the space. Any definition we choose must satisfy the basic requirements (3.14) and (3.15) of a product and must also have the properties that $(\mathbf{r}, \mathbf{s})=0$ if either $\mathbf{r}=\mathbf{0}$ or $\mathbf{s}=\mathbf{0}$ and that if $\mathbf{r}\neq\mathbf{0}$ the product $(\mathbf{r}, \mathbf{r})$ of a vector with itself must be a positive number different from zero.

We assume that this can be done for our vector space. (In the next section we discuss the appropriate form to take for the scalar product in a function space.) Then a *unit vector* in the space is one whose scalar product with itself is unity. If $\mathbf{r}$ is any vector of the space ($\neq\mathbf{0}$) then the vector $\mathbf{r}'=(1/N)\mathbf{r}$ is a unit vector where $N^2=(\mathbf{r}, \mathbf{r})$. If two nonzero vectors of the space are such that their scalar product vanishes they are said to be *orthogonal*. This is the analogue of the notion of two perpendicular vectors in ordinary space.

Two orthogonal vectors are necessarily linearly independent for if

$$\alpha\mathbf{r}+\beta\mathbf{s} = \mathbf{0},$$

we have $0=(\mathbf{r}, \mathbf{0})=(\mathbf{r}, \alpha\mathbf{r}+\beta\mathbf{s})=\alpha(\mathbf{r}, \mathbf{r})+\beta(\mathbf{r}, \mathbf{s})$. Then if the vectors $\mathbf{r}$ and $\mathbf{s}$ are orthogonal so that $(\mathbf{r}, \mathbf{s})=0$, this equation gives $\alpha=0$ since $(\mathbf{r}, \mathbf{r})\neq0$. Similarly $\beta=0$ and these are the only values of α and β that are consistent with the equation.

We can now show that it is always possible to find a set of n orthogonal unit vectors in an n-dimensional vector space. For suppose that by the process described in Section 3.3 we have obtained n linearly independent base vectors $\mathbf{a}_1, \mathbf{a}_2, \ldots, \mathbf{a}_n$. Then if $\mathbf{a}_1$ and $\mathbf{a}_2$ are not orthogonal, so that $(\mathbf{a}_1, \mathbf{a}_2)\neq0$, we can produce the pair of vectors $\mathbf{a}_1$ and $\mathbf{a}'_2=\mathbf{a}_2-\beta\mathbf{a}_1$ where $\beta=(\mathbf{a}_1, \mathbf{a}_2)/(\mathbf{a}_1, \mathbf{a}_1)$. These vectors are still linearly independent and they are orthogonal, as the reader can readily verify by expanding the product $(\mathbf{a}_1, \mathbf{a}_2-\beta\mathbf{a}_1)$. If now $\mathbf{a}_3$ is not orthogonal to $\mathbf{a}_1$ and $\mathbf{a}'_2$, we can form a new vector $\mathbf{a}'_3$ which is a linear combination of $\mathbf{a}_1, \mathbf{a}'_2$ and $\mathbf{a}_3$ and which is orthogonal to both $\mathbf{a}_1$ and $\mathbf{a}'_2$. We can proceed in this fashion until we have found altogether n orthogonal vectors $\mathbf{a}_1, \mathbf{a}'_2, \mathbf{a}'_3, \ldots, \mathbf{a}'_n$. Finally we can turn these into unit vectors by multiplying them by the appropriate factors.

These n orthogonal unit vectors can serve as a basis for a coordinate system in our vector space. We call such a coordinate system an *orthogonal coordinate system* and say that its base vectors $\mathbf{e}_1, \mathbf{e}_2, \ldots, \mathbf{e}_n$ form an *orthonormal* basis for the coordinate system. These base vectors satisfy the equations

$$(\mathbf{e}_i, \mathbf{e}_j) = \delta_{ij} \quad (i = 1, 2, \ldots, n; j = 1, 2, \ldots, n) \quad (3.17)$$

where δ_{ij} is defined by (3.13).

If $\mathbf{r}=x_1\mathbf{e}_1+x_2\mathbf{e}_2+\cdots+x_n\mathbf{e}_n$ and $\mathbf{r}'=x'_1\mathbf{e}_1+x'_2\mathbf{e}_2+\cdots+x'_n\mathbf{e}_n$ are two vectors of the space, their scalar product is

$$(\mathbf{r}, \mathbf{r}') = x_1x'_1+x_2x'_2+x_3x'_3+\cdots+x_nx'_n. \quad (3.18)$$

In all this we have tacitly assumed that we are dealing with a *real* vector space in which the components of the vectors are all real. The more general case in which we can allow them to be complex numbers is dealt with at the end of the next section.

3.5 Orthogonal Functions

In this section we show how it is possible to apply the general idea of a scalar product and of orthogonality to the functions of a function space. We think first of a function space consisting of *real* functions of a number of variables and wish to define a suitable scalar product (f, g) of two functions f and g of the space. This product must be a number which is associated with the two functions as a whole; it cannot depend on their values for a particular set of values of the variables of which they are functions. It is natural, there-fore, to think of integrating the functions over a range of values of their arguments and we proceed to define the scalar product of two real functions f and g by

$$(f, g) = \int fg \, d\tau, \tag{3.19}$$

where $\int \cdots d\tau$ indicates integration, with respect to all the variables of which f and g are functions, over a suitably defined range. The scalar product (f, g) is then simply a number associated with the functions f and g and it is easily seen that it has the required properties, namely

$$(f, bg) = b(f, g) \quad \text{and} \quad (f, g+h) = (f, g)+(f, h), \tag{3.20}$$

where f, g, h are any three functions and b is any number. The scalar product of a function with itself is

$$(f, f) = \int f^2 \, d\tau. \tag{3.21}$$

The right-hand side here is $\geqslant 0$, and $(f, f)=0$ if and only if f is the function which is zero everywhere. We write, if $f \not\equiv 0$,

$$(f, f) = N_f^2.$$

We call the real number N_f, which is analogous to the length of a position vector, the *normalization* of f. If f is such that $N_f = 1$ we say that f is *normalized*; any given function f can always be turned into a normalized function by multiplying it by the factor $(1/N_f)$ and such normalized functions are 'unit vectors' in the function space.

Two non-zero functions f and g which are such that $(f, g)=0$ are said to be orthogonal and the arguments of Section 3.4 show that in a function space of n dimensions we can always find n orthogonal and normalized basis functions $f_1, f_2, \ldots, f_n$ which satisfy the relations

$$(f_i, f_j) = \delta_{ij} \quad (i = 1, 2, \ldots, n; j = 1, 2, \ldots, n). \tag{3.22}$$

In terms of such a set of orthonormal base functions, if two functions of the space are

$$f = \alpha_1 f_1 + \alpha_2 f_2 + \cdots + \alpha_n f_n \quad \text{and} \quad f' = \alpha_1' f_1 + \alpha_2' f_2 + \cdots + \alpha_n' f_n,$$

then
$$(f, f') = \alpha_1 \alpha_1' + \alpha_2 \alpha_2' + \cdots + \alpha_n \alpha_n'.$$

In particular the normalization of f is given by

$$N_f^2 = \alpha_1^2 + \alpha_2^2 + \cdots + \alpha_n^2, \tag{3.23}$$

and f and f' are orthogonal if

$$\alpha_1 \alpha_1' + \alpha_2 \alpha_2' + \cdots + \alpha_n \alpha_n' = 0. \tag{3.24}$$

EXAMPLES

(i) The function space formed by the solutions of (3.6) consists of functions of the form $f = \alpha_1 f_1 + \alpha_2 f_2$ where $f_1 = \cos x$ and $f_2 = \sin x$. If we consider these functions for values of x between $-\pi$ and π we could define the scalar product to be

$$(f, f') = \int_{-\pi}^{\pi} f(x) f'(x) \, dx.$$

With this definition we find

$$(f_1, f_1) = \int_{-\pi}^{\pi} \cos^2 x \, dx = \pi,$$

$$(f_2, f_2) = \int_{-\pi}^{\pi} \sin^2 x \, dx = \pi,$$

$$(f_1, f_2) = \int_{-\pi}^{\pi} \cos x \sin x \, dx = 0.$$

Thus f_1 and f_2 are orthogonal to each other and the functions

$$f_1' = \frac{1}{\sqrt{\pi}} f_1 \quad \text{and} \quad f_2' = \frac{1}{\sqrt{\pi}} f_2$$

will be normalized and will form an orthonormal basis for this two dimensional function space.

(ii) Consider the wave functions (or atomic orbitals) of a p electron in an atom. A p state has a threefold degeneracy and in terms of an (x, y, z) coordinate system in physical space we can take the three linearly independent functions

$$p_x = F(r)x/r, \quad p_y = F(r)y/r, \quad p_z = F(r)z/r,$$

where $F(r)$ is the radial wave function, as the base functions of the three-dimensional function space of the p atomic orbitals. Then any real p orbital can be expressed as a linear combination of p_x, p_y, p_z, say

$$\psi = \beta_1 p_x + \beta_2 p_y + \beta_3 p_z$$

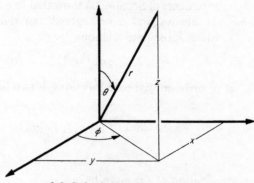

3.8 Spherical polar coordinates.

where $\beta_1, \beta_2, \beta_3$ are three real numbers. The scalar product of two functions ψ and ψ' in this space is the threefold integral

$$(\psi, \psi') = \int_{-\infty}^{\infty} \int_{-\infty}^{\infty} \int_{-\infty}^{\infty} \psi \psi' \, dx \, dy \, dz.$$

This type of integral is made easier to handle by introducing spherical polar coordinates (r, θ, ϕ) as in Fig. 3.8; these are such that

$$x = r \sin \theta \cos \phi, \quad y = r \sin \theta \sin \phi, \quad z = r \cos \theta.$$

In the integral the volume element $dxdydz$ is replaced by $r^2 dr \sin \theta d\theta d\phi$ and r ranges from 0 to ∞, θ from 0 to π, ϕ from 0 to 2π. Then

$$(p_y, p_z) = \int_0^\infty [F(r)]^2 r^2 \, dr \int_0^\pi \sin \theta \cos \theta (\sin \theta \, d\theta) \int_0^{2\pi} \sin \phi \, d\phi = 0.$$

Similarly, one finds

$$(p_x, p_y) = (p_z, p_x) = 0,$$

so that our three base functions are all orthogonal to each other. They clearly all have the same normalization N and

$$N^2 = (p_z, p_z) = \int_0^\infty [F(r)]^2 r^2 \, dr \int_0^\pi \cos^2 \theta (\sin \theta \, d\theta) \int_0^{2\pi} d\phi$$

$$= \tfrac{2}{3} \cdot 2\pi,$$

if we impose the normalization condition

$$\int_0^\infty [F(r)]^2 r^2 \, dr = 1$$

on the radial function $F(r)$ as is usually done. Dividing p_x, p_y, p_z by N then gives three normalized functions

$$p_1 = (3/4\pi)^{\frac{1}{2}} F(r)x/r; \quad p_2 = (3/4\pi)^{\frac{1}{2}} F(r)y/r; \quad p_3 = (3/4\pi)^{\frac{1}{2}} F(r)z/r \quad (3.25)$$

which form an orthonormal basis for the function space of the p atomic orbitals. With respect to this basis, a real p orbital can be written as

$$\psi = \alpha_1 p_1 + \alpha_2 p_2 + \alpha_3 p_3.$$

It will be normalized if

$$\alpha_1{}^2 + \alpha_2{}^2 + \alpha_3{}^2 = 1,$$

and two such functions with 'components' $(\alpha_1, \alpha_2, \alpha_3)$ and $(\alpha_1', \alpha_2', \alpha_3')$ will be orthogonal to each other if

$$\alpha_1 \alpha_1' + \alpha_2 \alpha_2' + \alpha_3 \alpha_3' = 0.$$

(iii) In the same way the d atomic orbitals form a five-dimensional function space and we can take the five normalized and orthogonal d orbitals

$$d_{xy} = cF(r)xy/r^2,$$

$$d_{yz} = cF(r)yz/r^2,$$

$$d_{zx} = cF(r)zx/r^2, \quad (3.26)$$

$$d_{x^2-y^2} = cF(r)(x^2-y^2)/2r^2,$$

$$d_{z^2} = cF(r)(3z^2-r^2)/2\sqrt{3}r^2,$$

where the radial wave function $F(r)$ satisfies

$$\int_0^\infty [F(r)]^2 r^2 \, dr = 1$$

and $c = (15/4\pi)^{\frac{1}{2}}$ is a normalizing constant.

So far we have assumed that all the functions of our function space are real. If they are complex we re-define the scalar product of two functions and write

$$(f, g) = \int f^*g \, d\tau, \tag{3.27}$$

where the asterisk denotes the complex conjugate. This means that in general (f, g) is a complex number and that

$$(f, g)^* = (g, f): \tag{3.28}$$

the order of the factors in the product is important and must be maintained. This definition satisfies the requirements (3.20) and it gives the normalization of a function f as

$$(f,f) = \int f^*f \, d\tau = \int |f|^2 \, d\tau.$$

This is a real number, positive and different from zero for any non-zero function f and we can still write

$$(f,f) = N_f{}^2,$$

where N_f is a real number, and use this to normalize f.

The condition for the orthogonality of two functions is $(f, g)=0$; we can still introduce an orthonormal set of base functions $f_1, f_2, \ldots, f_n$ and write a general function of our space as

$$f = \alpha_1 f_1 + \alpha_2 f_2 + \cdots + \alpha_n f_n, \tag{3.29}$$

where the components $(\alpha_1, \alpha_2, \ldots, \alpha_n)$ will be complex numbers. The scalar product of two functions f and f' with components $(\alpha_1, \ldots, \alpha_n)$ and $(\alpha_1', \ldots, \alpha_n')$ is

$$(f, f') = \alpha_1^* \alpha_2' + \cdots + \alpha_n^* \alpha_n', \tag{3.30}$$

so that the normalization of f is given by

$$(f,f) = \alpha_1^* \alpha_1 + \alpha_2^* \alpha_2 + \cdots + \alpha_n^* \alpha_n = |\alpha_1|^2 + |\alpha_2|^2 + \cdots + |\alpha_n|^2, \tag{3.31}$$

and f and f' are orthogonal to each other if

$$\alpha_1^* \alpha_1' + \alpha_2^* \alpha_2' + \cdots + \alpha_n^* \alpha_n' = 0. \tag{3.32}$$

EXAMPLES

(i) Instead of taking the functions p_1, p_2, p_3 of (3.25) as the basis for the three-dimensional function space of the p atomic orbitals one might take the three linearly independent combinations

$$p_{+1}' = \frac{1}{\sqrt{2}} (p_1 + ip_2),$$

$$p_{-1}' = \frac{1}{\sqrt{2}} (p_1 - ip_2), \tag{3.33}$$

$$p_0' = p_3.$$

These are examples of equations like (3.29) with complex coefficients (α_1, α_2, α_3). Thus, with respect to p_1, p_2, p_3 as basis, p'_{+1} has components $(1/\sqrt{2}, i/\sqrt{2}, 0)$, p'_{-1} has components $(1/\sqrt{2}, -i/\sqrt{2}, 0)$, and p'_0 has components $(0, 0, 1)$. Using (3.31) and (3.32) it is readily verified that p'_{+1}, p'_{-1}, p'_0 are all normalized and orthogonal, so that they form a possible orthonormal basis for the function space of p atomic orbitals. In terms of spherical polar coordinates these functions may be written as

$$p'_{\pm 1} = (3/8\pi)^{\frac{1}{2}}F(r)(x \pm iy)/r = (3/8\pi)^{\frac{1}{2}}F(r) \sin \theta \, e^{\pm i\phi}, \qquad (3.34a)$$

since $(x \pm iy)/r = \sin \theta (\cos \phi \pm i \sin \phi) = \sin \theta \, e^{\pm i\phi}$;

$$p'_0 = (3/4\pi)^{\frac{1}{2}}F(r) \cos \theta. \qquad (3.34b)$$

They are p atomic orbitals whose magnetic quantum numbers are $m = +1, -1, 0$.

(ii) In similar fashion one may construct other orthonormal sets of complex d functions from the set defined in (3.26). One such set of five functions is d'_{+2}, d'_{+1}, d'_0, d'_{-1}, d'_{-2} where

$$d'_{\pm 2} = \frac{1}{\sqrt{2}} (d_{x^2-y^2} \pm id_{xy}) = (15/32\pi)^{\frac{1}{2}}F(r) \sin^2 \theta \, e^{\pm 2i\phi},$$

$$d'_{\pm 1} = \frac{1}{\sqrt{2}} (d_{xz} \pm id_{yz}) = (15/8\pi)^{\frac{1}{2}}F(r) \sin \theta \cos \theta \, e^{\pm i\phi}, \qquad (3.35)$$

$$d'_0 = d_{z^2} = (5/16\pi)^{\frac{1}{2}}F(r)(3 \cos^2 \theta - 1).$$

These are the d orbitals whose magnetic quantum numbers are $m = \pm 2, \pm 1, 0$.

3.6 Vector Spaces and Molecules

Consider a molecule made up of N nuclei and n electrons. We can introduce an orthonormal coordinate system, with base vectors $\mathbf{e}_1$, $\mathbf{e}_2$, $\mathbf{e}_3$, into the physical space in which these $n + N$ particles move and describe the position of the kth particle by its coordinates $(x_1^{(k)}, x_2^{(k)}, x_3^{(k)})$ with respect to this basis. (The suffix k serves to label the different particles and takes the values $k = 1, 2, \ldots, n+N$.) The positions of all the particles making up the molecule are then specified by the values of the $3(n+N)$ quantities $x_1^{(1)}, x_2^{(1)}, x_3^{(1)}; \ldots;$ $x_1^{(k)}, x_2^{(k)}, x_3^{(k)}; \ldots; x_1^{(n+N)}, x_2^{(n+N)}, x_3^{(n+N)}$. Any particular set of numerical values of these quantities describes a specific *configuration* of the molecule.

Instead of regarding these $3(n+N)$ numbers as describing the positions of $n+N$ particles moving in a common three-dimensional space, we may regard them as the components of a single vector in a space of $3(n+N)$ dimensions and say that each possible configuration of the molecule is represented by a single 'point' in this *configuration space*. When we think of the configurations of the molecule in this way we must suppose that each particle is referred to its own individual coordinate system in physical space, with base vectors $\mathbf{e}_1^{(k)}$, $\mathbf{e}_2^{(k)}$, $\mathbf{e}_3^{(k)}$, $k = 1, 2, \ldots, n+N$; then we can take the set of $3(n+N)$ vectors $\mathbf{e}_1^{(1)}, \ldots, \mathbf{e}_3^{(n+N)}$ as a basis for the configuration space of the molecule.

Any particular state of motion of the particles constituting the molecule will be described by a wave function which is a function of all the coordinates. This wave function associates a numerical value with each possible configuration of the molecule; i.e. it attaches a number to each point in the configuration space of the molecule. As we have seen, the wave functions belonging to any particular energy level of the molecule themselves form a function space whose dimension is equal to the degeneracy of the energy level concerned.

Thus in dealing with a molecule we are concerned with vector spaces at different levels of abstraction: the physical space in which the particles that constitute the molecule are moving, the configuration space of the molecule as a whole, and the function spaces associated with the various energy levels of the molecule.

The complete Schrödinger equation for all the particles of a molecule is extremely complicated. The Born–Oppenheimer approximation is, however, sufficient for most purposes. This approximation allows us to discuss separately the translations and rotations of the molecular framework as a whole, the vibrations of the nuclei forming the framework about their equilibrium positions, and the motions of the electrons moving in a fixed framework of nuclei. Thus, in discussing the electronic structure of a molecule, one uses a $3n$-dimensional configuration space for the electrons and considers the function spaces formed by the electronic wave functions in which the variables are the coordinates $x_1^{(1)}, \ldots, x_3^{(n)}$ of the n electrons and in which the coordinates of the nuclei appear as fixed parameters. When the vibrations of the molecule are under consideration, one uses a configuration space whose 'points' correspond to displacements of the nuclei from their equilibrium positions and one considers the function spaces formed by the vibrational wave functions whose variables are these displacements.

In both these problems one is concerned with vector spaces which are intimately connected with the framework of the molecule formed by its nuclei in their equilibrium positions. The symmetry of this framework, summed up in the set of symmetry operations which constitutes the point group of the molecule, can be used to describe and classify these vector spaces; it is the task of the following chapters to show how this is done.

Chapter 4

OPERATORS, MATRICES, REPRESENTATIONS

4.1 Symmetry Operations and Operators

The connection between the various vector spaces that are associated with a molecule and its point group depends upon an extension of the idea of a symmetry operation. In the discussion of Chapter 2 we regarded a symmetry operation simply as a rotation or a reflection or a combination of rotations and reflections which moved a given molecular framework into coincidence with itself. We now proceed to think of symmetry operations in a more active way, regarding them as operators which can act upon the vectors of a vector space to produce other vectors of the space according to some definite rule.

As an example of this way of thinking of a symmetry operation consider the n electrons of a molecule in the approximation in which the nuclei forming the molecular framework are regarded as fixed, and consider a particular configuration X of the electrons in which they occupy the points $P_1, \ldots, P_k, \ldots, P_n$. Now take a particular symmetry operation R and imagine that it is applied to the electron positions so that each point P_k is rotated or reflected into a new point P_k' and X is changed into a new configuration X'. We may say that R operates on X to produce X'; there will be a definite relation, characteristic of R, between the coordinates of the points P_k which define X and the coordinates of the points P_k' which define X'.

We may further extend the notion of a symmetry operation and imagine its effect on the wave function Ψ of the electrons. This wave function associates a definite number $\Psi(X)$ with every possible configuration X of the electrons and an obvious way of defining the effect of R on Ψ is to say that when R changes X to X' it transfers the value that Ψ had at X to the new configuration X'. In this way R operates on Ψ to change it into a new function Ψ' whose value at X' is equal to the value of Ψ at X:

$$\Psi'(X') = \Psi(X).$$

These examples indicate how it is possible to regard a symmetry operation as an operator which acts upon a general vector of a vector space, in our examples a point in configuration space or a function of a function space, to change it into some other vector. The remainder of this chapter is concerned to give quantitative expression to this idea and to show how it gives rise to the concept of the representation of a group by means of matrices. Chapters 5 and 6 continue the mathematical development of the theory of group representations; once the theory has been established, we shall be able, in Chapter 7, to return to the ideas sketched out above and to show their relevance to the quantum mechanical problem of dealing with the Schrödinger equation for the electrons or nuclei of a molecule.

4.2 Operators and Matrices in Physical Space

We begin the discussion of the theory of group representations by considering the effect of a symmetry operation on a point in ordinary three-dimensional physical space. Suppose that we introduce an orthogonal coordinate system (coordinates x, y, z or x_1, x_2, x_3) with an orthonormal set of base vectors e_1, e_2, e_3. The origin O of this coordinate system is to be at a point which is left unmoved by all the symmetry operations of the molecule under consideration.

The effect of a symmetry operation R on the position vector $\mathbf{p}$ of a point P is to rotate it about an axis passing through the origin or to reflect it in a plane passing through the origin or to perform a combination of these operations on $\mathbf{p}$. The result will be to change $\mathbf{p}$ into a new vector $\mathbf{p}'$, the position vector of the point P' to which P is moved by R; we express this relation between $\mathbf{p}'$ and $\mathbf{p}$ by writing

$$\mathbf{p}' = R\mathbf{p}.$$

The operation R changes the direction of $\mathbf{p}$ but cannot change its length. Hence if a is any number we have

$$R(a\mathbf{p}) = a(R\mathbf{p}). \tag{4.1}$$

Further, the parallelogram relation between the vectors $\mathbf{p}$, $\mathbf{q}$ and $\mathbf{p}+\mathbf{q}$ (Fig. 3.1) is not altered if the parallelogram is rotated about an axis through its vertex O or if it is reflected in a plane containing O. Thus $R(\mathbf{p}+\mathbf{q})$ must be the diagonal of the parallelogram whose sides are $R\mathbf{p}$ and $R\mathbf{q}$, i.e.

$$R(\mathbf{p}+\mathbf{q}) = R\mathbf{p} + R\mathbf{q}. \tag{4.2}$$

In this notation the symbol R, which stands for the symmetry operation, is an *operator* which operates on any position vector $\mathbf{p}$ to produce a new vector $\mathbf{p}' = R\mathbf{p}$. Equations (4.1) and (4.2) show that it is a linear operator and that we can treat the combination of symbols $R\mathbf{p}$ as if it were an ordinary product.

Consider now a general point P of space with position vector

$$\mathbf{p} = x_1\mathbf{e}_1 + x_2\mathbf{e}_2 + x_3\mathbf{e}_3. \tag{4.3}$$

The operator R changes this to the position vector $\mathbf{p}'$ of some other point P' and from (4.3), using (4.1) and (4.2),

$$\mathbf{p}' = R\mathbf{p} = x_1(R\mathbf{e}_1) + x_2(R\mathbf{e}_2) + x_3(R\mathbf{e}_3). \tag{4.4}$$

The problem then is to express the three vectors $R\mathbf{e}_1$, $R\mathbf{e}_2$, $R\mathbf{e}_3$ in terms of the base vectors $\mathbf{e}_1$, $\mathbf{e}_2$, $\mathbf{e}_3$. These new vectors are the position vectors of points in space and so must be expressible in the form (4.3). We write

$$R\mathbf{e}_1 = r_{11}\mathbf{e}_1 + r_{21}\mathbf{e}_2 + r_{31}\mathbf{e}_3,$$

$$R\mathbf{e}_2 = r_{12}\mathbf{e}_1 + r_{22}\mathbf{e}_2 + r_{32}\mathbf{e}_3, \tag{4.5}$$

$$R\mathbf{e}_3 = r_{13}\mathbf{e}_1 + r_{23}\mathbf{e}_2 + r_{33}\mathbf{e}_3,$$

or, in more compact form,

$$R\mathbf{e}_k = \sum_{j=1}^{3} r_{jk}\mathbf{e}_j \quad (k = 1, 2 \text{ or } 3). \tag{4.5'}$$

In these equations the three sets of numbers (r_{1k}, r_{2k}, r_{3k}) with $k = 1, 2, 3$ are the components of the vectors $R\mathbf{e}_k$ with respect to the original base vectors $\mathbf{e}_1$, $\mathbf{e}_2$, $\mathbf{e}_3$.

Substituting (4.5) into (4.4) gives

$$\mathbf{p}' = R\mathbf{p} = x_1(r_{11}\mathbf{e}_1 + r_{21}\mathbf{e}_2 + r_{31}\mathbf{e}_3) + x_2(r_{12}\mathbf{e}_1 + r_{22}\mathbf{e}_2 + r_{32}\mathbf{e}_3)$$
$$+ x_3(r_{13}\mathbf{e}_1 + r_{23}\mathbf{e}_2 + r_{33}\mathbf{e}_3).$$

Hence, collecting up the coefficients of $\mathbf{e}_1$, $\mathbf{e}_2$, $\mathbf{e}_3$, we obtain

$$\mathbf{p}' = R\mathbf{p} = x_1'\mathbf{e}_1 + x_2'\mathbf{e}_2 + x_3'\mathbf{e}_3,$$

where

$$x_1' = r_{11}x_1 + r_{12}x_2 + r_{13}x_3,$$

$$x_2' = r_{21}x_1 + r_{22}x_2 + r_{23}x_3, \tag{4.6}$$

$$x_3' = r_{31}x_1 + r_{32}x_2 + r_{33}x_3,$$

or, in more compact form,

$$x_k' = \sum_{j=1}^{3} r_{kj}x_j \quad (k = 1, 2 \text{ or } 3). \tag{4.6'}$$

The reader should carefully note the different ways in which the summation over the suffix j appears in (4.5') and (4.6'). (Readers unfamiliar with the suffix notation are referred to Appendix B.)

To summarize these results we can say that the effect of the operator R on the base vectors of the coordinate system is given by equations (4.5) in which the coefficients r_{jk} are numbers which depend on the relation between R and the base vectors. Once these numbers are known equations (4.6) give the relations between the coordinates (x_1, x_2, x_3) of a general point P and the coordinates (x'_1, x'_2, x'_3) of the point P' into which P is moved by R. The set of nine numbers r_{jk} ($j, k = 1, 2, 3$) gives a numerical representation of the operator R with respect to the base vectors e_1, e_2, e_3.

The numbers r_{jk} representing R are conveniently displayed by writing them down in a square array of three rows and three columns. Written in this form we say that they form a *square matrix* and we denote this matrix by the symbol R:

$$R = \begin{bmatrix} r_{11} & r_{12} & r_{13} \\ r_{21} & r_{22} & r_{23} \\ r_{31} & r_{32} & r_{33} \end{bmatrix}. \tag{4.7}$$

The numbers $r_{11}, r_{12}, \ldots, r_{33}$ are the *matrix elements*. The first suffix labels the row, the second suffix labels the column, so that r_{jk} is the element which lies at the intersection of row j with column k. The way in which R is related to (4.5) and (4.6) should be noted; the components (r_{1k}, r_{2k}, r_{3k}) of the vector Re_k are written in order down the kth *column* while the coefficients (r_{k1}, r_{k2}, r_{k3}) which appear in equations (4.6) for the x'_k are written across the kth *row* of the matrix.

The matrices representing the different types of symmetry operations are easily obtained and are given below.

(a) The identical operation

Since E leaves everything unchanged we have

$$Ee_1 = 1 \cdot e_1 + 0 \cdot e_2 + 0 \cdot e_3,$$
$$Ee_2 = 0 \cdot e_1 + 1 \cdot e_2 + 0 \cdot e_3,$$
$$Ee_3 = 0 \cdot e_1 + 0 \cdot e_2 + 1 \cdot e_3.$$

The matrix representing E is therefore

$$E = \begin{bmatrix} 1 & 0 & 0 \\ 0 & 1 & 0 \\ 0 & 0 & 1 \end{bmatrix}. \tag{4.8}$$

Such a matrix with unity in each diagonal place and zero everywhere else is called a *unit matrix*.

(b) A rotation about e_3

Suppose that $R = C(\alpha)$ is a rotation through an angle α about the e_3 axis, positive α corresponding to a right-handed screw rotation about the direction of e_3. Then e_3 is left unchanged by the rotation whilst e_1 and e_2 are rotated to the positions $C(\alpha)e_1$ and $C(\alpha)e_2$ shown in Fig. 4.1(a). These are unit vectors with no components along the e_3 direction; the x_1 and x_2 components of $C(\alpha)e_1$ are $\cos \alpha$ and $\sin \alpha$ respectively while those of $C(\alpha)e_2$ are $-\sin \alpha$ and $\cos \alpha$. Thus

$$
\begin{aligned}
C(\alpha)e_1 &= \quad\cos \alpha \cdot e_1 + \sin \alpha \cdot e_2 + 0 \cdot e_3, \\
C(\alpha)e_2 &= -\sin \alpha \cdot e_1 + \cos \alpha \cdot e_2 + 0 \cdot e_3, \\
C(\alpha)e_3 &= \quad 0 \cdot e_1 \quad + \quad 0 \cdot e_2 \quad + 1 \cdot e_3,
\end{aligned}
\tag{4.9}
$$

and the matrix of $C(\alpha)$ with respect to this coordinate system is

$$
\mathsf{C}(\alpha) = \begin{bmatrix} \cos \alpha & -\sin \alpha & 0 \\ \sin \alpha & \cos \alpha & 0 \\ 0 & 0 & 1 \end{bmatrix}.
\tag{4.10}
$$

If the rotation $C(\alpha)$ takes the point (x_1, x_2, x_3) to the point with coordinates (x_1', x_2', x_3') equations (4.6) give

$$
\begin{aligned}
x_1' &= \cos \alpha \cdot x_1 - \sin \alpha \cdot x_2 + 0 \cdot x_3, \\
x_2' &= \sin \alpha \cdot x_1 + \cos \alpha \cdot x_2 + 0 \cdot x_3, \\
x_3' &= \quad 0 \cdot x_1 \quad + \quad 0 \cdot x_2 \quad + 1 \cdot x_3.
\end{aligned}
\tag{4.11}
$$

The geometrical meaning of these equations is illustrated in Fig. 4.1(b).

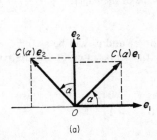
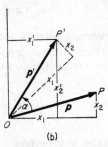

(a)   (b)

4.1 The effect of a rotation about e_3: (a) on the base vectors, (b) on a general point.

(e$_3$ is perpendicular to the plane of the paper.)

(c) A reflection in a plane containing e_3

If $R = \sigma$, a reflection in a plane containing the e_3 axis which makes an angle β with the plane of e_3 and e_1, we have the situation shown in Fig. 4.2. From this figure we can see that

$$
\begin{aligned}
\sigma e_1 &= \cos 2\beta \cdot e_1 + \sin 2\beta \cdot e_2 + 0 \cdot e_3, \\
\sigma e_2 &= \sin 2\beta \cdot e_1 - \cos 2\beta \cdot e_2 + 0 \cdot e_3, \\
\sigma e_3 &= \quad 0 \cdot e_1 \quad + \quad 0 \cdot e_2 \quad + 1 \cdot e_3.
\end{aligned}
\tag{4.12}
$$

Hence the matrix representing σ is

$$
\sigma = \begin{bmatrix} \cos 2\beta & \sin 2\beta & 0 \\ \sin 2\beta & -\cos 2\beta & 0 \\ 0 & 0 & 1 \end{bmatrix}.
\tag{4.13}
$$

(d) A reflection in the plane perpendicular to e_3

A reflection in the plane of e_1 and e_2 will leave these two vectors unaltered and will reverse the direction of e_3. Thus it will be represented by the matrix

$$\sigma_h = \begin{bmatrix} 1 & 0 & 0 \\ 0 & 1 & 0 \\ 0 & 0 & -1 \end{bmatrix}. \tag{4.14}$$

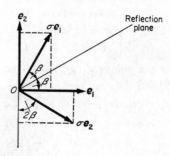

4.2 The effect of a reflection in a plane containing e_3 on the base vectors.

(*e_3 is perpendicular to the plane of the paper.*)

(e) An improper rotation about e_3

The effect of the improper rotation $S(\alpha)$ on e_1 and e_2 will be as for $C(\alpha)$ and it will also reverse the direction of e_3. Hence it is represented by the matrix

$$S(\alpha) = \begin{bmatrix} \cos\alpha & -\sin\alpha & 0 \\ \sin\alpha & \cos\alpha & 0 \\ 0 & 0 & -1 \end{bmatrix}. \tag{4.15}$$

(f) Inversion in the origin

The effect of the inversion is simply to reverse the directions of e_1, e_2, e_3 and the corresponding matrix is

$$i = \begin{bmatrix} -1 & 0 & 0 \\ 0 & -1 & 0 \\ 0 & 0 & -1 \end{bmatrix}. \tag{4.16}$$

Note that, with the exception of E and i, these matrices depend on how we choose the directions of the coordinate axes. A rotation through an angle α about some line different from the e_3 axis would have a matrix whose elements are different from (4.10) and a reflection in a plane which does not contain the e_3 axis would have a matrix different from (4.13). These special cases are, however, sufficient for our purposes.

4.3 Matrix Products and Inverses

In Section 2.2 we defined the product $T = SR$ of two symmetry operations S and R as the symmetry operation which is the result of first applying R and following it by S. In our representation of symmetry operations by their effects on position vectors we accordingly say that if R changes $\mathbf{p}$ to $\mathbf{p}'$ and S changes $\mathbf{p}'$ to $\mathbf{p}''$ then the product operation $T = SR$ will change $\mathbf{p}$ directly to $\mathbf{p}''$;

$$Tp = (SR)\mathbf{p} = S(R\mathbf{p}). \tag{4.17}$$

The matrix representing T is found by calculating the effects of SR on the base vectors $\mathbf{e}_1$, $\mathbf{e}_2$, $\mathbf{e}_3$. Suppose that R is represented by R with elements r_{jk}, that S is represented by S with elements s_{ij}, and that $T = SR$ is represented by T with elements t_{ik}, i.e. in accordance with (4.5′) suppose that

$$R\mathbf{e}_k = \sum_{j=1}^{3} r_{jk}\mathbf{e}_j; \qquad S\mathbf{e}_j = \sum_{i=1}^{3} s_{ij}\mathbf{e}_i;$$

and that

$$T\mathbf{e}_k = \sum_{i=1}^{3} t_{ik}\mathbf{e}_i. \tag{4.18}$$

We wish to express the elements t_{ik} of T in terms of those of R and S. This can be done as follows:

$$T\mathbf{e}_k = (SR)\mathbf{e}_k = S(R\mathbf{e}_k) = S\left(\sum_{j=1}^{3} r_{jk}\mathbf{e}_j \right) = \sum_{j=1}^{3} r_{jk}(S\mathbf{e}_j)$$

$$= \sum_{j=1}^{3} r_{jk}\left(\sum_{i=1}^{3} s_{ij}\mathbf{e}_i \right)$$

i.e.
$$T\mathbf{e}_k = \sum_{i=1}^{3} \left(\sum_{j=1}^{3} s_{ij}r_{jk} \right)\mathbf{e}_i.$$

This is an equation of exactly the form of (4.18) if we put

$$t_{ik} = \sum_{j=1}^{3} s_{ij}r_{jk}, \tag{4.19}$$

and we therefore deduce that the matrix which represents the product operation $T = SR$ is the matrix whose elements are the numbers t_{ik} defined in terms of the elements of R and S by (4.19). It is natural to call this matrix the *product* of R and S and to symbolize the content of (4.19) by writing

$$T = SR; \tag{4.20}$$

i.e. we say that the matrix representing the product of two symmetry operations is the product of their representative matrices, where by the product of two matrices we understand the relation (4.19) between the elements of the product matrix and the elements of the two matrices forming the factors in the product. This definition of the product of S and R when written out explicitly says that the element in row i and column k of the product matrix is

$$t_{ik} = s_{i1}r_{1k} + s_{i2}r_{2k} + s_{i3}r_{3k};$$

it is the number obtained by multiplying each element of *row i* of S by the corresponding element of *column k* of R and adding up the results. In a schematic way we can say that the *ik* element of SR is

$$[SR]_{ik} = (\text{row } i \text{ of S}) \times (\text{column } k \text{ of R}).$$

EXAMPLES

(i) Suppose that $R = C(\alpha)$ and $S = C(\beta)$, two rotations about the $\mathbf{e}_3$ axis. Their product is the rotation $C(\alpha+\beta)$ about $\mathbf{e}_3$. The matrix which represents R is given by (4.10) and S is represented by a similar matrix with α replaced by β. Thus

$$SR = \begin{bmatrix} \cos\beta & -\sin\beta & 0 \\ \sin\beta & \cos\beta & 0 \\ 0 & 0 & 1 \end{bmatrix} \begin{bmatrix} \cos\alpha & -\sin\alpha & 0 \\ \sin\alpha & \cos\alpha & 0 \\ 0 & 0 & 1 \end{bmatrix}.$$

Applying the rule for forming the product of two matrices, we find:

$$[SR]_{11} = \cos\beta\cos\alpha + (-\sin\beta)\sin\alpha + 0 \quad = \cos(\alpha+\beta),$$
$$[SR]_{12} = \cos\beta(-\sin\alpha) + (-\sin\beta)\cos\alpha + 0 = -\sin(\alpha+\beta),$$
$$[SR]_{13} = \cos\beta\cdot 0 + (-\sin\beta)\cdot 0 + 0.1 \quad = 0.$$

The remaining elements of SR may be calculated in similar fashion. One finds

$$SR = \begin{bmatrix} \cos(\alpha+\beta) & -\sin(\alpha+\beta) & 0 \\ \sin(\alpha+\beta) & \cos(\alpha+\beta) & 0 \\ 0 & 0 & 1 \end{bmatrix},$$

which is, indeed, according to (4.10) the matrix which represents the rotation $C(\alpha+\beta)$.

(ii) The relation $\sigma^2 = E$ for the product of a reflection with itself should be represented in terms of the corresponding matrices by the equation

$$\sigma\sigma = E,$$

and we proceed to verify this. From (4.13) we have

$$\sigma\sigma = \begin{bmatrix} \cos 2\beta & \sin 2\beta & 0 \\ \sin 2\beta & -\cos 2\beta & 0 \\ 0 & 0 & 1 \end{bmatrix} \begin{bmatrix} \cos 2\beta & \sin 2\beta & 0 \\ \sin 2\beta & -\cos 2\beta & 0 \\ 0 & 0 & 1 \end{bmatrix}.$$

Thus

$$[\sigma\sigma]_{11} = \cos 2\beta\cos 2\beta + \sin 2\beta\sin 2\beta + 0 \quad = 1,$$
$$[\sigma\sigma]_{12} = \cos 2\beta\sin 2\beta + \sin 2\beta(-\cos 2\beta) + 0 = 0,$$
$$[\sigma\sigma]_{13} = \cos 2\beta\cdot 0 + \sin 2\beta\cdot 0 + 0.1 \quad = 0.$$

In similar fashion, one finds that $[\sigma\sigma]_{22} = [\sigma\sigma]_{33} = 1$, and that the remaining elements of $\sigma\sigma$ all vanish, which is what we set out to prove.

The definition of the product of two matrices may be extended to products containing any number of factors. Suppose that A, B and C are three matrices with elements a_{ij}, b_{ij}, c_{ij}. Then we can form the matrix BC and multiply it by A (on the left) to form A(BC). Similarly we can form the matrix AB and multiply it (on the right) by C to obtain the matrix (AB)C. The resultant matrices are identical, for by successive applications of the rule (4.19) we obtain for their ik elements the expression:

$$[A(BC)]_{ik} = \sum_j a_{ij}[BC]_{jk} = \sum_j a_{ij}\left(\sum_l b_{jl}c_{lk}\right) = \sum_j \sum_l a_{ij}b_{jl}c_{lk};$$

$$[(AB)C]_{ik} = \sum_l [AB]_{il}c_{lk} = \sum_l \left(\sum_j a_{ij}b_{jl}\right)c_{lk} = \sum_l \sum_j a_{ij}b_{jl}c_{lk}.$$

Thus the matrix product, like the product of symmetry operations, is associative: A(BC)=(AB)C. One must take care, however, in such a product to maintain the correct order of the factors since matrix multiplication is not commutative in general and, except in special cases, $AB \neq BA$.

The inverse of the symmetry operation R is the operation R^{-1} satisfying $RR^{-1}=R^{-1}R=E$. The corresponding relation between their representative matrices is

$$RR^{-1} = R^{-1}R = E$$

and we call the matrix R^{-1} the *inverse* of the matrix R. In general, if A and B are two matrices satisfying

$$AB = BA = E, \tag{4.21}$$

then B is the inverse matrix to A and we write

$$B = A^{-1}.$$

Now E is the unit matrix of (4.8) and its elements are the numbers

$$\delta_{ik} = \begin{cases} 1 & \text{if } i = k \\ 0 & \text{if } i \neq k. \end{cases}$$

Thus equations (4.21) expressed in terms of the elements of A and B become

$$\sum_{j=1}^{3} a_{ij}b_{jk} = \sum_{j=1}^{3} b_{ij}a_{jk} = \delta_{ik} \quad (i, k = 1, 2 \text{ or } 3). \tag{4.22}$$

EXAMPLES

(i) The inverse of the rotation $C(\alpha)$ about the e_3 axis is the rotation $C(-\alpha)$ about the same axis through an equal but opposite angle. The corresponding matrix is given by (4.10) when α is replaced by $-\alpha$;

$$C^{-1}(\alpha) = C(-\alpha) = \begin{bmatrix} \cos(-\alpha) & -\sin(-\alpha) & 0 \\ \sin(-\alpha) & \cos(-\alpha) & 0 \\ 0 & 0 & 1 \end{bmatrix} = \begin{bmatrix} \cos\alpha & \sin\alpha & 0 \\ -\sin\alpha & \cos\alpha & 0 \\ 0 & 0 & 1 \end{bmatrix}.$$

(ii) Since $\sigma^2 = E$, a reflection σ is its own inverse. Consequently the matrix σ is its own inverse, and the same is true for the matrix i representing inversion.

(iii) Just as for symmetry operations (compare (2.4)) the inverse of a product of two matrices R and S is given by

$$(SR)^{-1} = R^{-1}S^{-1}.$$

4.4 Matrix Representations

Our discussion so far has shown that we can effectively replace the abstract symmetry operations of a molecular point group by the matrices that represent their effects on the base vectors of a coordinate system set up in the physical space of the molecule. The product of two symmetry operations is represented by the product of their representative matrices and all the relations that hold between symmetry operations are mirrored by the same relations between their matrices. We say that the set of matrices representing the symmetry operations of a point group forms a *representation of the group*; the set of base vectors e_1, e_2, e_3 of the coordinate system with respect to which the matrices are defined by (4.5) forms the *basis of the representation*.

EXAMPLE: *The point group $\mathscr{C}_{3v}$ of ammonia*

Choose the coordinate system shown in Fig. 4.3. Then the elements of $\mathscr{C}_{3v}$

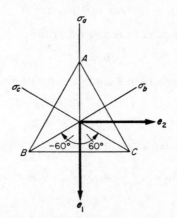

4.3 Coordinate system for $\mathscr{C}_{3v}$.

(e$_3$ is perpendicular to the plane of the paper.)

are: the identical operation E; a rotation C_3 through $120°$ about e_3; a rotation C_3^{-1} through $-120°$ about e_3; three reflections σ_a, σ_b, σ_c in the three planes of symmetry containing e_3. Thus C_3 and C_3^{-1} are represented by matrices of the form (4.10) with $\alpha = 120°$ and $\alpha = -120°$ respectively, and σ_a, σ_b, σ_c are represented by matrices of the form (4.13) with $\beta = 0$, $-60°$, $60°$ respectively. Putting in these values of α and β gives the set of matrices

$$E = \begin{bmatrix} 1 & 0 & 0 \\ 0 & 1 & 0 \\ 0 & 0 & 1 \end{bmatrix}, \quad C_3 = \begin{bmatrix} -\frac{1}{2} & -\frac{\sqrt{3}}{2} & 0 \\ \frac{\sqrt{3}}{2} & -\frac{1}{2} & 0 \\ 0 & 0 & 1 \end{bmatrix}, \quad C_3^{-1} = \begin{bmatrix} -\frac{1}{2} & \frac{\sqrt{3}}{2} & 0 \\ -\frac{\sqrt{3}}{2} & -\frac{1}{2} & 0 \\ 0 & 0 & 1 \end{bmatrix},$$

$$\sigma_a = \begin{bmatrix} 1 & 0 & 0 \\ 0 & -1 & 0 \\ 0 & 0 & 1 \end{bmatrix}, \quad \sigma_b = \begin{bmatrix} -\frac{1}{2} & -\frac{\sqrt{3}}{2} & 0 \\ -\frac{\sqrt{3}}{2} & \frac{1}{2} & 0 \\ 0 & 0 & 1 \end{bmatrix}, \quad \sigma_c = \begin{bmatrix} -\frac{1}{2} & \frac{\sqrt{3}}{2} & 0 \\ \frac{\sqrt{3}}{2} & \frac{1}{2} & 0 \\ 0 & 0 & 1 \end{bmatrix}.$$

Relations between the products of these matrices will mirror the relations (2.1) between the symmetry operations of $\mathscr{C}_{3v}$. Thus for example

$$\sigma_b \sigma_c = \begin{bmatrix} -\frac{1}{2} & -\frac{\sqrt{3}}{2} & 0 \\ -\frac{\sqrt{3}}{2} & \frac{1}{2} & 0 \\ 0 & 0 & 1 \end{bmatrix} \begin{bmatrix} -\frac{1}{2} & \frac{\sqrt{3}}{2} & 0 \\ \frac{\sqrt{3}}{2} & \frac{1}{2} & 0 \\ 0 & 0 & 1 \end{bmatrix}$$

$$= \begin{bmatrix} \frac{1}{4} - \frac{3}{4} + 0 & -\frac{\sqrt{3}}{4} - \frac{\sqrt{3}}{4} + 0 & 0 + 0 + 0 \\ \frac{\sqrt{3}}{4} + \frac{\sqrt{3}}{4} + 0 & -\frac{3}{4} + \frac{1}{4} + 0 & 0 + 0 + 0 \\ 0 + 0 + 0 & 0 + 0 + 0 & 0 + 0 + 1 \end{bmatrix}$$

$$= \begin{bmatrix} -\frac{1}{2} & -\frac{\sqrt{3}}{2} & 0 \\ \frac{\sqrt{3}}{2} & -\frac{1}{2} & 0 \\ 0 & 0 & 1 \end{bmatrix} = C_3$$

which is the matrix representation of the equation $\sigma_b \sigma_c = C_3$ relating the symmetry operations σ_b, σ_c and C_3.

Again

$$\sigma_c \sigma_a = \begin{bmatrix} -\frac{1}{2} & \frac{\sqrt{3}}{2} & 0 \\ \frac{\sqrt{3}}{2} & \frac{1}{2} & 0 \\ 0 & 0 & 1 \end{bmatrix} \begin{bmatrix} 1 & 0 & 0 \\ 0 & -1 & 0 \\ 0 & 0 & 1 \end{bmatrix} = \begin{bmatrix} -\frac{1}{2} & -\frac{\sqrt{3}}{2} & 0 \\ \frac{\sqrt{3}}{2} & -\frac{1}{2} & 0 \\ 0 & 0 & 1 \end{bmatrix} = C_3$$

corresponding to the relation $\sigma_c \sigma_a = C_3$ between the symmetry operations.

4.5 Representations in General

The representation of a point group by matrices in the way we have discussed arose from the idea of regarding a symmetry operation as an operator which rotates or reflects any position vector **p** into a new vector **p'**. The possibility of representing such an operator by a matrix, and the fact that the product of two operators is represented by the product of their matrices, depends on the facts that the operators are linear, with the properties (4.1) and (4.2) and that their products have the property (4.17).

These ideas can be extended to a general vector space, for example the function space of the wave functions belonging to a particular energy level of a molecule, if one associates with every symmetry operation R of the molecule a corresponding linear operator O_R which can act on any vector of the space to produce another vector belonging to the same space according to some suitably defined rule.

Suppose that a general vector of the space is denoted by f. (Henceforth, bold face symbols like **r**, **s**, **e** will be used for position vectors only.) Then we denote the new vector f', obtained by applying the operator O_R to f, by $f' = O_R f$. The fact that O_R is a linear operator means that

$$O_R(af) = a(O_R f); \quad O_R(f+g) = O_R f + O_R g, \tag{4.23}$$

where a is any number and f and g are any two vectors of the space. (Compare (4.23) with (4.1) and (4.2).)

The correspondence between the symmetry operations R and the linear operators O_R must be such as to preserve the multiplication rules for the symmetry operations: if T, S, R are three symmetry operations related by $T = SR$, then the corresponding operators O_T, O_S and O_R must be related by

$$O_T f = O_{(SR)} f = O_S(O_R f), \tag{4.24}$$

where f is any vector of the space under consideration. That is to say, the result of operating on f with O_T is exactly the same as the result obtained by operating on f with O_R to produce an intermediate vector $O_R f$ and then operating on this intermediate vector with O_S. (Compare (4.24) with (4.17).) Equation (4.24) effectively defines the product of two operators and, just as is the case with the symmetry operations themselves, this product is associative.

The correspondence between symmetry operations and the operators O_R implies that there will be a unit operator O_E, associated with the identical symmetry operation E, such that

$$O_R O_E = O_E O_R = O_R$$

for every R. Also each operator O_R will have an inverse $(O_R)^{-1}$ such that

$$(O_R)^{-1} O_R = O_R(O_R)^{-1} = O_E;$$

this inverse operator is the operator corresponding to the symmetry operation R^{-1} so that

$$(O_R)^{-1} = O_{R^{-1}}.$$

The set of symmetry operations belonging to a particular molecule forms a group, its point group. Correspondingly the set of operators associated with the symmetry operations will form a group whose structure resembles that of the point group of the molecule. Just as the introduction of a coordinate system into three-dimensional physical space enabled us to represent the point group of symmetry operations (regarded as operators acting on the position vectors of points in physical space) by a set of 3×3 matrices, so by introducing a coordinate system into the general vector space we shall obtain a representation of the group of operators O_R, and so ultimately of the point group of symmetry operations, by a set of matrices multiplying together in the same way as the operators which they represent. If the vector space under consideration has n dimensions, the matrices representing the symmetry operations will be $n \times n$ matrices with n rows and n columns.

Suppose that the base vectors of a coordinate system in the vector space are $f_1, f_2, \ldots, f_n$. (It is usually convenient in particular applications to choose these to be an orthonormal set but this is not an essential requirement.) Since an operator O_R can operate on any vector of the space to produce another vector which must be expressible in terms of the chosen base vectors $f_1, \ldots, f_n$, the effect of O_R on each of the base vectors can be expressed by equations, analogous to (4.5′), of the form

$$O_R f_k = \sum_{j=1}^{n} [D(R)]_{jk} f_j \quad (k = 1, 2, \ldots, n). \tag{4.25}$$

The set of coefficients $[D(R)]_{jk}$ in (4.25) may be written as a matrix $\mathsf{D}(R)$ of n rows and columns; the number $[D(R)]_{jk}$ is the element of this matrix which stands at the intersection of row j and column k. We thus obtain an $n \times n$ matrix which represents the operator O_R, and consequently the symmetry operation R itself, in the coordinate system with basis $f_1, f_2, \ldots, f_n$.

Applying O_R to a general vector

$$f = \alpha_1 f_1 + \alpha_2 f_2 + \cdots + \alpha_n f_n = \sum_{k=1}^{n} \alpha_k f_k$$

of the space, and using the fact that O_R is a linear operator, gives

$$O_R f = \sum_{k=1}^{n} \alpha_k (O_R f_k) = \sum_{k=1}^{n} \alpha_k \left(\sum_{j=1}^{n} [D(R)]_{jk} f_j \right)$$

i.e. $$O_R f = \sum_{j=1}^{n} \alpha'_j f_j \quad \text{where} \quad \alpha'_j = \sum_{k=1}^{n} [D(R)]_{jk} \alpha_k. \tag{4.26}$$

This is the analogue of (4.6′) in the general case.

The $n \times n$ matrices $D(R)$ will multiply together in the same way as the symmetry operations which they represent because of the property (4.24) of the operators O_R. This follows because, if

$$O_R f_k = \sum_{j=1}^{n} [D(R)]_{jk} f_j, \quad O_S f_j = \sum_{i=1}^{n} [D(S)]_{ij} f_i, \quad O_T f_k = \sum_{i=1}^{n} [D(T)]_{ik} f_i,$$

(4.27)

then

$$O_T f_k = O_{(SR)} f_k = O_S(O_R f_k) = O_S\left(\sum_{j=1}^{n} [D(R)]_{jk} f_j \right)$$

$$= \sum_{j=1}^{n} [D(R)]_{jk}(O_S f_j) = \sum_{j=1}^{n} [D(R)]_{jk}\left(\sum_{i=1}^{n} [D(S)]_{ij} f_i \right);$$

i.e.
$$O_T f_k = \sum_{i=1}^{n} \left(\sum_{j=1}^{n} [D(S)]_{ij}[D(R)]_{jk} \right) f_i.$$
(4.28)

(Note that it is necessary for this result that the operators O_R should be linear.) Comparing (4.28) with the last of the equations in (4.27) shows that the matrix which represents O_T has elements

$$[D(T)]_{ik} = \sum_{j=1}^{n} [D(S)]_{ij}[D(R)]_{jk},$$
(4.29)

which is the obvious generalization of the multiplication rule (4.19) for 3×3 matrices. The matrix $D(T)$ whose elements are given by (4.29) is the product of $D(S)$ and $D(R)$ and we write

$$D(T) = D(SR) = D(S)D(R).$$
(4.30)

This discussion shows that if, in an n-dimensional vector space, we can define linear operators O_R which, by (4.24), reflect the multiplication rules of the symmetry operations to which they correspond, then we can represent each symmetry operation R by an $n \times n$ matrix $D(R)$, defined by (4.25) with respect to the basis $f_1, f_2, \ldots, f_n$. The products of these matrices correspond to the products of the symmetry operations which they represent and the set of matrices representing the symmetry operations of a point group forms an *n-dimensional representation of the group*.

EXAMPLE

As a simple example of the general theory given above consider the set of all positive and negative real numbers and let O_E be the unit operator which leaves the sign of a number unchanged and O_I be an operator which reverses the sign of any number to which it is applied:

$$O_E x = x, \quad O_I x = -x,$$
(4.31)

for any number x. These are clearly linear operators and their multiplication rules are

$$O_E O_E = O_E, \quad O_I O_I = O_E, \quad O_I O_E = O_E O_I = O_I. \tag{4.32}$$

The set of all positive and negative real numbers forms a one-dimensional vector space and (4.31) shows that in this space the operator O_E is represented by the 1×1 matrix $+1$ while O_I is represented by the 1×1 matrix -1. (A matrix with one row and one column is of course just a single number.) These numbers multiply together exactly according to the rules for O_E and O_I since

$$(+1) \times (+1) = +1, (-1) \times (-1) = +1, (-1) \times (+1) = (+1) \times (-1) = -1.$$

They form a one-dimensional representation of the group whose two elements are the operators O_E and O_I.

Now consider the point group $\mathscr{C}_{3v}$ whose elements E, C_3, C_3^{-1}, σ_a, σ_b, σ_c multiply together according to the rules (2.1). These rules can all be fitted into a scheme resembling (4.32) of the form

$$(\text{Rotation}) \times (\text{Rotation}) = \text{Rotation or } E,$$

$$(\text{Reflection}) \times (\text{Reflection}) = \text{Rotation or } E,$$

$$(\text{Rotation}) \times (\text{Reflection}) = \text{Reflection}.$$

Thus the multiplication rules (2.1) will be preserved, albeit in a much simplified form, if we make the three symmetry operations E, C_3, C_3^{-1} all correspond to the operator O_E and the three reflections σ_a, σ_b, σ_c all correspond to O_I. We then arrive at a one-dimensional representation of the point group $\mathscr{C}_{3v}$ in which E, C_3, C_3^{-1} are all represented by the number $+1$ while σ_a, σ_b, σ_c are all represented by the number -1.

An even simpler representation can be obtained by making all the elements of $\mathscr{C}_{3v}$ correspond to the single operator O_E. This gives a one-dimensional representation, called the *identical representation*, in which all the group elements are represented by the number $+1$; this is a representation which reflects the group multiplication rules in a trivial way but which, as we shall see later, is of considerable importance.

4.6 Operators in a Function Space

In this section we shall apply the general ideas developed above to a function space and we consider first of all functions of position in physical space. A typical function f will then be a function $f(x_1, x_2, x_3)$ of the coordinates (x_1, x_2, x_3) of a point P in physical space; i.e. the function f assigns to each point P of space with coordinates (x_1, x_2, x_3) the numerical value $f(x_1, x_2, x_3)$.

Suppose that the symmetry operation R moves P to P' with coordinates (x_1', x_2', x_3'). Then, in accordance with the ideas outlined in Section 4.1, we *define* the operator O_R associated with R by saying that $O_R f$ is a new function which assigns to P' the same numerical value that the original function f assigned to P. We express this relation between the two functions by writing

$$(O_R f)(x_1', x_2', x_3') = f(x_1, x_2, x_3), \tag{4.33}$$

where it is to be understood that x'_1, x'_2, x'_3 are related to x_1, x_2, x_3 by equations of the form (4.6). The values of the coefficients r_{jk} which appear in these equations are determined by the specific symmetry operation R under consideration. The, unfortunately, rather clumsy notation on the left-hand side of (4.33) indicates the value of the new function $O_R f$ at the point with coordinates (x'_1, x'_2, x'_3).

We can make use of (4.33) to obtain the actual form of $O_R f$ if we use (4.6) to express x_1, x_2, x_3 in terms of x'_1, x'_2, x'_3 and substitute these expressions into the right-hand side of (4.33) so that the same variables appear on both sides of the equation.

EXAMPLE

Suppose that $R = C(\alpha)$, a rotation about the $\mathbf{e}_3$ axis, and take the function

$$p_1(x_1, x_2, x_3) = F(r)x_1/r$$

where $r = (x_1{}^2 + x_2{}^2 + x_3{}^2)^{1/2}$ is the distance of the point (x_1, x_2, x_3) from the origin. (This is a p type atomic orbital like those of (3.25); we have simply labelled the coordinates by x_1, x_2, x_3 in place of x, y, z and have omitted a numerical factor.)

Under $C(\alpha)$ the point (x_1, x_2, x_3) moves to a point whose coordinates (x'_1, x'_2, x'_3) are given by (4.11). These equations can be solved to express the x_k in terms of the x'_k and give

$$x_1 = \quad \cos\alpha \cdot x'_1 + \sin\alpha \cdot x'_2,$$
$$x_2 = -\sin\alpha \cdot x'_1 + \cos\alpha \cdot x'_2, \tag{4.34}$$
$$x_3 = x'_3.$$

The rotation leaves the distance from the origin unchanged so that $r = r'$.

When the operator O_C corresponding to $C(\alpha)$ is applied to p_1 it produces a new function $O_C p_1$ which at the point (x'_1, x'_2, x'_3) has the value

$$(O_C p_1)(x'_1, x'_2, x'_3) = p_1(x_1, x_2, x_3) = F(r)x_1/r.$$

Substituting for x_1 and r from (4.34) we obtain

$$(O_C p_1)(x'_1, x'_2, x'_3) = F(r')(\cos\alpha \cdot x'_1 + \sin\alpha \cdot x'_2)/r'. \tag{4.35}$$

Since both sides of (4.35) are expressed in terms of the same variables (x'_1, x'_2, x'_3) and these variables can be the coordinates of any point, we can drop the primes in (4.35) and say that the value of $O_C p_1$ at a general point (x_1, x_2, x_3) is given by

$$(O_C p_1)(x_1, x_2, x_3) = \cos\alpha \cdot F(r)x_1/r + \sin\alpha \cdot F(r)x_2/r. \tag{4.36}$$

The definition (4.33) of the effect of O_R on a function is one which seems intuitively to be natural and convenient. Before adopting it without question, however, we must make sure that the operators defined in this way are linear and that they multiply together according to the rule (4.24). In proving that the operators do indeed satisfy these conditions we shall use a simplified notation in which x stands for the set of coordinates (x_1, x_2, x_3) and x' stands for the set (x'_1, x'_2, x'_3).

PROOF OF LINEARITY

(i) Let f be a function, a a multiplying number, and consider the function $h = af$. Then

$$(O_R h)(x') = h(x) = af(x) = a(O_R f)(x'),$$

since by definition $f(x) = (O_R f)(x')$. This equation must hold for any point x' and we therefore deduce that

$$O_R(af) = a(O_R f).$$

(ii) Take two functions f and g and let $h = f + g$. Then

$$(O_R f)(x') = f(x), \qquad (O_R g)(x') = g(x),$$

and $\qquad (O_R h)(x') = h(x) = f(x) + g(x) = (O_R f)(x') + (O_R g)(x').$

Since this equation holds for any x', we deduce that

$$O_R(f + g) = O_R f + O_R g.$$

The results of (i) and (ii) taken together show that (4.33) does define a linear operator satisfying the conditions (4.23).

PROOF OF THE PROPERTY (4.24)

Consider two symmetry operations R and S and suppose that R moves x to x' while S moves x' to x''. Then the combined operation SR will move x directly to x'' and the operator O_{SR} corresponding to this combined operation is such that

$$(O_{SR} f)(x'') = f(x). \qquad (4.37)$$

Now if g is any function (4.33) tells us that, since S moves x' to x'',

$$(O_S g)(x'') = g(x'). \qquad (4.38)$$

Suppose in particular that g is the function $O_R f$. Then

$$g(x') = (O_R f)(x') = f(x)$$

and (4.38) becomes

$$[O_S(O_R f)](x'') = f(x). \qquad (4.39)$$

(Note that the left-hand side of (4.39) indicates the value of the function $O_S(O_R f)$ at the point x''.)

Now (4.37) and (4.39) hold wherever the point x, and the corresponding point x'', may be. Since their right-hand sides are identical the same must be true of their left-hand sides and

$$O_{SR} f = O_S(O_R f),$$

which is the required property (4.24) of the operators O_R.

The results we have obtained apply to functions of the coordinates (x_1, x_2, x_3) of a point in physical space but they can easily be generalized to apply to functions of any number of variables provided that we know how the variables themselves change under the action of a symmetry operation. Thus we can consider electronic or vibrational wave functions which are functions of the coordinates of all the electrons or nuclei of a molecule. If we let X stand for a complete specification of all these coordinates, i.e. if X stands for the coordinates of a point in configuration space, X will be moved to a new point X' of configuration space by a symmetry operation R and there will be a definite relation, characteristic of R, between the coordinates of X and X'. We then define the corresponding operator O_R acting on a function F of the coordinates by

$$(O_R F)(X') = F(X). \tag{4.40}$$

The arguments given above are clearly also valid in this more general case and (4.40) gives a satisfactory definition of the operators O_R for functions of this type.

To summarize the results of this section, we have shown that (4.33) for functions of position in physical space or, more generally, (4.40) for functions of position in a configuration space give a satisfactory definition of the operators O_R to be associated with the symmetry operations R. These definitions of the rule by which O_R acts on a function to produce a new function can then be used to apply the general theory of Section 4.5 to obtain representations of the point group of a molecule in a function space. Some examples of this process are given in the next section.

4.7 Examples

EXAMPLE 1: *p orbitals*

Consider the three-dimensional space whose base functions are the three p orbitals of (3.25). With a change of notation from x, y, z to x_1, x_2, x_3 for the coordinates of a point and the omission of the common normalizing factor these functions are

$$p_1 = F(r)x_1/r, \quad p_2 = F(r)x_2/r, \quad p_3 = F(r)x_3/r.$$

We have already discussed the effect on p_1 of a rotation $C(\alpha)$ about the e_3 axis. The result is given in (4.36); the functions p_1 and p_2 can be recognized on the right-hand side of this equation and (4.36) can be written as

$$O_C p_1 = \cos \alpha \cdot p_1 + \sin \alpha \cdot p_2 + 0 \cdot p_3.$$

In similar fashion one finds

$$O_C p_2 = -\sin \alpha \cdot p_1 + \cos \alpha \cdot p_2 + 0 \cdot p_3,$$

$$O_C p_3 = \quad 0 \cdot p_1 \quad + \quad 0 \cdot p_2 \quad + 1 \cdot p_3.$$

These are examples of the general equations (4.25) representing the effect of an operator on a set of base vectors. The coefficients of the functions p_1, p_2, p_3 form the matrix

$$\mathsf{D}(C) = \begin{bmatrix} \cos \alpha & -\sin \alpha & 0 \\ \sin \alpha & \cos \alpha & 0 \\ 0 & 0 & 1 \end{bmatrix}, \tag{4.41}$$

which then represents the operation $C(\alpha)$ in the function space of p_1, p_2, p_3. This matrix is identical with the matrix (4.10) which represents $C(\alpha)$ in physical space, an example of the way in which the same representation of a symmetry operation may appear in quite different contexts. The reason for the similarity between physical space and the function space with basis p_1, p_2, p_3 is that the p orbitals are directed along the three coordinate axes so that a symmetry operation has the same effect on the p orbitals as it has on the coordinate axes. Thus it will be found that the matrices (4.13–16), which represent symmetry operations in physical space, are reproduced when one considers the effects of the corresponding operations on the functions p_1, p_2, p_3.

EXAMPLE 2: *d orbitals*

The five d orbitals of (3.26) span a five-dimensional function space. If we omit the factor $(15/4\pi)^{1/2}F(r)/r^2$ which is common to all these functions and which remains unaltered by any symmetry operation (since we always take the origin of coordinates at a point which is left unmoved by the operations of a point group), and if we use x_1, x_2, x_3 in place of x, y, z, these five base functions are

$$d_1 = \tfrac{1}{2}(x_1{}^2 - x_2{}^2), \quad d_2 = x_1 x_2, \quad d_3 = x_1 x_3,$$
$$d_4 = x_2 x_3, \quad d_5 = (3x_3{}^2 - r^2)/2\sqrt{3}.$$

(i) Consider the rotation $C(\alpha)$ and the corresponding operator O_C in this five-dimensional function space. The application of O_C to d_1 gives, according to (4.33),

$$(O_C d_1)(x_1', x_2', x_3') = d_1(x_1, x_2, x_3) = \tfrac{1}{2}(x_1{}^2 - x_2{}^2).$$

We express x_1 and x_2 in terms of x_1', x_2', x_3' by (4.34) and find

$$\tfrac{1}{2}(x_1{}^2 - x_2{}^2) = \cos 2\alpha \cdot \tfrac{1}{2}(x_1'^2 - x_2'^2) + \sin 2\alpha \cdot x_1' x_2'$$
$$= \cos 2\alpha \cdot d_1(x_1', x_2', x_3') + \sin 2\alpha \cdot d_2(x_1', x_2', x_3').$$

Since these relations hold for any point x_1', x_2', x_3', it follows that the function $O_C d_1$ can be expressed in terms of d_1 and d_2 by

$$O_C d_1 = \cos 2\alpha \cdot d_1 + \sin 2\alpha \cdot d_2.$$

Similarly one finds

$$O_C d_2 = -\sin 2\alpha \cdot d_1 + \cos 2\alpha \cdot d_2,$$

$$O_C d_3 = \cos \alpha \cdot d_3 + \sin \alpha \cdot d_4,$$

$$O_C d_4 = -\sin \alpha \cdot d_3 + \cos \alpha \cdot d_4,$$

$$O_C d_5 = d_5.$$

From these equations we can write down the matrix representing $C(\alpha)$ in the function space with base functions $d_1, \ldots, d_5$; it is

$$\mathsf{D}(C) = \begin{bmatrix} \cos 2\alpha & -\sin 2\alpha & 0 & 0 & 0 \\ \sin 2\alpha & \cos 2\alpha & 0 & 0 & 0 \\ 0 & 0 & \cos \alpha & -\sin \alpha & 0 \\ 0 & 0 & \sin \alpha & \cos \alpha & 0 \\ 0 & 0 & 0 & 0 & 1 \end{bmatrix}. \tag{4.42a}$$

(ii) Now consider a reflection σ in a plane which contains the $\mathbf{e}_3$ axis and which makes an angle β with the plane of $\mathbf{e}_1$ and $\mathbf{e}_3$. The reflection moves a point with coordinates (x_1, x_2, x_3) to the point (x_1', x_2', x_3'); the relations between these coordinates are obtained by substituting the matrix of (4.13) into (4.6). A calculation similar to that described above for $C(\alpha)$ shows that in the space of $d_1, \ldots, d_5$ σ is represented by the matrix

$$\mathsf{D}(\sigma) = \begin{bmatrix} \cos 4\beta & \sin 4\beta & 0 & 0 & 0 \\ \sin 4\beta & -\cos 4\beta & 0 & 0 & 0 \\ 0 & 0 & \cos 2\beta & \sin 2\beta & 0 \\ 0 & 0 & \sin 2\beta & -\cos 2\beta & 0 \\ 0 & 0 & 0 & 0 & 1 \end{bmatrix}. \tag{4.42b}$$

EXAMPLE 3: *A representation of* $\mathscr{C}_{3v}$

We can use the results of Example 2 to write down a five-dimensional representation of $\mathscr{C}_{3v}$. If we use the coordinate system of Fig. 4.3, the matrices representing C_3 and C_3^{-1} are obtained from (4.42a) by putting $\alpha = 120°$ and $-120°$ respectively; the matrices representing the reflections σ_a, σ_b, σ_c are obtained from (4.42b) by putting $\beta = 0°$, $-60°$, $60°$ respectively. The elements of these matrices can be expressed in terms of the quantities

$$c = \cos 60° = 1/2 \quad \text{and} \quad s = \sin 60° = \sqrt{3}/2,$$

and the matrices themselves are found to be:

$$\mathsf{D}(C_3) = \begin{bmatrix} -c & s & \cdot & \cdot & \cdot \\ -s & -c & \cdot & \cdot & \cdot \\ \cdot & \cdot & -c & -s & \cdot \\ \cdot & \cdot & s & -c & \cdot \\ \cdot & \cdot & \cdot & \cdot & 1 \end{bmatrix}, \quad \mathsf{D}(C_3^{-1}) = \begin{bmatrix} -c & -s & \cdot & \cdot & \cdot \\ s & -c & \cdot & \cdot & \cdot \\ \cdot & \cdot & -c & s & \cdot \\ \cdot & \cdot & -s & -c & \cdot \\ \cdot & \cdot & \cdot & \cdot & 1 \end{bmatrix},$$

$$D(\sigma_a) = \begin{bmatrix} 1 & 0 & . & . & . \\ 0 & -1 & . & . & . \\ . & . & 1 & 0 & . \\ . & . & 0 & -1 & . \\ . & . & . & . & 1 \end{bmatrix}, \qquad D(\sigma_b) = \begin{bmatrix} -c & s & . & . & . \\ s & c & . & . & . \\ . & . & -c & -s & . \\ . & . & -s & c & . \\ . & . & . & . & 1 \end{bmatrix}$$

$$D(\sigma_c) = \begin{bmatrix} -c & -s & . & . & . \\ -s & c & . & . & . \\ . & . & -c & s & . \\ . & . & s & c & . \\ . & . & . & . & 1 \end{bmatrix}$$

(In writing down these matrices we have used dots to indicate matrix elements which vanish.)

These matrices, together with the unit matrix $D(E)$, form a five-dimensional representation of $\mathscr{C}_{3v}$. It is easy to verify that they do actually multiply together according to the rules (2.1).

A noteworthy feature of this representation is that the matrices all have the same *block-diagonal form*; all their non-vanishing elements occur in blocks down the diagonal. This particular form of the matrices is a consequence of the facts that, for all the operations of $\mathscr{C}_{3v}$, (i) the functions $O_R d_1$ and $O_R d_2$ are linear combinations of d_1 and d_2, independent of d_3, d_4, d_5; (ii) $O_R d_3$ and $O_R d_4$ are linear combinations of d_3 and d_4, independent of d_1, d_2, d_5; (iii) $O_R d_5 = d_5$ and does not depend on the other base functions.

It follows from this that the functions d_1 and d_2 by themselves form a basis for a two-dimensional representation of $\mathscr{C}_{3v}$; the matrices of this representation are the 2×2 matrices in the upper left-hand corners of the 5×5 matrices above, and it is easy to check that these 2×2 matrices do multiply together in the correct way. In the same way the pair of functions d_3 and d_4 forms the basis of a two-dimensional representation whose matrices are the 2×2 matrices occupying the central positions in the 5×5 matrices. Finally, the function d_5, left unaltered by all the operations of $\mathscr{C}_{3v}$, generates the one-dimensional identical representation which represents all the elements of $\mathscr{C}_{3v}$ by the number $+1$.

4.8 Unitary Operators

The operators which we have introduced to describe the effects of symmetry operations on position vectors and functions of position have an important property which we now discuss.

Consider, first, two position vectors **r** and **s** with a scalar product $(\mathbf{r}, \mathbf{s})$ defined by (3.10). The scalar product depends only on the lengths of **r** and **s** and on the angle between them. A symmetry operation R applied simultaneously to both **r** and **s** will rotate or reflect them in the same way to produce new vectors $R\mathbf{r}$ and $R\mathbf{s}$, but it will not change their lengths nor will it change the angle between them. R, therefore, has no effect on the scalar product, and

$$(R\mathbf{r}, R\mathbf{s}) = (\mathbf{r}, \mathbf{s}). \tag{4.43}$$

Consider, next, functions of position. In a general case these functions might be complex and the scalar product of two complex functions is, by (3.27), the integral

$$(f, g) = \int f^*(P)g(P)\, d\tau_P, \tag{4.44}$$

where P is a general point with coordinates (x_1, x_2, x_3) and $d\tau_P = dx_1\, dx_2\, dx_3$ is the volume element at P. The integration extends over all points P, i.e. over all values of the x_i from $-\infty$ to ∞. Now a symmetry operation R will move P to a point P' with coordinates (x_1', x_2', x_3') and it will move the volume element $d\tau_P$ to an equal volume element $d\tau_{P'} = dx_1'\, dx_2'\, dx_3'$ situated at P'. Furthermore, the operator O_R is defined by (4.33) in such a way that $f(P) = (O_R f)(P')$ and $g(P) = (O_R g)(P')$. Hence

$$\int f^*(P)g(P)\, d\tau_P = \int [(O_R f)(P')]^*[(O_R g)(P')]\, d\tau_{P'}, \tag{4.45}$$

since the range of integration extends over all points P or P'. But, according to the definition (4.44), the right-hand side of (4.45) is the scalar product $(O_R f, O_R g)$. Thus we have shown that the operators O_R defined by (4.33) have the property

$$(O_R f, O_R g) = (f, g). \tag{4.46}$$

This result is clearly also valid for functions of position in a general configuration space where the operators O_R satisfy (4.40).

Operators which have this property of leaving the scalar product unchanged are called *unitary operators* and all the operators with which we shall be concerned are unitary operators which satisfy (4.46).

We examine the consequences of (4.43) for the special case of position vectors. Suppose that we have chosen three mutually perpendicular unit vectors $\mathbf{e}_1, \mathbf{e}_2, \mathbf{e}_3$ to serve as a basis for a coordinate system in physical space. Then the vectors $R\mathbf{e}_1, R\mathbf{e}_2, R\mathbf{e}_3$ will also be mutually perpendicular unit vectors with scalar products satisfying

$$(R\mathbf{e}_i, R\mathbf{e}_j) = (\mathbf{e}_i, \mathbf{e}_j) = \delta_{ij}, \quad (i, j = 1, 2, 3). \tag{4.47}$$

Now, by (4.5), $\qquad R\mathbf{e}_i = r_{1i}\mathbf{e}_1 + r_{2i}\mathbf{e}_2 + r_{3i}\mathbf{e}_3,$

and $\qquad\qquad\qquad R\mathbf{e}_j = r_{1j}\mathbf{e}_1 + r_{2j}\mathbf{e}_2 + r_{3j}\mathbf{e}_3,$

and their scalar product is, by (3.16),

$$(R\mathbf{e}_i, R\mathbf{e}_j) = r_{1i}r_{1j} + r_{2i}r_{2j} + r_{3i}r_{3j} = \sum_{k=1}^{3} r_{ki}r_{kj}.$$

Hence (4.47) becomes

$$\sum_{k=1}^{3} r_{ki} r_{kj} = \delta_{ij}, \tag{4.48}$$

which expresses the fact that the columns of the matrix R, which represents R in the physical space of position vectors, are the components of mutually perpendicular unit vectors. A matrix with this property is called an *orthogonal matrix*. As an example, the reader may verify that all the matrices given in Section 4.4 are orthogonal matrices whose elements satisfy (4.48).

We can express the content of (4.48) in matrix form if we introduce a new matrix $\tilde{R}$, called the *transpose* of R, which is obtained from R by interchanging its rows and columns: row k of R becomes column k of $\tilde{R}$ and column i of R becomes row i of $\tilde{R}$, so that the ik element of the transposed matrix $\tilde{R}$ is

$$\tilde{r}_{ik} = r_{ki}.$$

We can then rewrite (4.48) as

$$\sum_{k=1}^{3} \tilde{r}_{ik} r_{kj} = \delta_{ij}.$$

Now the left-hand side of this equation is simply the ij element of the product matrix $\tilde{R}R$ and δ_{ij} is the ij element of the unit matrix E. Hence (4.48) can be expressed in matrix form as

$$\tilde{R}R = E. \tag{4.49}$$

If we multiply this equation on the right by the inverse matrix R^{-1} we see that (4.48) is equivalent to the statement that

$$\tilde{R} = R^{-1}. \tag{4.50}$$

Equations (4.49) and (4.50) are simply different ways of writing (4.48) and any of these equations may be taken to define what is meant by an orthogonal matrix. We may note that R^{-1} itself must be an orthogonal matrix since it represents some symmetry operation and the same arguments will apply to it as do to R. Hence the columns of $\tilde{R}$ must be components of mutually perpendicular unit vectors and so the *rows* of R will satisfy equations similar to (4.48), namely

$$\sum_{k=1}^{3} r_{ik} r_{jk} = \delta_{ij}. \tag{4.51}$$

EXAMPLE

The matrices given in Section 4.4 form a representation of $\mathscr{C}_{3v}$ with respect to an orthonormal basis in physical space. In this representation the matrix representing C_3^{-1} is the transpose of the matrix representing C_3. The matrices representing σ_a, σ_b, σ_c are left unaltered by a transposition of rows and columns (they are *symmetrical* matrices) since, for a reflection, $\sigma^{-1} = \sigma$ and consequently, by (4.50), $\tilde{\sigma} = \sigma$.

These ideas are readily extended to matrices of n rows and columns. An $n \times n$ matrix A with elements a_{ij} is orthogonal if

$$\sum_{k=1}^{n} a_{ki}a_{kj} = \delta_{ij}, \qquad (4.52)$$

and if $\tilde{\mathsf{A}}$ is the transpose of A

$$\tilde{\mathsf{A}}\mathsf{A} = \mathsf{E} \quad \text{or} \quad \tilde{\mathsf{A}} = \mathsf{A}^{-1}. \qquad (4.53)$$

Chapter 5

REDUCIBLE AND IRREDUCIBLE
REPRESENTATIONS

5.1 Introduction

In the last chapter we saw how to represent the symmetry operations of a molecular point group by a set of matrices which multiply together in the same way as the symmetry operations. These matrices are found by associating a group of linear operators with the symmetry operations of the point group and by calculating the effects of these operators on the base vectors of an n-dimensional vector space. Our object in this and the subsequent chapter is to show how it is possible to classify and characterize all the possible representations of a group. It is this classification of the representations which results in the main applications of group theory to quantum mechanics.

The classification might, at first sight, seem an impossible task since in constructing a representation we can consider vector spaces of any dimension, and even in a given vector space the choice of a basis is quite arbitrary. Thus for any group it will be possible to construct representations of arbitrary dimension n, and even for a given n there will be many numerically different sets of matrices which multiply together in the right way.

The problem of classification can, however, be solved firstly by regarding all the representations which arise from a given vector space, irrespective of the choice of basis, as essentially equivalent, and, secondly, by proving that any representation can be described in terms of a small number of fundamental irreducible representations. The irreducible representations of the molecular point groups can be described and classified once and for all. This classification is contained in the character table of the group and the end result of representation theory is a set of simple rules for using these tables of characters. Thus the key concepts of representation theory are those of the *equivalence* of two representations, the *character* of a representation, and the *reduction* of a representation into its *irreducible* components.

5.2 Equivalent Representations

To find a matrix representation of a group of linear operators acting on the vectors of a given space it is necessary to choose a definite basis for the space and to calculate the effects of the operators on each base vector. A different choice of basis would produce a numerically different set of representative matrices, but once a definite choice has been made, (4.25) and (4.26) tell us all we need to know in order to calculate the effects of the operators on any vector of the space.

Now the choice of a basis for a vector space is arbitrary (although in particular applications one choice may be more natural or convenient than another) since any set of n linearly independent vectors will provide a basis for an n-dimensional space. Thus there will be many sets of matrices that can serve to represent a group of operators in a given vector space. All these possible sets are, however, essentially equivalent to each other since they all contain exactly the same information, namely the effects of the operators on a general vector of the space. The problem then arises of how the matrices of these equivalent representations are related to each other; it is necessary to find the relation between matrices representing the same operator with respect to different bases.

Suppose that we have two different sets of linearly independent base vectors in an n-dimensional space and that we denote these by $f_1, \ldots, f_n$ and $g_1, \ldots, g_n$. Then we can express either set of base vectors in terms of the other and numbers a_{jk}, b_{ij} must exist such that

$$f_k = \sum_{j=1}^{n} a_{jk} g_j, \quad k = 1, 2, \ldots, n; \tag{5.1a}$$

$$g_j = \sum_{i=1}^{n} b_{ij} f_i, \quad j = 1, 2, \ldots, n. \tag{5.1b}$$

The sets of coefficients a_{jk} and b_{ij} can be formed into matrices A and B and we first show that these matrices are inverse to each other. This follows by substituting the expression (5.1b) for g_j into (5.1a). One finds

$$f_k = \sum_{j=1}^{n} a_{jk} \left(\sum_{i=1}^{n} b_{ij} f_i \right) = \sum_{i=1}^{n} \left(\sum_{j=1}^{n} b_{ij} a_{jk} \right) f_i.$$

For this equation to be true, the sum $\sum_{j=1}^{n} b_{ij} a_{jk}$ must vanish when $i \neq k$ and must equal unity when $i = k$;

i.e.

$$\sum_{j=1}^{n} b_{ij} a_{jk} = \delta_{ik}. \tag{5.2a}$$

Similarly one can prove that

$$\sum_{j=1}^{n} a_{ij} b_{jk} = \delta_{ik}. \tag{5.2b}$$

The summations on the left-hand sides of these equations are the ik elements of the product matrices BA and AB respectively, and δ_{ik} is the ik element of the unit matrix E. Hence (5.2a,b) show that A and B are related by $AB = BA = E$, which is the same thing as saying that A and B are inverse to each other; $B = A^{-1}$ and $A = B^{-1}$. (Compare (4.21) and (4.22) which refer to 3×3 matrices.)

Now consider an operator O_R. We can find the matrix $D^{(f)}(R)$ representing O_R with respect to the basis $f_1, \ldots, f_n$ by calculating the coefficients $[D^{(f)}(R)]_{ki}$ in the equations

$$O_R f_i = \sum_{k=1}^{n} [D^{(f)}(R)]_{ki} f_k. \tag{5.3a}$$

In the same way we can find the matrix $D^{(g)}(R)$ representing O_R with respect to the basis $g_1, \ldots, g_n$ by calculating the coefficients $[D^{(g)}(R)]_{lj}$ in the equations

$$O_R g_j = \sum_{l=1}^{n} [D^{(g)}(R)]_{lj} g_l. \tag{5.3b}$$

But instead of calculating the coefficients in (5.3b) directly from the rule by which O_R acts on the vectors of the space we can proceed as follows:

$$O_R g_j = O_R \left(\sum_{i=1}^{n} b_{ij} f_i \right) = \sum_{i=1}^{n} b_{ij} (O_R f_i)$$

$$= \sum_{i=1}^{n} b_{ij} \sum_{k=1}^{n} [D^{(f)}(R)]_{ki} f_k = \sum_{i=1}^{n} b_{ij} \sum_{k=1}^{n} [D^{(f)}(R)]_{ki} \sum_{l=1}^{n} a_{lk} g_l.$$

(In deriving this we have used the fact that O_R is a linear operator and made use also of (5.1a,b) and (5.3a).) A rearrangement of the order of the summations then gives

$$O_R g_j = \sum_{l=1}^{n} \left\{ \sum_{k=1}^{n} \sum_{i=1}^{n} a_{lk} [D^{(f)}(R)]_{ki} b_{ij} \right\} g_l. \tag{5.4}$$

In (5.4) the coefficient of g_l, enclosed in parentheses, is the lj element of the matrix $AD^{(f)}(R)B$; equally we see by comparing (5.4) with (5.3b) that it must be the lj element of the matrix $D^{(g)}(R)$ representing O_R with respect to the basis $g_1, \ldots, g_n$. Thus, since $B = A^{-1}$, we have found the relation between the matrices representing O_R with respect to the two bases:

$$D^{(g)}(R) = AD^{(f)}(R)A^{-1}. \tag{5.5}$$

If we are given a set of matrices $D^{(f)}(R)$ representing a group of operators with respect to a particular basis $f_1, \ldots, f_n$, (5.5) tells us what the matrices representing the operators will become if we change to another basis whose vectors $g_1, \ldots, g_n$ are related to $f_1, \ldots, f_n$ by equations of the form (5.1).

This change of basis does not, of course, affect the multiplication rules of the matrices: if

$$D^{(f)}(SR) = D^{(f)}(S)D^{(f)}(R),$$

then equally

$$D^{(g)}(SR) = AD^{(f)}(SR)A^{-1} = AD^{(f)}(S)D^{(f)}(R)A^{-1}$$
$$= AD^{(f)}(S)A^{-1}AD^{(f)}(R)A^{-1} = D^{(g)}(S)D^{(g)}(R).$$

In some particular applications it may be necessary to set up a definite basis in a vector space and to work explicitly with the matrices arising from this choice of basis; normally, however, one is interested in what can be said about a representation irrespective of the basis. From this point of view all the different sets of matrices that can be used to represent a group of operators in a given space are merely different realizations of what is essentially the same representation; one set of matrices can be obtained from another by using the appropriate transformation matrix A in (5.5). This equation, there-fore, gives us a definition of equivalent representations: *two representations of a point group by $n \times n$ matrices $D^{(f)}(R)$ and $D^{(g)}(R)$ are equivalent if a matrix A, with inverse A^{-1}, exists for which (5.5) holds for every operation R of the group.*

5.3 Examples

As examples of (5.5) we discuss two representations of $\mathscr{C}_{3v}$ which can be obtained from the representation given in Section 4.4. This representation arose from a consideration of the effects of the operations of $\mathscr{C}_{3v}$ on the base vectors of an orthonormal coordinate system in physical space, but, as we saw in Example 1 of Section 4.7, it also appears when one considers the function space of p atomic orbitals. The matrices of this representation are reproduced in the column of Table 5.1 which is headed Γ_1, the symbol we shall use to signify this particular representation.

EXAMPLE 1

Equations (3.33) define a change of basis in the function space of the p orbitals from the base functions p_1, p_2, p_3 of (3.25) to the functions p'_1, p'_{-1}, p'_0 of (3.34a,b). Take p_1, p_2, p_3 to be the 'f' basis and p'_1, p'_{-1}, p'_0 to be the 'g' basis. Then, in this case, (5.1b) is

$$p'_1 = \frac{1}{\sqrt{2}} p_1 + \frac{i}{\sqrt{2}} p_2 + 0 \cdot p_3,$$

$$p'_{-1} = \frac{1}{\sqrt{2}} p_1 - \frac{i}{\sqrt{2}} p_2 + 0 \cdot p_3,$$

$$p'_0 = 0 \cdot p_1 + 0 \cdot p_2 + 1 \cdot p_3,$$

so that the transformation matrix $\mathbf{B}$ is

$$\mathbf{B} = \begin{bmatrix} \dfrac{1}{\sqrt{2}} & \dfrac{1}{\sqrt{2}} & 0 \\[2mm] \dfrac{i}{\sqrt{2}} & -\dfrac{i}{\sqrt{2}} & 0 \\[2mm] 0 & 0 & 1 \end{bmatrix} = \mathbf{A}^{-1}. \tag{5.6a}$$

We can easily express the p functions in terms of the p' functions; this gives the matrix

$$\mathbf{A} = \mathbf{B}^{-1} = \begin{bmatrix} \dfrac{1}{\sqrt{2}} & -\dfrac{i}{\sqrt{2}} & 0 \\[2mm] \dfrac{1}{\sqrt{2}} & \dfrac{i}{\sqrt{2}} & 0 \\[2mm] 0 & 0 & 1 \end{bmatrix} \tag{5.6b}$$

(It can readily be verified by forming the matrix product $\mathbf{AB}$ that these matrices are indeed inverse to each other.)

Consider now a rotation $C(\alpha)$ about the $\mathbf{e}_3$ axis. The matrix representing this operation in the 'f' basis is $\mathbf{D}^{(f)}(C)$ and is given by (4.41). Consequently, by (5.5) the matrix representing $C(\alpha)$ in the 'g' basis will be

$$\mathbf{D}^{(g)}[C(\alpha)] = \mathbf{A}\mathbf{D}^{(f)}[C(\alpha)]\mathbf{A}^{-1}$$

$$= \begin{bmatrix} \dfrac{1}{\sqrt{2}} & -\dfrac{i}{\sqrt{2}} & 0 \\[2mm] \dfrac{1}{\sqrt{2}} & \dfrac{i}{\sqrt{2}} & 0 \\[2mm] 0 & 0 & 1 \end{bmatrix} \begin{bmatrix} \cos\alpha & -\sin\alpha & 0 \\ \sin\alpha & \cos\alpha & 0 \\ 0 & 0 & 1 \end{bmatrix} \begin{bmatrix} \dfrac{1}{\sqrt{2}} & \dfrac{1}{\sqrt{2}} & 0 \\[2mm] \dfrac{i}{\sqrt{2}} & -\dfrac{i}{\sqrt{2}} & 0 \\[2mm] 0 & 0 & 1 \end{bmatrix}$$

On multiplying these matrices together one finds

$$\mathbf{D}^{(g)}(C) = \begin{bmatrix} e^{-i\alpha} & 0 & 0 \\ 0 & e^{i\alpha} & 0 \\ 0 & 0 & 1 \end{bmatrix}$$

using $e^{\pm i\alpha} = \cos\alpha \pm i\sin\alpha$.

This result may be verified by a direct calculation of the effect of $C(\alpha)$ on the functions p'_1, p'_{-1}, p'_0. These functions are written down explicitly in (3.34a,b) in terms of the spherical polar coordinates (r, θ, ϕ) defined in Fig. 3.8. The rotation $C(\alpha)$ applied to a point with coordinates (r, θ, ϕ) rotates it through an angle α about the $\mathbf{e}_3$ axis and moves it to the point with coordinates (r', θ', ϕ') where $r' = r$, $\theta' = \theta$, $\phi' = \phi + \alpha$. The corresponding operator O_C applied to a function $f(r, \theta, \phi)$ changes it to the function $O_C f$ where

$$(O_C f)(r', \theta', \phi') = f(r, \theta, \phi) = f(r', \theta', \phi' - \alpha).$$

In this equation (r', θ', ϕ') may be the coordinates of any point; we may therefore omit the primes on the coordinates and write

$$(O_C f)(r, \theta, \phi) = f(r, \theta, \phi - \alpha).$$

Thus

$$O_C p_1' = (3/8\pi)^{1/2} F(r) \sin\theta \cdot e^{i(\phi-\alpha)} \quad = e^{-i\alpha} p_1',$$

$$O_C p_{-1}' = (3/8\pi)^{1/2} F(r) \sin\theta \cdot e^{-i(\phi-\alpha)} = e^{i\alpha} p_{-1}',$$

$$O_C p_0' = (3/4\pi)^{1/2} F(r) \cos\theta \qquad\qquad = p_0',$$

and the matrix representing $C(\alpha)$ in this basis is indeed the matrix $D^{(g)}(C)$ found above.

Consider next a reflection σ in a plane, containing the e_3 axis, which makes an angle β with the e_1, e_3 plane. This operation is represented in the p_1, p_2, p_3 basis by the matrix (4.13). It will be found that transformation of this matrix by the matrices (5.6a,b) according to (5.5) gives

$$D^{(g)}(\sigma) = \begin{bmatrix} 0 & e^{-2i\beta} & 0 \\ e^{2i\beta} & 0 & 0 \\ 0 & 0 & 1 \end{bmatrix},$$

a result which may be verified by a direct calculation of the effect of the operator O_σ on the base functions p_1', p_{-1}', p_0'. (To perform this calculation, note that σ changes (r, θ, ϕ) to (r', θ', ϕ') where $r' = r$, $\theta' = \theta$, $\phi' = 2\beta - \phi$.)

If these results are applied to the point group $\mathscr{C}_{3v}$ with rotations C_3, $C_3{}^{-1}$ through angles $\alpha = 120°$, $-120°$ respectively, and reflections σ_a, σ_b, σ_c with angles $\beta = 0°$, $-60°$, $60°$ respectively, we obtain the representation of $\mathscr{C}_{3v}$ whose matrices are given in Table 5.1 in the column headed Γ_2.

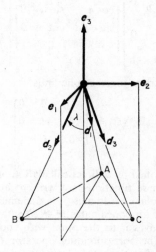

5.1 Coordinate systems for ammonia.

EXAMPLE 2

$\mathscr{C}_{3v}$ is the point group of the ammonia molecule, and the coordinate system of Fig. 4.3, which gave rise to the representation Γ_1 of $\mathscr{C}_{3v}$, is shown again in Fig. 5.1 in relation to this molecule. The figure also shows three unit vectors d_1, d_2, d_3

which point along the directions of the three NH bonds. These vectors could be taken as the basis of a coordinate system in physical space; one might, for example, choose this basis in a discussion of directed valence in ammonia. If we were to choose $\mathbf{d}_1$, $\mathbf{d}_2$, $\mathbf{d}_3$ as a basis we should obtain a representation of $\mathscr{C}_{3v}$ which would be equivalent to the representation Γ_1. The matrices of this representation, which we shall call Γ_3, are easily found by examining the effects of the operations of $\mathscr{C}_{3v}$ on $\mathbf{d}_1$, $\mathbf{d}_2$, and $\mathbf{d}_3$. For example, the rotation C_3 moves $\mathbf{d}_1$ to $\mathbf{d}_2$, $\mathbf{d}_2$ to $\mathbf{d}_3$, and $\mathbf{d}_3$ to $\mathbf{d}_1$ so that

$$C_3\mathbf{d}_1 = 0\cdot\mathbf{d}_1 + 1\cdot\mathbf{d}_2 + 0\cdot\mathbf{d}_3,$$

$$C_3\mathbf{d}_2 = 0\cdot\mathbf{d}_1 + 0\cdot\mathbf{d}_2 + 1\cdot\mathbf{d}_3,$$

$$C_3\mathbf{d}_3 = 1\cdot\mathbf{d}_1 + 0\cdot\mathbf{d}_2 + 0\cdot\mathbf{d}_3,$$

and the matrix representing C_3 is

$$\begin{bmatrix} 0 & 0 & 1 \\ 1 & 0 & 0 \\ 0 & 1 & 0 \end{bmatrix}. \tag{5.7}$$

The other matrices of this representation may be found in the same way; they are written down the column of Table 5.1 headed Γ_3.

Since Γ_3 is a representation which is equivalent to Γ_1, its matrices must be obtainable from the matrices of Γ_1 by changing the basis of the coordinate system from $\mathbf{e}_1$, $\mathbf{e}_2$, $\mathbf{e}_3$ to $\mathbf{d}_1$, $\mathbf{d}_2$, $\mathbf{d}_3$. Let us examine this change of basis in detail. Suppose that in Fig. 5.1 the NH bonds make an angle λ with the direction of $-\mathbf{e}_3$. Then from the geometry of the figure

$$\mathbf{d}_1 = -\mathbf{e}_1 \sin\lambda - \mathbf{e}_3 \cos\lambda,$$

$$\mathbf{d}_2 = \tfrac{1}{2}(\mathbf{e}_1 - \sqrt{3}\mathbf{e}_2)\sin\lambda - \mathbf{e}_3 \cos\lambda, \tag{5.8a}$$

$$\mathbf{d}_3 = \tfrac{1}{2}(\mathbf{e}_1 + \sqrt{3}\mathbf{e}_2)\sin\lambda - \mathbf{e}_3 \cos\lambda.$$

Solving these equations for $\mathbf{e}_1$, $\mathbf{e}_2$, $\mathbf{e}_3$ gives

$$\mathbf{e}_1 = (-2\mathbf{d}_1 + \mathbf{d}_2 + \mathbf{d}_3)/3\sin\lambda,$$

$$\mathbf{e}_2 = (0\cdot\mathbf{d}_1 - \mathbf{d}_2 + \mathbf{d}_3)/\sqrt{3}\sin\lambda, \tag{5.8b}$$

$$\mathbf{e}_3 = (-\mathbf{d}_1 - \mathbf{d}_2 - \mathbf{d}_3)/3\cos\lambda.$$

These are the forms taken by equations (5.1) in this case. If we regard $\mathbf{e}_1$, $\mathbf{e}_2$, $\mathbf{e}_3$ as the 'f' basis and $\mathbf{d}_1$, $\mathbf{d}_2$, $\mathbf{d}_3$ as the 'g' basis, the transformation matrices are

$$\mathsf{A} = \begin{bmatrix} -\dfrac{2}{3a} & 0 & -\dfrac{1}{3b} \\[2ex] \dfrac{1}{3a} & -\dfrac{1}{\sqrt{3}a} & -\dfrac{1}{3b} \\[2ex] \dfrac{1}{3a} & \dfrac{1}{\sqrt{3}a} & -\dfrac{1}{3b} \end{bmatrix} \quad \text{and} \quad \mathsf{A}^{-1} = \begin{bmatrix} -a & \dfrac{a}{2} & \dfrac{a}{2} \\[2ex] 0 & -\dfrac{\sqrt{3}a}{2} & \dfrac{\sqrt{3}a}{2} \\[2ex] -b & -b & -b \end{bmatrix}$$

where we have written $\sin \lambda = a$ and $\cos \lambda = b$. (Here we have an example of a transformation to a set of base vectors which are not necessarily orthogonal. Equation (5.8a) shows that

$$(\mathbf{d}_1, \mathbf{d}_2) = (\mathbf{d}_2, \mathbf{d}_3) = (\mathbf{d}_3, \mathbf{d}_1) = -\tfrac{1}{2}\sin^2 \lambda + \cos^2 \lambda;$$

these scalar products vanish only if $\tan \lambda = \sqrt{2}$. In this case $a = \sin \lambda = \sqrt{(2/3)}$, $b = \cos \lambda = \sqrt{(1/3)}$ and it is only for these particular values of a and b that A is orthogonal and $\tilde{A} = A^{-1}$.) The matrices $D^{(g)}(R)$ of Γ_3 are obtained from the matrices $D^{(f)}(R)$ of Γ_1 by forming the products $AD^{(f)}(R)A^{-1}$. Thus, for example, the matrix representing C_3 in the $\mathbf{d}$ basis must be

$$\begin{bmatrix} -\dfrac{2}{3a} & 0 & -\dfrac{1}{3b} \\ \dfrac{1}{3a} & -\dfrac{1}{\sqrt{3}a} & -\dfrac{1}{3b} \\ \dfrac{1}{3a} & \dfrac{1}{\sqrt{3}a} & -\dfrac{1}{3b} \end{bmatrix} \begin{bmatrix} -\dfrac{1}{2} & -\dfrac{\sqrt{3}}{2} & 0 \\ \dfrac{\sqrt{3}}{2} & -\dfrac{1}{2} & 0 \\ 0 & 0 & 1 \end{bmatrix} \begin{bmatrix} -a & \dfrac{a}{2} & \dfrac{a}{2} \\ 0 & -\dfrac{\sqrt{3}a}{2} & \dfrac{\sqrt{3}a}{2} \\ -b & -b & -b \end{bmatrix}$$

It is readily verified that this product is equal to the matrix given in (5.7).

TABLE 5.1. *Equivalent representations of $\mathscr{C}_{3v}$*

(*Note*: In this table, $c = \cos \pi/3 = 1/2$, $s = \sin \pi/3 = \sqrt{3}/2$, and $\epsilon = e^{-2\pi i/3} = -(c+is)$.)

	Γ_1	Γ_2	Γ_3
E	$\begin{bmatrix} 1&0&0\\0&1&0\\0&0&1 \end{bmatrix}$	$\begin{bmatrix} 1&0&0\\0&1&0\\0&0&1 \end{bmatrix}$	$\begin{bmatrix} 1&0&0\\0&1&0\\0&0&1 \end{bmatrix}$
C_3	$\begin{bmatrix} -c&-s&0\\s&-c&0\\0&0&1 \end{bmatrix}$	$\begin{bmatrix} \epsilon&0&0\\0&\epsilon^*&0\\0&0&1 \end{bmatrix}$	$\begin{bmatrix} 0&0&1\\1&0&0\\0&1&0 \end{bmatrix}$
C_3^{-1}	$\begin{bmatrix} -c&s&0\\-s&-c&0\\0&0&1 \end{bmatrix}$	$\begin{bmatrix} \epsilon^*&0&0\\0&\epsilon&0\\0&0&1 \end{bmatrix}$	$\begin{bmatrix} 0&1&0\\0&0&1\\1&0&0 \end{bmatrix}$
σ_a	$\begin{bmatrix} 1&0&0\\0&-1&0\\0&0&1 \end{bmatrix}$	$\begin{bmatrix} 0&1&0\\1&0&0\\0&0&1 \end{bmatrix}$	$\begin{bmatrix} 1&0&0\\0&0&1\\0&1&0 \end{bmatrix}$
σ_b	$\begin{bmatrix} -c&-s&0\\-s&c&0\\0&0&1 \end{bmatrix}$	$\begin{bmatrix} 0&\epsilon^*&0\\\epsilon&0&0\\0&0&1 \end{bmatrix}$	$\begin{bmatrix} 0&0&1\\0&1&0\\1&0&0 \end{bmatrix}$
σ_c	$\begin{bmatrix} -c&s&0\\s&c&0\\0&0&1 \end{bmatrix}$	$\begin{bmatrix} 0&\epsilon&0\\\epsilon^*&0&0\\0&0&1 \end{bmatrix}$	$\begin{bmatrix} 0&1&0\\1&0&0\\0&0&1 \end{bmatrix}$

5.4 Characters

The discussion so far has shown us how the matrices of a representation change when the basis of the representation is changed and how the matrices of two equivalent representations are related to each other. The question we wish now to discuss is that of how to describe a representation in general without referring to some specific basis; we wish to discover if there are quantities associated with a representation which are the same for all equivalent representations and which are different for non-equivalent representations.

Such quantities must be associated with the matrices of the representation and must remain invariant if the basis of the representation is changed. Suppose that we denote an invariant quantity associated with the matrix $D(R)$ of a representation by $\chi[D(R)]$. Since a change of basis changes $D(R)$ to $AD(R)A^{-1}$, where A is the matrix describing the change of basis, the invariant quantity χ must be defined in such a way that

$$\chi[D(R)] = \chi[AD(R)A^{-1}] \tag{5.9}$$

for any matrix A with inverse A^{-1}. It turns out that for our purposes the appropriate invariant quantity to associate with a matrix D is what is called the *trace* of the matrix, denoted by Tr(D). (In German, and in many English texts, this is called the *spur* of the matrix and is denoted by Sp(D).) The trace of a matrix is defined to be the algebraic sum of its diagonal elements; if D is an $n \times n$ matrix with elements d_{ij}, then

$$\mathrm{Tr}(D) = \sum_{i=1}^{n} d_{ii}. \tag{5.10}$$

The invariance of the trace of a matrix under a transformation like that of (5.5) follows from the fact that if P and Q are any two matrices, then

$$\mathrm{Tr}(PQ) = \mathrm{Tr}(QP); \tag{5.11}$$

i.e. even though in general the matrices PQ and QP are quite different, nevertheless the sums of their diagonal elements will be equal. This follows from the definition of the trace:

$$\mathrm{Tr}(PQ) = \sum_{i=1}^{n} [PQ]_{ii} = \sum_{i=1}^{n} \sum_{k=1}^{n} p_{ik}q_{ki} = \sum_{k=1}^{n} \sum_{i=1}^{n} q_{ki}p_{ik}$$

$$= \sum_{k=1}^{n} [QP]_{kk} = \mathrm{Tr}(QP).$$

We now apply this result to the matrix ADA^{-1} with $P=AD$ and $Q=A^{-1}$ to obtain

$$\mathrm{Tr}(ADA^{-1}) = \mathrm{Tr}(A^{-1}AD) = \mathrm{Tr}(D). \tag{5.12}$$

Thus the trace of a matrix does possess the required invariance property (5.9), and we conclude that if two representations of a group, with matrices $D^{(f)}(R)$ and $D^{(g)}(R)$, are equivalent then it follows that

$$\text{Tr}[D^{(f)}(R)] = \text{Tr}[D^{(g)}(R)] \tag{5.13}$$

for every element R of the group.

EXAMPLE

Table 5.2 lists the traces of the matrices, belonging to three equivalent representations of $\mathscr{C}_{3v}$, which are given in Table 5.1. The table illustrates the way in which the trace remains invariant when the basis of a representation is changed. (In column Γ_2 of the table we have used the fact that $\epsilon + \epsilon^* = -1$.)

TABLE 5.2. *The traces of the matrices of Table 5.1.*

	Γ_1	Γ_2	Γ_3
E	$1+1+1 = 3$	$1+1+1 = 3$	$1+1+1 = 3$
C_3	$-\frac{1}{2}-\frac{1}{2}+1 = 0$	$\epsilon + \epsilon^* + 1 = 0$	$0+0+0 = 0$
C_3^{-1}	$-\frac{1}{2}-\frac{1}{2}+1 = 0$	$\epsilon^* + \epsilon + 1 = 0$	$0+0+0 = 0$
σ_a	$1-1+1 = 1$	$0+0+1 = 1$	$1+0+0 = 1$
σ_b	$-\frac{1}{2}+\frac{1}{2}+1 = 1$	$0+0+1 = 1$	$0+1+0 = 1$
σ_c	$-\frac{1}{2}+\frac{1}{2}+1 = 1$	$0+0+1 = 1$	$0+0+1 = 1$

So far we have seen that the trace of a representative matrix remains invariant under a change of basis and that (5.13) holds for the matrices of two equivalent representations. There might well be other quantities associated with the matrices which also remain invariant, but the special importance of the trace of a matrix in representation theory is a consequence of the fact that (5.13) can be used as a *criterion* for deciding whether or not two representations are equivalent. As we shall see in Section 6.4, two representations of a group whose matrices are such that (5.13) is valid for every element R of the group are *necessarily* equivalent to each other.

The proof of this statement depends on some properties of representations that we have yet to establish. If for the moment we assume that it is true we see that we have found an answer to the question, posed at the beginning of this section, of how to characterize a representation in general terms without having to refer it to a specific basis. We can do this by stating, for each element R of a group, the value of the trace of the matrix $D(R)$ which represents R. This gives us a set of numbers which is characteristic of the representation in the sense that all equivalent representations give rise to the same set of numbers while non-equivalent representations have different sets.

For this reason, the number $\text{Tr}[D(R)]$ is called the *character* of the group element R in the representation with matrices $D(R)$. We denote the character by the symbol $\chi(R)$:

$$\chi(R) = \text{Tr}[D(R)]. \tag{5.14}$$

The complete set of characters, one for each element of the group, is called *the character of the representation*, and, with these definitions, we say that *two representations are equivalent if, and only if, they have the same character.*

The description of a representation in terms of its character is simplified if one makes use of the fact, discussed in Section 2.5, that the elements of a group can be divided into mutually exclusive classes of conjugate elements. The definition (2.5) of the relation between two conjugate group elements P and Q must, in any representation, be mirrored by the matrices representing these elements. Thus if P and Q are conjugate elements there must be some group element R for which

$$D(P) = D(R^{-1})D(Q)D(R). \tag{5.15}$$

Since $D(R^{-1}) = D^{-1}(R)$, (5.15) is a relation between the matrices $D(P)$ and $D(Q)$ of precisely the same form as (5.5). It follows by the same argument that led to (5.13) that

$$\text{Tr}[D(P)] = \text{Tr}[D(Q)].$$

Thus, in any representation of a group, $\chi(P) = \chi(Q)$ if P and Q are conjugate elements: in order to specify the character of a representation it suffices to state the character of a typical element from each class of the group.

EXAMPLE

The elements of $\mathscr{C}_{3v}$ divide into three classes: the identical operation E; the two rotations C_3 and C_3^{-1}; and the three reflections σ_a, σ_b, σ_c. In the equivalent representations of this group that we have considered, Table 5.2 shows that

$$\chi(E) = 3; \quad \chi(C_3) = \chi(C_3^{-1}) = 0; \quad \chi(\sigma_a) = \chi(\sigma_b) = \chi(\sigma_c) = 1.$$

These characters are conveniently exhibited in the form of a *character table* as shown below.

Class	E	C_3, C_3^{-1}	$\sigma_a, \sigma_b, \sigma_c$
Character χ	3	0	1

5.5 Reducible Representations: An Example

Our discussion so far has shown us how the matrices of a representation change when the basis of the representation is changed and how one can characterize a given representation. With these matters out of the way, we are now in a position to introduce the concepts of reducible and irreducible representations, concepts which lie at the very heart of the applications of group theory in quantum mechanics.

Before we embark on a general discussion of reducibility we shall, however, illustrate the ideas involved by considering once again the representation of $\mathscr{C}_{3v}$ which arises from evaluating the effects of its symmetry operations on position vectors in physical space. Any set of three non-coplanar vectors, with origin at a point which is left unmoved by the operations of $\mathscr{C}_{3v}$, will serve as the basis for a coordinate system in this space and can be used to obtain a set of 3×3 matrices representing $\mathscr{C}_{3v}$. All the different sets of matrices that can be obtained in this way give representations which are equivalent to one another and one such representation can be transformed into another by a suitable choice of the transformation matrix A in (5.5). The representations given in Table 5.1 are examples of equivalent representations of this kind.

Of all the possible coordinate systems that might be used as a basis for this representation there is one general type which, from our present point of view, may be regarded as particularly simple. The operations of $\mathscr{C}_{3v}$ are such as to leave unaltered any position vector which points along the axis of symmetry and to change any vector which is perpendicular to this axis into another vector perpendicular to the axis. If, therefore, one chooses a coordinate system one of whose base vectors, say e_3, points along the symmetry axis and whose other two vectors, say e_1 and e_2, are perpendicular to this axis, any operation of $\mathscr{C}_{3v}$ will leave e_3 unaltered and will turn e_1 or e_2 into linear combinations of each other. Thus, if R denotes any one of the operations of $\mathscr{C}_{3v}$,

$$Re_1 = r_{11}e_1 + r_{21}e_2 + 0 \cdot e_3,$$
$$Re_2 = r_{12}e_1 + r_{22}e_2 + 0 \cdot e_3, \qquad (5.16)$$
$$Re_3 = 0 \cdot e_1 + 0 \cdot e_2 + 1 \cdot e_3.$$

In a basis of this kind, therefore, all the matrices of the representation have the same form:

$$D(R) = \begin{bmatrix} r_{11} & r_{12} & 0 \\ r_{21} & r_{22} & 0 \\ 0 & 0 & 1 \end{bmatrix}. \qquad (5.17)$$

It is evident that e_1 and e_2, which form a basis for a two-dimensional space (the plane through the origin perpendicular to the axis of symmetry), generate a two-dimensional representation of $\mathscr{C}_{3v}$ whose matrices, $D'(R)$ say, appear in the upper left-hand corner of (5.17), and that e_3 by itself, being left unaltered by all the operations of $\mathscr{C}_{3v}$, generates the identical representation whose matrices $D''(R) = 1$ appear in the lower right-hand corner of (5.17). Thus symbolically we may write (5.17) as

$$D(R) = \left[\begin{array}{c|c} D'(R) & 0 \\ \hline 0 & D''(R) \end{array}\right].$$
(5.18)

We say that $D(R)$ is the *direct sum* of the matrices $D'(R)$ and $D''(R)$.

There are, of course, many different ways of choosing the two vectors e_1 and e_2 and so there will be many different possible sets of 2×2 matrices $D'(R)$. All these possible two-dimensional representations are, however, equivalent to each other. Let us use the symbol Γ' to stand for any one of these equivalent two-dimensional representations and let Γ''' stand for the identical representation. Further, let Γ symbolize any of the equivalent three-dimensional representations of $\mathscr{C}_{3v}$ with which we began the discussion. We can then summarize our results by saying that it is possible to choose a basis for Γ in such a way that its matrices appear in the *reduced form* (5.18) as direct sums of matrices belonging to the representations Γ' and Γ'''; alternatively, we say that Γ is a *reducible representation* which can be *reduced* into the component representations Γ' and Γ'' by a suitable choice of basis. We express this in symbols by writing

$$\Gamma = \Gamma' + \Gamma''.$$
(5.19)

EXAMPLE

Table 5.1 shows three equivalent representations of $\mathscr{C}_{3v}$. Of these, both Γ_1 and Γ_2 have the reduced form of (5.18). For Γ_1, the base vectors e_1 and e_2 of the two-dimensional representation Γ' are two unit vectors perpendicular to e_3 and to each other; for Γ_2, the base vectors of Γ' are the complex combinations $e_1' = (e_1 + ie_2)/\sqrt{2}$ and $e_2' = (e_1 - ie_2)/\sqrt{2}$. The matrices of the equivalent representation Γ_3 do not have the reduced form (5.18) but, as we have seen, Γ_3 can be transformed into Γ_1 by the change of basis described by (5.8); i.e. Γ_3 is a reducible representation which can be reduced by the change of basis (5.8).

We may now apply the concept of reducibility to the 2×2 matrices $D'(R)$ of the representation Γ' and ask whether it may not be possible to find a basis for Γ' in which the matrices $D'(R)$ themselves appear in reduced form as the direct sums of two one-dimensional representations. This would require us to choose the base vectors e_1, e_2 in such a way that, for every operation R of $\mathscr{C}_{3v}$,

$$Re_1 = r_1 e_1; \qquad Re_2 = r_2 e_2.$$

Then the matrices of Γ' in this representation would all have the same diagonal form

$$D'(R) = \begin{bmatrix} r_1 & 0 \\ 0 & r_2 \end{bmatrix}.$$
(5.20)

That it is in fact impossible to find such a basis for Γ' may be shown by the following argument. Suppose that we had succeeded in finding a basis for Γ' in which all the matrices had the reduced form (5.20). Then for any two operations R and S of $\mathscr{C}_{3v}$ we should have

$$D'(RS) = D'(R)D'(S) = \begin{bmatrix} r_1 & 0 \\ 0 & r_2 \end{bmatrix}\begin{bmatrix} s_1 & 0 \\ 0 & s_2 \end{bmatrix} = \begin{bmatrix} r_1 s_1 & 0 \\ 0 & r_2 s_2 \end{bmatrix}$$

$$= \begin{bmatrix} s_1 & 0 \\ 0 & s_2 \end{bmatrix}\begin{bmatrix} r_1 & 0 \\ 0 & r_2 \end{bmatrix} = D'(S)D'(R) = D'(SR).$$

Thus the group operations RS and SR would be represented by the *same* matrix in this representation. If one now changed to any other basis for Γ' one would obtain, by (5.5), an equivalent representation in which the matrices representing RS and SR were the same. One such equivalent representation is given by the 2×2 matrices in the upper left-hand corners of the matrices Γ_1 of Table 5.1. In this particular representation the operations $\sigma_a = \sigma_c C_3$ and $\sigma_b = C_3\sigma_c$, for example, are represented by *different* matrices and this representation cannot, therefore, be equivalent to a representation whose matrices have the reduced form (5.20). The supposition that a basis for Γ' can be found which reduces it to the form (5.20) thus leads to a contradiction and must be false. It follows that no reduction of Γ' is possible; Γ' is an *irreducible representation* of $\mathscr{C}_{3v}$ which cannot be reduced to a direct sum of two one-dimensional representations by any change of basis whatsoever.

5.6 Reducible and Irreducible Representations

The idea, which we introduced above in a special case, that it may be possible to choose the basis for a representation in such a way that its matrices are exhibited as direct sums of matrices belonging to irreducible representations can easily be generalized. Suppose that Γ is an n-dimensional representation of a group of operators O_R acting on the vectors of an n-dimensional vector space V, and suppose that the relations between the operators and the vector space are such that it is possible to find a basis $f_1, f_2, \ldots, f_n$ for V with the property that the first m of these base vectors are transformed amongst themselves by all the operators O_R; i.e. suppose that, for every R and a given fixed value of m,

$$O_R f_1 = [D(R)]_{11}f_1 + \cdots + [D(R)]_{m1}f_m + 0 \cdot f_{m+1} + \cdots + 0 \cdot f_n,$$

$$O_R f_2 = [D(R)]_{12}f_1 + \cdots + [D(R)]_{m2}f_m + 0 \cdot f_{m+1} + \cdots + 0 \cdot f_n,$$

$$\cdot \quad \cdot \quad \cdot \quad \cdot \quad \cdot \quad \cdot \quad \cdot \quad \cdot \quad \cdot \quad \cdot \quad \cdot \quad \cdot \quad \cdot \quad \cdot \quad \cdot \quad \cdot \quad (5.21a)$$

$$O_R f_m = [D(R)]_{1m}f_1 + \cdots + [D(R)]_{mm}f_m + 0 \cdot f_{m+1} + \cdots + 0 \cdot f_n.$$

(Compare the first two equations of (5.16).)

If the representation is such that a basis of this kind can be found, the m base vectors $f_1, f_2, \ldots, f_m$ by themselves define a space V' of m dimensions, a *sub-space* of the original space V, which has the property that any vector of V' is transformed into another vector of V' by the operators O_R. (One says that V' is an *invariant sub-space* of V.) If we restrict ourselves to considering only orthonormal bases, as we are perfectly entitled to do, the remaining base vectors $f_{m+1}, \ldots, f_n$ of V define another sub-space, V'' say, which has $n-m$ dimensions and which is such that any vector belonging to V'' is orthogonal to any vector belonging to V'. Thus, if f' is any vector belonging to V' and f'' is a vector belonging to V'', their scalar product must vanish and $(f'', f') = 0$. Now the operators O_R will be unitary operators of the type discussed in Section 4.8 and so, by (4.46), $(O_R f'', O_R f') = 0$. But, by the hypothesis made above, $O_R f'$ is a vector belonging to V', and since f' and hence $O_R f'$ may be any vector of V' we deduce that $O_R f''$ must be orthogonal to every vector of V'. It must therefore belong to the sub-space V'' and be a linear combination of the vectors $f_{m+1}, \ldots, f_n$. If we let f'' run successively through the vectors $f_{m+1}, \ldots, f_n$ it follows that we shall obtain a set of companion equations to (5.21a) of the form

$$O_R f_{m+1} = 0 \cdot f_1 + \cdots + 0 \cdot f_m + [D(R)]_{m+1, m+1} f_{m+1} + \cdots + [D(R)]_{n, m+1} f_n,$$
$$\cdot\quad\cdot\quad\cdot\quad\cdot\quad\cdot\quad\cdot\quad\cdot\quad\cdot\quad\cdot\quad\cdot\quad\cdot\quad\cdot\quad\cdot\quad\cdot\quad\cdot$$
$$O_R f_n = \quad 0 \cdot f_1 + \cdots + 0 \cdot f_m + [D(R)]_{m+1, n} f_{m+1} \quad + \cdots + [D(R)]_{nn} f_n.$$
$$(5.21b)$$

(Compare the third equation of (5.16).)

If the original representation Γ is such that it is possible to find an orthonormal basis which can be divided in this way into two independent sets of base vectors for some value of m less than n, we say that Γ is a *reducible representation*. If no such basis exists then Γ is an *irreducible representation*.

If Γ is reducible, so that it is possible to find a basis in which equations (5.21) hold, then, with respect to this basis, all the matrices of Γ will have the same *reduced form*

$$D(R) = \begin{bmatrix} [D(R)]_{11} \cdots [D(R)]_{1m} & 0 \cdots\cdots\cdots 0 \\ \vdots \qquad \vdots & \vdots \qquad \vdots \\ [D(R)]_{m1} \cdots [D(R)]_{mm} & 0 \cdots\cdots\cdots 0 \\ \hline 0 \cdots\cdots 0 & [D(R)]_{m+1,m+1} \cdots [D(R)]_{m+1,n} \\ \vdots \qquad \vdots & \vdots \qquad \vdots \\ 0 \cdots\cdots 0 & [D(R)]_{n,m+1} \cdots [D(R)]_{nn} \end{bmatrix} \begin{matrix} \\ \Big\} \ m \text{ rows} \\ \\ \\ \Big\} \ (n-m) \text{ rows} \\ \\ \end{matrix} \quad (5.22)$$

$\underbrace{\qquad}_{m \text{ columns}} \qquad \underbrace{\qquad}_{(n-m) \text{ columns}}$

Denote the $m \times m$ matrix in the upper left hand corner of $D(R)$ by $D'(R)$ and the $(n-m) \times (n-m)$ matrix in the lower right hand corner by $D''(R)$.

Then $D(R)$ is the direct sum of $D'(R)$ and $D''(R)$ and we can write (5.22) in schematic form as

$$D(R) = \left[\begin{array}{c|c} D'(R) & 0 \\ \hline 0 & D''(R) \end{array}\right]. \qquad (5.23)$$

From the form of (5.21a,b) it is clear that the two invariant sub-spaces of the original vector space V, namely V' with basis $f_1, \ldots, f_m$ and V'' with basis $f_{m+1}, \ldots, f_n$, give rise to two independent representations of the group of operators O_R; V' produces a representation, Γ' say, with matrices $D'(R)$ and V'' produces a representation, Γ''' say, with matrices $D''(R)$. The relation between the original representation Γ and the representations Γ' and Γ''' is symbolized by writing

$$\Gamma = \Gamma' + \Gamma''.$$

The meaning of this 'equation' is that Γ is a reducible representation whose matrices can, by a suitable choice of basis, be put into the reduced form (5.23) and expressed as direct sums of matrices belonging to Γ' and Γ''.

The actual basis used to reduce Γ is to a large extent arbitrary. The essential point is that it should be an orthonormal basis which clearly separates from each other the two invariant sub-spaces V' and V'' into which the original vector space V can be divided. Within V' and V'' themselves any suitable basis can be chosen; a change of basis for V' from $f_1, \ldots, f_m$ to another set of m base vectors lying within V' will merely replace the matrices $D'(R)$ by an equivalent set of matrices, and the same remark applies to the basis chosen for V''.

We now go on to consider the representations Γ' and Γ'', and ask whether they are reducible. It may be that V' and V'' themselves contain invariant sub-spaces and that Γ' and Γ''' can themselves be reduced, by a suitable change of basis within V' or V'', so that their matrices $D'(R)$ and $D''(R)$ are expressed as direct sums of matrices belonging to representations of smaller dimension. The reducibility of these representations can be examined in their turn. If this process is continued we shall eventually divide the original space V into a number of invariant sub-spaces each of which gives rise independently to a representation of the group of operators O_R and none of which can be divided into invariant sub-spaces of smaller dimension. When this final stage has been reached, the matrices of Γ will all have been transformed into diagonal block form,

$$D(R) = \left[\begin{array}{cccc} D^{(1)}(R) & & & \\ & D^{(2)}(R) & & \\ & & D^{(3)}(R) & \\ & & & D^{(p)}(R) \end{array}\right] \qquad (5.24)$$

where the various sub-matrices $D^{(1)}(R)$, $D^{(2)}(R), \ldots, D^{(p)}(R)$ belong to *irreducible representations* $\Gamma_1, \Gamma_2, \ldots, \Gamma_p$ which cannot be further reduced by any change of basis whatsoever. We shall then have arrived at a situation where the reducible representation Γ has been completely decomposed into its component irreducible representations, and we write

$$\Gamma = \Gamma_1 + \Gamma_2 + \Gamma_3 + \cdots + \Gamma_p. \qquad (5.25)$$

In the reduction of Γ the same irreducible representation may turn up more than once. For instance, it might well happen that $D^{(1)}(R)$ and $D^{(2)}(R)$ had the same dimension and were related by an equation of the form (5.5) with some particular matrix A. In this case the representations Γ_1 and Γ_2 would be equivalent to each other and a change in the basis of the invariant sub-space giving rise to Γ_2 would make $D^{(2)}(R)$ identical with $D^{(1)}(R)$. If this were the case, we should indicate the decomposition of Γ into its irreducible components by writing

$$\Gamma = 2\Gamma_1 + \Gamma_3 + \cdots + \Gamma_p.$$

EXAMPLES

(i) In the last section we discussed the representation of $\mathscr{C}_{3v}$ which arises when one considers position vectors in physical space. There are two invariant sub-spaces: the plane perpendicular to the symmetry axis, which has two dimensions, and the symmetry axis itself. The representation can accordingly be reduced into one two-dimensional and one one-dimensional representation, and, as we have seen, the two-dimensional representation is itself irreducible. The reduction is therefore complete; the columns Γ_1 and Γ_2 of Table 5.1 give two equivalent forms of the completely reduced representation.

(ii) In Example 3 of Section 4.7 we found the matrices of the five-dimensional representation of $\mathscr{C}_{3v}$ afforded by the d atomic orbitals. Here there are three invariant sub-spaces with bases d_1, d_2; d_3, d_4; d_5 and the matrices of the representation accordingly appear in reduced form as direct sums of two two-dimensional matrices and one one-dimensional matrix. As they are written down, the two sets of two-dimensional matrices are not the same, but it is easily seen that a change of basis in the d_1, d_2 sub-space from d_1, d_2 to d_1, $-d_2$ makes them identical. Thus we have here an example where the same representation occurs twice in the decomposition of a five-dimensional representation. It will be further noted that the matrices of this two-dimensional representation are the same as the matrices of the two-dimensional component representation occurring in column Γ_1 of Table 5.1. Since we know that this is an irreducible representation, we see that the matrices of the five-dimensional representation written down in Section 4.7 are already expressed in terms of irreducible representations and that they cannot be decomposed any further.

The ideas that we have discussed in this section are fundamental for the application of group theory to quantum mechanical problems. As we shall see, the problem of classifying the normal modes of vibration of a molecule or its electronic energy levels and of finding the selection rules which operate for transitions between its vibrational or electronic states turns into the problem of finding the irreducible representations into which a representation of the point group of the molecule can be decomposed. Before we can get down to these applications, however, we must describe the irreducible representations of the molecular point groups and derive the very simple rules, based on the characters of the irreducible representations, which enable us to identify the irreducible representations into which any given representation can be decomposed. These matters are the subject of the next chapter.

Chapter 6

IRREDUCIBLE REPRESENTATIONS

6.1 Properties of Irreducible Representations*

As we have seen, an IR of a group is one whose matrices cannot be brought into reduced form and exhibited as direct sums of matrices belonging to representations of smaller dimension by any change of basis whatsoever. The matrices of the IRs of a point group possess a number of remarkable properties which enable us to enumerate and classify, once and for all, every possible IR of any given point group, and which, further, enable us to find the irreducible components of any reducible representation of the group. A fair degree of mathematical sophistication is needed to establish these properties of IRs and we shall content ourselves with merely stating the main results that will be of interest to us. The significance of the theorems we need can be understood against the conceptual background that has been developed in the preceding chapters and the interested reader is referred to the books mentioned in the bibliography for detailed proofs.

Suppose that we are considering a group $\mathscr{G}$ which contains altogether g elements (including the identical operation) and that the elements of $\mathscr{G}$ can be divided into k different classes of mutually conjugate elements, in the manner described in Section 2.5. One can then prove:

THEOREM I: *The group $\mathscr{G}$ possesses precisely k different (i.e. non-equivalent) IRs $\Gamma_1, \Gamma_2, \ldots, \Gamma_k$ whose dimensions $n_1, n_2, \ldots, n_k$ satisfy the equation*

$$n_1{}^2 + n_2{}^2 + \cdots + n_k{}^2 = g. \qquad (6.1)$$

All the molecular point groups have a g and a k which are such that there is only one possible set of k integers the sum of whose squares is equal to g. Thus, apart from the arbitrary numbering of the different IRs, Theorem I tells us both how many IRs are possessed by a given point group and also what their dimensions are.

---

* The words 'irreducible representation' will occur so frequently in the rest of this book that we shall abreviate them to IR.

In any representation, as we saw in Section 5.4, all the group elements which belong to the same class will have the same character. We denote the k different classes into which the group $\mathscr{G}$ can be divided by $\mathscr{K}_1, \mathscr{K}_2, \ldots, \mathscr{K}_k$ and suppose that they contain $g_1, g_2, \ldots, g_k$ group elements respectively. Further, we denote the character, in the representation Γ_μ, of a group element which belongs to the class $\mathscr{K}_i$ by $\chi_i^{(\mu)}$. Then our second theorem is:

THEOREM II: *The characters $\chi_i^{(\mu)}$ of the different IRs satisfy the relations*

$$\sum_{i=1}^{k} g_i \chi_i^{*(\mu)} \chi_i^{(\nu)} = g \delta_{\mu\nu}, \tag{6.2}$$

where $\chi_i^{*(\mu)}$ is the complex conjugate of $\chi_i^{(\mu)}$. (In many cases, $\chi_i^{(\mu)}$ is in fact real and $\chi_i^{*(\mu)} = \chi_i^{(\mu)}$.)

Two different possible cases are summarized in (6.2):

(i) If μ and ν refer to different IRs ($\mu \neq \nu$; $\delta_{\mu\nu} = 0$) then

$$\sum_{i=1}^{k} g_i \chi_i^{*(\mu)} \chi_i^{(\nu)} = 0; \tag{6.2'}$$

(ii) If μ and ν refer to the same IR ($\mu = \nu$; $\delta_{\mu\nu} = 1$) then

$$\sum_{i=1}^{k} g_i \chi_i^{*(\mu)} \chi_i^{(\mu)} = \sum_{i=1}^{k} g_i |\chi_i^{(\mu)}|^2 = g. \tag{6.2''}$$

One consequence of this theorem is that the sets of characters $\chi_i^{(\mu)}$, $i = 1, 2, \ldots, k$ belonging to the different IRs must be different so that the characters may be used to classify the IRs and to distinguish them from each other. This classification is conveniently shown in the form of a *character table* for the group in the manner indicated in Table 6.1.

TABLE 6.1. *The character table of a group $\mathscr{G}$*

$\mathscr{G}$	$\mathscr{K}_1$	$\mathscr{K}_2$	$\cdots$	$\mathscr{K}_i$	$\cdots$	$\mathscr{K}_k$
Γ_1	$\chi_1^{(1)}$	$\chi_2^{(1)}$	$\cdots$	$\chi_i^{(1)}$	$\cdots$	$\chi_k^{(1)}$
$\vdots$	$\vdots$	$\vdots$		$\vdots$		$\vdots$
Γ_μ	$\chi_1^{(\mu)}$	$\chi_2^{(\mu)}$	$\cdots$	$\chi_i^{(\mu)}$	$\cdots$	$\chi_k^{(\mu)}$
$\vdots$	$\vdots$	$\vdots$		$\vdots$		$\vdots$
Γ_k	$\chi_1^{(k)}$	$\chi_2^{(k)}$	$\cdots$	$\chi_i^{(k)}$	$\cdots$	$\chi_k^{(k)}$

In any group, the identical operation E is always in a class by itself and this is conventionally taken to be the class $\mathscr{K}_1$ so that the first column of the table shows the character of E in the various IRs. In the representation Γ_μ, with dimension n_μ, E is represented by the unit matrix with n_μ rows and columns. Thus $\chi_1^{(\mu)} = \chi^{(\mu)}(E) = n_\mu$, and the first column of the table simply gives the dimensions of the different IRs of $\mathscr{G}$.

EXAMPLE

We illustrate these theorems by considering, once again, the point group $\mathscr{C}_{3v}$. This group contains six elements divided into three classes. These classes are: $\mathscr{K}_1$, containing the identical operation E; $\mathscr{K}_2$, the class of the two rotations C_3, C_3^{-1}; and $\mathscr{K}_3$, the class of the three reflections σ_a, σ_b, σ_c. Thus in this group we have $g = 6$; $g_1 = 1$, $g_2 = 2$, and $g_3 = 3$.

Since the group contains three classes, Theorem I tells us that it has three different IRs whose dimensions n_1, n_2, n_3 satisfy

$$n_1^2 + n_2^2 + n_3^2 = 6.$$

It is easily seen that the only set of three integers the sum of whose squares is equal to six is the set $(1, 1, 2)$; we conclude that $\mathscr{C}_{3v}$ possesses three IRs one of which is two-dimensional while the remaining two both have one dimension.

In our various discussions of $\mathscr{C}_{3v}$ we have already found these IRs. They are:

(i) The identical representation, of one dimension, which associates the number $+1$ with every element of $\mathscr{C}_{3v}$. We call this the representation A_1.

(ii) There is another representation, also of one dimension, which associates the number $+1$ with the group elements E, C_3, C_3^{-1} and the number -1 with the elements σ_a, σ_b, σ_c. This representation is called A_2. Both these representations were discussed at the end of Section 4.5.

(iii) In Section 5.5 we found a two-dimensional IR of $\mathscr{C}_{3v}$; the matrices of one particular form of this representation are the 2×2 sub-matrices in the upper left-hand corners of the matrices listed in column Γ_1 of Table 5.1. We call this the representation E. (This use of E to denote a representation is not to be confused with the symbol for the identical operation. The notation used for naming IRs is described in the next section.)

The characters of the one-dimensional representations are obvious; those of the two-dimensional representation E can be read off from the matrices of Table 5.1. The character table of $\mathscr{C}_{3v}$ is shown in Table 6.2.

TABLE 6.2. *The character table of* $\mathscr{C}_{3v}$

$\mathscr{C}_{3v}$	E	$2C_3$	3σ
A_1	1	1	1
A_2	1	1	-1
E	2	-1	0

This table has the form of Table 6.1. The names of the IRs are written down the left-hand column under the name of the group, and the headings of the remaining columns show the various classes of the group. The symbols used for the classes give a general indication of the type of element contained in the class (E, C_3 or σ) and the number g_i of elements in the class.

We can use the characters entered in this table to illustrate Theorem II. Suppose that we number the IRs by $\Gamma_1 = A_1$, $\Gamma_2 = A_2$, $\Gamma_3 = E$. Then, in the notation of Theorem II, the various characters are

$$\chi_1^{(1)} = 1, \quad \chi_2^{(1)} = 1, \quad \chi_3^{(1)} = 1;$$

$$\chi_1^{(2)} = 1, \quad \chi_2^{(2)} = 1, \quad \chi_3^{(2)} = -1;$$

$$\chi_1^{(3)} = 2, \quad \chi_2^{(3)} = -1, \quad \chi_3^{(3)} = 0.$$

We then find:

$$(a) \quad \sum_{i=1}^{3} g_i \chi_i^{*(1)} \chi_i^{(2)} = 1 \cdot 1 \cdot 1 + 2 \cdot 1 \cdot 1 + 3 \cdot 1 \cdot (-1) = 1 + 2 - 3 = 0,$$

$$(b) \quad \sum_{i=1}^{3} g_i \chi_i^{*(2)} \chi_i^{(3)} = 1 \cdot 1 \cdot 2 + 2 \cdot 1 \cdot (-1) + 3 \cdot (-1) \cdot 0 = 2 - 2 - 0 = 0,$$

$$(c) \quad \sum_{i=1}^{3} g_i \chi_i^{*(1)} \chi_i^{(3)} = 1 \cdot 1 \cdot 2 + 2 \cdot 1 \cdot (-1) + 3 \cdot 1 \cdot 0 = 2 - 2 + 0 = 0,$$

in accordance with (6.2′), and also

$$(d) \quad \sum_{i=1}^{3} g_i \chi_i^{*(1)} \chi_i^{(1)} = 1 \cdot 1 \cdot 1 + 2 \cdot 1 \cdot 1 + 3 \cdot 1 \cdot 1 = 1 + 2 + 3 = 6,$$

$$(e) \quad \sum_{i=1}^{3} g_i \chi_i^{*(2)} \chi_i^{(2)} = 1 \cdot 1 \cdot 1 + 2 \cdot 1 \cdot 1 + 3 \cdot (-1) \cdot (-1) = 1 + 2 + 3 = 6,$$

$$(f) \quad \sum_{i=1}^{3} g_i \chi_i^{*(3)} \chi_i^{(3)} = 1 \cdot 2 \cdot 2 + 2 \cdot (-1) \cdot (-1) + 3 \cdot 0 \cdot 0 = 4 + 2 + 0 = 6,$$

in accordance with (6.2″).

A more interesting application of Theorem II is to show how it may be used to deduce the characters of the two-dimensional IR E from a knowledge of the characters of A_1 and A_2. If we treat the characters $\chi_i^{(3)}$ as unknowns, Theorem II tells us that

$$\sum_{i=1}^{3} g_i \chi_i^{*(1)} \chi_i^{(3)} = 0, \quad \text{i.e.} \quad \chi_1^{(3)} + 2\chi_2^{(3)} + 3\chi_3^{(3)} = 0;$$

$$\sum_{i=1}^{3} g_i \chi_i^{*(2)} \chi_i^{(3)} = 0, \quad \text{i.e.} \quad \chi_1^{(3)} + 2\chi_2^{(3)} - 3\chi_3^{(3)} = 0.$$

From these equations it follows that $\chi_3^{(3)} = 0$, and that $\chi_2^{(3)} = -\frac{1}{2}\chi_1^{(3)}$. But we know, from Theorem I, that we are dealing with a two-dimensional IR so that in fact $\chi_1^{(3)} = 2$. Hence $\chi_2^{(3)} = -1$ and we have found the character of the two-dimensional IR without any need to write down its matrices explicitly.

This example shows how it is possible to build up the character table of a group from a knowledge of some of its simpler IRs using general arguments based on our theorems, without having explicitly to construct the matrices of the representation. The character tables for all the point groups have been found by methods of this kind and a selection of those likely to be of chemical interest is given in Appendix H. As well as the characters of the IRs, the tables give, in the columns on the right, certain additional information the meaning of which will be discussed later on. For the moment we are concerned just with the IRs and we pass now to a description of the notation used to name them.

6.2 Notation for Irreducible Representations

The symbols A_1, A_2, E that we used above for the IRs of $\mathscr{C}_{3v}$ are part of a general scheme for labelling the IRs of the molecular point groups that was introduced in definitive form by Mulliken [11]. Although the Mulliken symbols may be regarded as arbitrary labels attached to the IRs, rather like the symbols used for the chemical elements, the scheme does have a rational basis which it is useful to understand. Some points of the scheme are mentioned below.

(a) None of the point groups we shall discuss has an IR with dimension greater than two, with the exception of the groups $\mathscr{T}_d$, $\mathscr{O}$ and $\mathscr{O}_h$ which have some three-dimensional IRs. The characters of the IRs are mostly real numbers; the only IRs with complex characters are certain one-dimensional IRs of the groups $\mathscr{C}_n$ and $\mathscr{C}_{nh}$ with $n > 2$, $\mathscr{S}_4$ and $\mathscr{S}_6$. These complex representations are discussed separately below. The dimensions of the IRs with real characters are indicated by using the symbols A or B for one-dimensional IRs, E for two-dimensional IRs and either T or F for three-dimensional IRs. (Generally speaking, one finds T used in discussions of the electronic structure of molecules while the same representations are labelled by F in the treatment of molecular vibrations. These alternative notations are both given in the character tables.) The choice between A and B for the one-dimensional IRs is determined by whether the character $\chi(C_n)$ of a rotation about the main n-fold symmetry axis is $+1$ (A representation) or -1 (B representation). Suffixes 1, 2, 3, ... are used, where necessary, to distinguish different IRs with the same dimension.

(b) For certain groups, the Mulliken symbols also have the suffixes g or u attached to them, or they may appear with primes or double primes. The significance of these additions to the symbols requires a little explanation.

In describing the group $\mathscr{O}_h$, we saw that it consisted of the elements of $\mathscr{O}$, the group of pure rotations which move a cube (or a regular octahedron) into itself, together with an equal number of elements obtained by multiplying each element of $\mathscr{O}$ by the inversion i. We indicate this relation between $\mathscr{O}$ and $\mathscr{O}_h$ by writing $\mathscr{O}_h = \mathscr{O} \times i$; in general, by the notation $\mathscr{G} \times i$ where $\mathscr{G}$ is a point group, we mean the enlarged group which is obtained by adding to $\mathscr{G}$ the set of elements obtained by multiplying each element of $\mathscr{G}$ by the inversion. Several of the point groups may be expressed in this way; for n even, $\mathscr{C}_{nh} = \mathscr{C}_n \times i$ and $\mathscr{D}_{nh} = \mathscr{D}_n \times i$; for n odd, $\mathscr{D}_{nd} = \mathscr{D}_n \times i$; and also $\mathscr{S}_6 = \mathscr{C}_3 \times i$ and $\mathscr{O}_h = \mathscr{O} \times i$.

The IRs of $\mathscr{G} \times i$ are closely related to those of the smaller group $\mathscr{G}$. Since inversion commutes with every other symmetry operation, it is easily seen that $\mathscr{G} \times i$ contains twice as many classes as $\mathscr{G}$; for each class $\mathscr{K}_l$ of $\mathscr{G}$, there will be, in $\mathscr{G} \times i$, a class $\mathscr{K}_l$ and a class $\mathscr{K}'_l = i\mathscr{K}_l$, obtained by multiplying each element of $\mathscr{K}_l$ by i. Theorem I then shows that $\mathscr{G} \times i$ has twice as many IRs as $\mathscr{G}$. It can further be shown (see Appendix C) that to each IR Γ_μ of $\mathscr{G}$

there correspond two IRs of $\mathscr{G} \times i$ with the same dimension as Γ_μ. In both these IRs the characters χ_l of the classes $\mathscr{K}_l$ which are common to $\mathscr{G}$ and to $\mathscr{G} \times i$ are the same as the characters of the IR Γ_μ of $\mathscr{G}$. In one of these IRs, called an *even representation*, the characters χ'_l of the corresponding classes $\mathscr{K}'_l = i\mathscr{K}_l$ satisfy $\chi'_l = \chi_l$, while in the other IR, an *odd representation*, they satisfy $\chi'_l = -\chi_l$. These two IRs of $\mathscr{G} \times i$, which both arise from the same IR Γ_μ of $\mathscr{G}$, are denoted respectively by $\Gamma_{\mu g}$ (g for German *gerade = even*) and $\Gamma_{\mu u}$ (u for German *ungerade = odd*).

EXAMPLE

The group $\mathscr{C}_2$ with two elements E and C_2 each in a separate class has two one-dimensional IRs A and B. The group $\mathscr{C}_{2h} = \mathscr{C}_2 \times i$ has four elements E, C_2, i and $\sigma_h = iC_2$, each in a separate class, and has four one-dimensional IRs A_g, A_u, B_g, B_u. The relations between the IRs of $\mathscr{C}_2$ and of $\mathscr{C}_{2h}$ can be seen by comparing their character tables. Thus, for instance, the IR B of $\mathscr{C}_2$, with characters $\chi(E) = 1$ and $\chi(C_2) = -1$, gives rise to the IRs B_g and B_u of $\mathscr{C}_{2h}$. The characters of B_g are $\chi(E) = 1$, $\chi(C_2) = -1$, $\chi(i) = 1$, $\chi(\sigma_h) = -1$; the characters of B_u are $\chi(E) = 1$, $\chi(C_2) = -1$, $\chi(i) = -1$, and $\chi(\sigma_h) = 1$.

Apart from the g and u notation, the relation between the IRs of $\mathscr{G}$ and $\mathscr{G} \times i$ has a useful practical consequence. As we shall see, one of the main uses of a character table is to identify the IRs. For this purpose we need not always consider the whole group $\mathscr{G} \times i$ but may, first of all, restrict ourselves to the smaller group $\mathscr{G}$ to determine the Γ_μ symbol for the IR and then examine the character of the inversion to determine whether we are dealing with a g ($\chi(i)$ positive) or a u ($\chi(i)$ negative) IR.

(c) Very similar considerations apply to the groups $\mathscr{C}_{3h}$, $\mathscr{C}_{5h}$, $\mathscr{D}_{3h}$ and $\mathscr{D}_{5h}$. $\mathscr{D}_{3h}$, for example, contains the elements of $\mathscr{D}_3$ together with a set of elements obtained by multiplying each element of $\mathscr{D}_3$ by the reflection σ_h, which commutes with all the elements of $\mathscr{D}_3$, and we write $\mathscr{D}_{3h} = \mathscr{D}_3 \times \sigma_h$. In general, we use $\mathscr{G} \times \sigma_h$ to denote a group obtained by adding to the elements of $\mathscr{G}$ the set of elements obtained by multiplying each element of $\mathscr{G}$ by σ_h. In the cases where one can think of the larger group in this way, σ_h will commute with all the elements of $\mathscr{G}$ and will play a role precisely analogous to the inversion in groups of the form $\mathscr{G} \times i$. Then $\mathscr{G} \times \sigma_h$ has classes $\mathscr{K}_l$ which are the same as those of $\mathscr{G}$, together with a set of corresponding classes $\mathscr{K}'_l = \sigma_h \mathscr{K}_l$, and has twice as many IRs as $\mathscr{G}$. Each IR Γ_μ of $\mathscr{G}$ gives rise to two IRs of $\mathscr{G} \times \sigma_h$. These are denoted by Γ'_μ and Γ''_μ. In both these IRs the characters χ_l of the classes $\mathscr{K}_l$ which are common to $\mathscr{G}$ and $\mathscr{G} \times \sigma_h$ are the same as the characters of Γ_μ; in Γ'_μ, the characters of the classes $\mathscr{K}'_l = \sigma_h \mathscr{K}_l$ satisfy $\chi'_l = \chi_l$, while in Γ''_μ they satisfy $\chi'_l = -\chi_l$. For the purpose of identifying the IRs of $\mathscr{G} \times \sigma_h$, we may use the character table of the smaller group $\mathscr{G}$ to identify the Γ_μ symbol and then add one prime if $\chi(\sigma_h)$ is positive or two primes if $\chi(\sigma_h)$ is negative.

Certain groups may be written either as $\mathscr{G} \times \sigma_h$ or $\mathscr{G} \times i$. For instance $\mathscr{D}_{4h}$ is obtained by adding a horizontal plane of symmetry to $\mathscr{D}_4$ and so may be written as $\mathscr{D}_4 \times \sigma_h$. Alternatively, we may pick out the element $i = \sigma_h C_2$ of $\mathscr{D}_{4h}$ and write $\mathscr{D}_{4h} = \mathscr{D}_4 \times i$. In these cases we always choose to express the group in the form $\mathscr{G} \times i$ and use the g, u notation.

(*d*) We finally come to consider the one-dimensional IRs with complex characters that were mentioned in (*a*) above. Suppose that a group with elements P, Q, R, ... and multiplication rules $PQ = R$, ... has a one-dimensional IR Γ_c in which the group elements are represented by complex numbers p, q, r, ... whose products mirror the multiplication rules of the group so that $pq = r$, ... If we now take the complex conjugates of the numbers p, q, r, ... their products will have multiplication rules of exactly the same structure, $p^*q^* = r^*$, ..., so that there will be another one-dimensional IR which represents the group elements by the complex conjugate numbers p^*, q^*, r^*, ... This representation we call Γ_c^*, the complex conjugate representation to Γ_c, and we see that the complex one-dimensional IRs of a group must always occur in complex conjugate pairs. In the Mulliken notation these pairs of representations are not given separate labels; they are bracketed together and given the symbol E appropriate to a two-dimensional IR.

EXAMPLE

Take the group $\mathscr{C}_3$ with elements E, C_3, $C_3^{-1} = C_3^2$. These elements commute with each other. They are, therefore, in three separate classes and so, by Theorem I, $\mathscr{C}_3$ has three one-dimensional IRs. Suppose that we take the representation which arises when we consider the effects of the symmetry operations of $\mathscr{C}_3$ on the base vectors $\mathbf{e}_1$, $\mathbf{e}_2$, $\mathbf{e}_3$ of an orthonormal coordinate system in physical space, and suppose that we choose $\mathbf{e}_3$ to point along the axis of symmetry. The matrices representing the rotations then have the form (4.10) with $\alpha = 120°$ and $-120°$ respectively, and they are given explicitly in column Γ_1 of Table 5.1, since $\mathscr{C}_3$ is the group that remains when we strike the reflections σ_a, σ_b, σ_c out of $\mathscr{C}_{3v}$. These matrices appear in reduced form as the direct sum of the identical representation A of $\mathscr{C}_3$ and a two-dimensional representation. Now suppose that we change to a complex basis $\mathbf{e}_1' = (\mathbf{e}_1 + i\mathbf{e}_2)/\sqrt{2}$, $\mathbf{e}_2' = (\mathbf{e}_1 - i\mathbf{e}_2)/\sqrt{2}$, $\mathbf{e}_3' = \mathbf{e}_3$. This will change the matrices representing E, C_3, C_3^{-1} into the equivalent forms given in column Γ_2 of Table 5.1. But these three matrices are in completely reduced form and are the direct sums of three one-dimensional matrices. From them we can write down the character table for $\mathscr{C}_3$. This is given in Table 6.3, where we have put $\epsilon = e^{-2\pi i/3}$. In the table the two complex conjugate representations Γ_c and Γ_c^* are bracketed together and given the single label E.

TABLE 6.3. *Character Table of* $\mathscr{C}_3$

$\mathscr{C}_3$	E	C_3	C_3^{-1}
A	1	1	1
$E = \left\{ \begin{array}{l} \Gamma_c \\ \Gamma_c^* \end{array} \right.$	1	ϵ	ϵ^*
	1	ϵ^*	ϵ

The reason for not giving separate labels to the complex IRs is that in physical applications they invariably occur together in their complex conjugate pairs. Whereas, generally speaking, we always want, for good physical reasons, to break down a reducible representation as far as we can into its irreducible components, it does not usually give us any further information if the reduction merely reduces a two-dimensional representation into the direct sum of two complex conjugate one-dimensional representations. This point will become clear when we discuss the physical applications of the theory. In the above example, for instance, we should generally be content to leave the representation in its original semi-reduced form as $A + E$, where E has the real characters $\chi(E) = 2$, $\chi(C_3) = \chi(C_3^{-1}) = \epsilon + \epsilon^* = -1$, rather than to decompose it further into the completely reduced form $A + \Gamma_c + \Gamma_c^*$.

The Mulliken notation has become almost standard but there is another notation which is occasionally found in the literature. Bethe, in a classic paper [10], was the first to point out the uses of group theory in discussing the splittings of the energy levels of ions in crystals. He derived the character tables of some of the point groups and his symbols for their IRs are still used by some authors, particularly in discussions of octahedrally coordinated complexes. The groups concerned are $\mathcal{O}$, $\mathcal{T}_d$ and $\mathcal{D}_4$. These all have five IRs which Bethe simply labelled $\Gamma_1, \ldots, \Gamma_5$. The corresponding Mulliken symbols are given below.

$$\text{Bethe } (\mathcal{O}, \mathcal{T}_d, \mathcal{D}_4): \quad \Gamma_1 \quad \Gamma_2 \quad \Gamma_3 \quad \Gamma_4 \quad \Gamma_5$$

$$\text{Mulliken } (\mathcal{O}, \mathcal{T}_d): \quad A_1 \quad A_2 \quad E \quad T_1 \quad T_2$$

$$\text{Mulliken } (\mathcal{D}_4): \quad A_1 \quad A_2 \quad B_1 \quad B_2 \quad E$$

6.3 Linear Molecules and Atoms

The point groups $\mathcal{C}_{\infty v}$ and $\mathcal{D}_{\infty h}$ of linear molecules, or the full rotation group $\mathcal{R}_3$ of an atom, differ from the point groups that we have been considering in that they have an infinity of elements. We can, nevertheless, construct reducible and irreducible representations of these groups in exactly the same way as for the point groups with a finite number of elements.

Thus, for example, $\mathcal{C}_{\infty v}$ consists of all possible rotations $C(\phi)$ about an axis of symmetry together with reflections σ_v in all possible planes of symmetry passing through the axis. If we were to take an origin on the axis of symmetry and to introduce an orthonormal coordinate basis in physical space with $\mathbf{e}_3$ pointing along the axis of symmetry and $\mathbf{e}_1$ and $\mathbf{e}_2$ perpendicular to the axis, we should obtain a representation of $\mathcal{C}_{\infty v}$ in which a rotation $C(\alpha)$ was represented by the matrix (4.10), one such matrix for each value of α in the range from 0 to 2π, and in which a reflection in a plane containing $\mathbf{e}_3$ making an angle β with the $\mathbf{e}_1$, $\mathbf{e}_3$ plane was represented by the matrix (4.13), one such matrix for each value of β in the range from 0 to π. It is clear from the form of these matrices that this representation is reducible and that $\mathbf{e}_3$ by itself generates the identical representation, in which all the elements of

$\mathscr{C}_{\infty v}$ are represented by the number $+1$, while the pair of base vectors e_1 and e_2 generate a two-dimensional representation of $\mathscr{C}_{\infty v}$ which, by an argument similar to that used in Section 5.5, can be seen to be irreducible. Similarly, the matrices (4.42a,b) give us a reducible representation of $\mathscr{C}_{\infty v}$ arising from the five-dimensional function space of the d atomic orbitals.

Because these groups have an infinity of elements and classes, the theorems used in Section 6.1 do not apply to them and other, more elaborate, methods are needed to find their IRs. We shall not discuss these methods at all but shall merely state the results that will be of use to us. In contrast to the finite point groups, these *continuous groups* have an infinite number of IRs. It is possible, however, to order these into a sequence and it turns out that in practice one is only concerned with the first few members of the sequence. The various groups are discussed below.

(a) $\mathscr{C}_{\infty v}$

In this group the pairs of rotations $C(\phi)$, $C(-\phi)$ through equal and opposite angles, belong to a class of two elements, one class for each value of ϕ, and all the reflections σ_v belong to one class. The group has two one-dimensional IRs and an infinite sequence of two-dimensional IRs. In the Mulliken notation these would be described by the symbols A_1, A_2, E_1, E_2, ..., but a completely different notation, which uses the Greek letters Σ, Π, Δ, Φ, ... and which dates back to the original spectroscopic investigations of linear molecules, is normally employed. The characters of these IRs are given in Table 6.4. The class headings in the table indicate, as usual, the number and kind of element in each class.

TABLE 6.4. *Character Table of* $\mathscr{C}_{\infty v}$

$\mathscr{C}_{\infty v}$	E	$2C(\phi)$	$\infty\sigma_v$
$A_1 = \Sigma^+$	1	1	1
$A_2 = \Sigma^-$	1	1	-1
$E_1 = \Pi$	2	$2\cos\phi$	0
$E_2 = \Delta$	2	$2\cos 2\phi$	0
$E_3 = \Phi$	2	$2\cos 3\phi$	0
...	...	...	...

(b) $\mathscr{D}_{\infty h}$

This group is obtained from $\mathscr{C}_{\infty v}$ by adding the inversion i and we can write $\mathscr{D}_{\infty h} = \mathscr{C}_{\infty v} \times i$. Each IR of $\mathscr{C}_{\infty v}$ gives rise to two IRs of $\mathscr{D}_{\infty h}$, distinguished by the suffixes g and u.

(c) $\mathscr{R}_3$

$\mathscr{R}_3$ consists of all possible rotations about all possible axes passing through a single point. All rotations through the same angle, irrespective of the axes of rotation, belong to the same class. The IRs of $\mathscr{R}_3$ are characterized by a number j which can take any of the values $j=0, \frac{1}{2}, 1, \frac{3}{2}, 2, \frac{5}{2}, \ldots$; there is one IR for each value of j and it has dimension $2j+1$. In our applications we shall mostly be concerned with the representations in which j is an *integer*. It is then usual to use the letter l in place of j and to label the irreducible representations belonging to the different values of l by the symbols $S, P, D, F, \ldots$ familiar in atomic spectroscopy according to the following scheme.

$$\text{Representation } l \ = 0 \quad 1 \quad 2 \quad 3 \quad 4 \quad \ldots$$
$$\text{Dimension } (2l+1) = 1 \quad 3 \quad 5 \quad 7 \quad 9 \quad \ldots$$
$$\text{Label} \qquad : S \quad P \quad D \quad F \quad G \quad \ldots$$

6.4 The Reduction of a Reducible Representation (i)

We come now to the matter which is central to most of the applications of group theory in quantum mechanics, the decomposition of a reducible representation into its component IRs. How and why it is that many molecular properties can be discussed in terms of representations are questions that will be considered in the following chapters. Here we are concerned with a mathematical problem: given a reducible representation Γ which arises from the operations of a point group $\mathscr{G}$ in a given vector space, to find a basis for the vector space such that all the matrices of Γ have the reduced form (5.24) and are expressed as direct sums of matrices belonging to IRs of $\mathscr{G}$. Usually the vector space will be defined by a given set of base vectors and the matrices of Γ with respect to this basis will not be in anything resembling a reduced form.

We shall discuss a systematic approach to this problem which divides it into two parts:

Problem (i): To decide which of the IRs of $\mathscr{G}$ will appear in the reduction of Γ; that is, to write down the appropriate form of (5.25).

Problem (ii): To find a new basis for the vector space in which the matrices of Γ have the fully reduced form (5.24); that is, essentially, to find a matrix A which, by (5.5), transforms the given matrices of Γ into their equivalent reduced forms.

Problem (i) can be solved very simply in terms of the characters of Γ and of the IRs of $\mathscr{G}$, without any need to write down the matrices of Γ explicitly. Its solution leads to the qualitative applications of group theory concerned with such things as the *classification* of the energy levels or modes of vibration of molecules by their symmetry, and the *selection rules* responsible for the qualitative features of molecular spectra.

The answer to problem (ii) is needed in the quantitative calculations which relate the measured values of physical quantities to theory. Thus, for example, the answer to problem (i), applied to the vibrations of a molecule, tells us the degeneracies and symmetry species of its normal modes of vibration and enables us to find out which of these are infra-red and which are Raman active; but, in order to relate the measured values of the fundamental frequencies to the force constants of the molecule we need to solve problem (ii). This second problem is much more difficult than the first; it is usually solved by combining some general principles provided by group theory with *ad hoc* methods which are geared to the particular molecule under consideration. This is discussed in Section 6.6; we shall in the rest of this section be concerned with problem (i) only.

We may state problem (i) in the following way: when the given representation Γ of $\mathscr{G}$ is fully reduced and all its matrices have the diagonal block form (5.24), the sub-matrices $D^{(1)}(R), \ldots, D^{(p)}(R)$ will belong to IRs of $\mathscr{G}$. As we saw in Section 5.6, the same IR may occur more than once in the reduction of Γ; equally well, of course, not every IR will necessarily appear. Suppose that the number of times that the IR Γ_v does appear is a_v; a_v may have any integral value 0, 1, 2, ... Then we may write (5.25), in terms of the k different IRs of $\mathscr{G}$, as

$$\Gamma = a_1\Gamma_1 + \cdots + a_v\Gamma_v + \cdots + a_k\Gamma_k = \sum_{v=1}^{k} a_v\Gamma_v, \qquad (6.3)$$

and problem (i) is simply to determine the numbers a_v.

Consider the matrix of Γ which represents the group element R. The trace of this matrix is the character of R in Γ, $\chi^{(\Gamma)}(R)$ say, and this number remains the same whatever basis is chosen for Γ. Thus $\chi^{(\Gamma)}(R)$ is equal to the trace of the reduced matrix (5.24). But, since the trace of a matrix is simply the sum of its diagonal elements, the trace of (5.24) is the sum of the traces of its sub-matrices $D^{(1)}(R), \ldots, D^{(p)}(R)$; the traces of these sub-matrices, in their turn, are the characters of R in the IRs to which the sub-matrices belong. Thus, if sub-matrices belonging to Γ_v appear a_v times in (5.24), their contribution to the trace of (5.24) is just $a_v\chi^{(v)}(R)$ where $\chi^{(v)}(R)$ is the character of R in Γ_v. It follows that

$$\chi^{(\Gamma)}(R) = a_1\chi^{(1)}(R) + \cdots + a_k\chi^{(k)}(R) = \sum_{v=1}^{k} a_v\chi^{(v)}(R).$$

This equation holds for each element R of $\mathscr{G}$. If we let R run through all the elements of $\mathscr{G}$ we shall, however, obtain only k different equations, where k is the number of classes of $\mathscr{G}$, since in any representation the characters of all the group elements belonging to the same class are equal. We can write these k equations as

$$\chi_i^{(\Gamma)} = \sum_{v=1}^{k} a_v\chi_i^{(v)}, \quad i = 1, 2, \ldots, k, \qquad (6.4)$$

where $\chi_i^{(\Gamma)}$ is the character, in the given representation Γ, of an element belonging to the class $\mathscr{K}_i$ and the $\chi_i^{(v)}$ are the characters of the IRs of $\mathscr{G}$.

Now take a particular IR Γ_μ of $\mathscr{G}$ with characters $\chi_i^{(\mu)}$, and multiply each equation of (6.4) by the corresponding $g_i\chi_i^{*(\mu)}$. If all the resulting equations are added together, one will obtain

$$\sum_{i=1}^{k} g_i\chi_i^{*(\mu)}\chi_i^{(\Gamma)} = \sum_{i=1}^{k} g_i\chi_i^{*(\mu)}\left(\sum_{v=1}^{k} a_v\chi_i^{(v)}\right) = \sum_{v=1}^{k} a_v\left(\sum_{i=1}^{k} g_i\chi_i^{*(\mu)}\chi_i^{(v)}\right).$$

But, by Theorem II, the sum enclosed in brackets is simply $g\delta_{\mu v}$, and so

$$\sum_{i=1}^{k} g_i\chi_i^{*(\mu)}\chi_i^{(\Gamma)} = \sum_{v=1}^{k} a_v g\delta_{\mu v} = ga_\mu.$$

(The last equality follows because, as v ranges over the values from 1 to k, $\delta_{\mu v}$ vanishes except for the particular value $v=\mu$ when $\delta_{\mu\mu}=1$.)

We conclude that the number of times that Γ_μ occurs in the reduction of Γ is

$$a_\mu = \frac{1}{g}\sum_{i=1}^{k} g_i\chi_i^{*(\mu)}\chi_i^{(\Gamma)}. \tag{6.5}$$

This is the solution of problem (i); it only requires a knowledge of the character table of the group and the characters $\chi_i^{(\Gamma)}$ of the given representation.

EXAMPLES

(i) Take the representation of $\mathscr{C}_{3v}$ given in column Γ_3 of Table 5.1. The characters of this representation for the three classes of C_{3v} are:

$$\chi^{(\Gamma)}(E) = 3, \quad \chi^{(\Gamma)}(C_3) = 0, \quad \chi^{(\Gamma)}(\sigma) = 1,$$

and the characters of the irreducible representations of $\mathscr{C}_{3v}$ are given in Table 6.2. Substituting these and the appropriate values of the g_i into (6.5) gives:

Representation A_1: $a_{A_1} = \frac{1}{6}(1\cdot1\cdot3+2\cdot1\cdot0+3\cdot1\cdot1) = 1$;

Representation A_2: $a_{A_2} = \frac{1}{6}(1\cdot1\cdot3+2\cdot1\cdot0+3\cdot(-1)\cdot1) = 0$;

Representation E: $a_E = \frac{1}{6}(1\cdot2\cdot3+2\cdot(-1)\cdot0+3\cdot0\cdot1) = 1.$

Thus the reduction of this representation gives

$$\Gamma = A_1 + E.$$

The characters of these representations are related by

$$\chi^{(\Gamma)} = \chi^{(A_1)} + \chi^{(E)},$$

a result that may be verified directly from the character table.

$\mathscr{C}_{3v}$	E	$2C_3$	3σ
A_1	1	1	1
E	2	-1	0
$\Gamma = A_1+E$	3	0	1

In this example the result is almost obvious by inspection of the character table. In more complicated examples, where representations of large dimension are involved, it is *always* advisable to check the numbers a_v found by substitution into (6.5) against the equations (6.4) and to verify that the characters of the IRs do add up correctly to give the character of Γ.

(ii) Take the representation of $\mathscr{C}_3$ given by the first three matrices in column Γ_3 of Table 5.1. The characters of this representation for the three classes of $\mathscr{C}_3$ are:

$$\chi^{(\Gamma)}(E) = 3, \quad \chi^{(\Gamma)}(C_3) = 0, \quad \chi^{(\Gamma)}(C_3{}^{-1}) = 0,$$

and the characters of the IRs of $\mathscr{C}_3$ are given in Table 6.3. Equation (6.5) gives:

Representation A : $\quad a_A = \tfrac{1}{3}(1 \cdot 1 \cdot 3 + 1 \cdot 1 \cdot 0 + 1 \cdot 1 \cdot 0) = 1;$

Representation Γ_c : $\quad a_{\Gamma_c} = \tfrac{1}{3}(1 \cdot 1 \cdot 3 + 1 \cdot \epsilon^* \cdot 0 + 1 \cdot \epsilon \cdot 0) = 1;$

Representation Γ_c^*: $\quad a_{\Gamma_c^*} = \tfrac{1}{3}(1 \cdot 1 \cdot 3 + 1 \cdot \epsilon \cdot 0 + 1 \cdot \epsilon^* \cdot 0) = 1.$

Thus $\Gamma = A + \Gamma_c + \Gamma_c^*$, a result we have previously found. As we have seen, the Mulliken notation lumps Γ_c and Γ_c^* together in a single representation E, and we would therefore tend to write the reduction as $\Gamma = A + E$. But E is a reducible representation and (6.5) is only valid for *irreducible* representations; for the purpose of reducing Γ, the complex representations *must* be regarded as separate IRs. It would be quite incorrect to argue as follows: Γ_c and Γ_c^* together form a reducible representation E whose characters are $\chi(E) = 2$, $\chi(C_3) = \chi(C_3{}^{-1}) = \epsilon + \epsilon^* = -1$. Therefore the number of times that E occurs in Γ is, by (6.5),

$$a_E = \tfrac{1}{3}(1 \cdot 2 \cdot 3 + 1 \cdot (-1) \cdot 0 + 1 \cdot (-1) \cdot 0) = 2.$$

This is not the right answer! Although we always pair the IRs with complex characters into two-dimensional reducible representations designated by a single Mulliken symbol, when we are working with these representations we must use their irreducible one-dimensional components.

In proving (6.5) we have, incidentally, justified the statement made in Section 5.4 that two representations with the same character are necessarily equivalent. This is true for the IRs since the characters of the different IRs of a group are different. If Γ and Γ' are two reducible representations with the same characters, so that for each class of the group $\chi_i^{(\Gamma)} = \chi_i^{(\Gamma')}$, (6.5) shows that each will have the same set of numbers a_v occuring in their reduction. This means that when Γ and Γ' are both completely reduced, their matrices will each contain a_1 sub-matrices belonging to Γ_1, a_2 sub-matrices belonging to Γ_2, etc. These sub-matrices may occur in different orders down the diagonals of the reduced representations, but then they can be brought into the same order by simply renumbering the base vectors of Γ or Γ'. If this is done, the reduced matrices of Γ and Γ' are obviously equivalent and so Γ and Γ' themselves must be equivalent representations.

6.5 An Important Theorem

The results of the previous section enable us to decide which of the IRs of a group $\mathscr{G}$ are contained in a reducible representation, Γ, of $\mathscr{G}$. In order to solve the more difficult problem of finding a basis in which the matrices of Γ have the completely reduced form (5.24) we need to make use of a theorem which we shall state without proof.

Imagine that, for each IR Γ_μ of $\mathscr{G}$, we have written down a definite set of $n_\mu \times n_\mu$ matrices $D^{(\mu)}(R)$ which represent the operations R of $\mathscr{G}$ and suppose that these matrices have been obtained by using an orthonormal basis. Then the theorem states:

THEOREM III: *The elements of the matrices of any two irreducible representations Γ_μ and Γ_ν of $\mathscr{G}$ satisfy the relations*

$$\sum_R [D^{(\mu)}(R)]_{ij}^*[D^{(\nu)}(R)]_{pq} = \frac{g}{n_\mu}\,\delta_{\mu\nu}\delta_{ip}\delta_{jq}, \qquad (6.6)$$

where g is the number of elements of $\mathscr{G}$ and the summation runs over all the elements of $\mathscr{G}$.

(6.6) covers three different cases:

(a) If Γ_μ and Γ_ν are different IRs, so that $\mu \neq \nu$ and $\delta_{\mu\nu}=0$, then

$$\sum_R [D^{(\mu)}(R)]_{ij}^*[D^{(\nu)}(R)]_{pq} = 0. \qquad (6.6a)$$

(b) If Γ_μ and Γ_ν are the same ($\mu=\nu$, $\delta_{\mu\nu}=1$) but $i \neq p$ and/or $j \neq q$, so that δ_{ip} and/or δ_{jq} are zero, then

$$\sum_R [D^{(\mu)}(R)]_{ij}^*[D^{(\mu)}(R)]_{pq} = 0. \qquad (6.6b)$$

(c) If $\mu=\nu$ and at the same time $i=p$ and $j=q$, so that $\delta_{ip}=\delta_{jq}=1$, then

$$\sum_R [D^{(\mu)}(R)]_{ij}^*[D^{(\mu)}(R)]_{ij} = \sum_R |[D^{(\mu)}(R)]_{ij}|^2 = \frac{g}{n_\mu}. \qquad (6.6c)$$

The statement in (6.6) may be put into words as follows: write down the set of matrices $D^{(\mu)}(R)$ belonging to Γ_μ and the set $D^{(\nu)}(R)$ belonging to Γ_ν; choose a definite set of numerical values for i, j, p, q and one of the group elements R; pick out the ij element of $D^{(\mu)}(R)$ and the pq element of $D^{(\nu)}(R)$ and form the number $[D^{(\mu)}(R)]_{ij}^*[D^{(\nu)}(R)]_{pq}$; do this for each element R of $\mathscr{G}$, using always the same values of i, j, p, q; add up the g numbers obtained in this way. This gives the sum on the left-hand side of (6.6) and the theorem tells us the value of the sum in the various cases depending on the values of μ, ν, i, j, p, q.

EXAMPLE: *Irreducible representations of $\mathscr{C}_{3v}$*

Table 6.5 contains matrices belonging to the three IRs of $\mathscr{C}_{3v}$. The matrices of E are taken from column Γ_2 of Table 5.1; in them $\epsilon = e^{-2\pi i/3}$ so that $\epsilon + \epsilon^* = -1$ and $\epsilon^*\epsilon = 1$.

TABLE 6.5. *Matrices of irreducible representations of* $\mathscr{C}_{3v}$

	E	C_3	C_3^{-1}	σ_a	σ_b	σ_c
$\Gamma_1 = A_1$	[1]	[1]	[1]	[1]	[1]	[1]
$\Gamma_2 = A_2$	[1]	[1]	[1]	[-1]	[-1]	[-1]
$\Gamma_3 = E$	$\begin{bmatrix} 1 & 0 \\ 0 & 1 \end{bmatrix}$	$\begin{bmatrix} \epsilon & 0 \\ 0 & \epsilon^* \end{bmatrix}$	$\begin{bmatrix} \epsilon^* & 0 \\ 0 & \epsilon \end{bmatrix}$	$\begin{bmatrix} 0 & 1 \\ 1 & 0 \end{bmatrix}$	$\begin{bmatrix} 0 & \epsilon^* \\ \epsilon & 0 \end{bmatrix}$	$\begin{bmatrix} 0 & \epsilon \\ \epsilon^* & 0 \end{bmatrix}$

For A_1, the suffixes must have the values $i=j=1$ and $[D^{(1)}(R)]_{11}=1$ for all R; for A_2, $i=j=1$ and $[D^{(2)}(R)]_{11}=1$ for $R=E$, C_3, C_3^{-1}, while $[D^{(2)}(R)]_{11}=-1$ for $R=\sigma_a$, σ_b, σ_c. Various cases of (6.6) give:

$\mu=\nu = 1$; $n_\mu=1$;

$$\sum_R [D^{(1)}(R)]_{11}^*[D^{(1)}(R)]_{11} = 1^2+1^2+1^2+1^2+1^2+1^2 = 6. \quad \text{[cf. (6.6}c)]}$$

$\mu=1$, $\nu=2$;

$$\sum_R [D^{(1)}(R)]_{11}^*[D^{(2)}(R)]_{11} = 1\cdot1+1\cdot1+1\cdot1+1\cdot(-1)+1\cdot(-1)+1\cdot(-1) = 0.$$
$$\text{[cf. (6.6}a)]}$$

$\mu=2$, $\nu=3$; $p=1$, $q=2$;

$$\sum_R [D^{(2)}(R)]_{11}^*[D^{(3)}(R)]_{12} = 1\cdot0+1\cdot0+1\cdot0+(-1)\cdot1+(-1)\epsilon^*+(-1)\epsilon = 0.$$
$$\text{[cf. (6.6}a)]}$$

$\mu=\nu=3$; $i=p=1$, $j=1$, $q=2$;

$$\sum_R [D^{(3)}(R)]_{11}^*[D^{(3)}(R)]_{12} = 1\cdot0+\epsilon^*\cdot0+\epsilon\cdot0+0\cdot1+0\cdot\epsilon^*+0\cdot\epsilon = 0. \quad \text{[cf. (6.6}b)]}$$

$\mu=\nu=3$; $i=p=1$, $j=q=2$; $n_\mu=2$;

$$\sum_R [D^{(3)}(R)]_{12}^*[D^{(3)}(R)]_{12} = 0+0+0+1\cdot1+\epsilon\epsilon^*+\epsilon^*\epsilon = 3 = 6/2. \quad \text{[cf. (6.6}c)]}$$

The reader may verify other cases of (6.6) and also that the results are equally valid if the matrices for E are chosen from the equivalent set contained in column Γ_1 of Table 5.1.

This theorem has been called the *key theorem of representation theory*. We have quoted it because it is required in some of the applications, but we note here that, in a strictly logical treatment, it should have been placed at the beginning of this chapter, since our Theorem II is a direct consequence of it and part of the proof of Theorem I also depends on it. We discuss these points below, before proceeding to an application of Theorem III.

PROOF OF THEOREM II

Put $i=j$ and $p=q$ in (6.6) so that it refers to diagonal elements of $D^{(\mu)}(R)$ and $D^{(\nu)}(R)$. Then, since $\delta_{ip}\delta_{ip} = \delta_{ip}$, we have

$$\sum_R [D^{(\mu)}(R)]_{ii}^*[D^{(\nu)}(R)]_{pp} = \frac{g}{n_\mu} \delta_{\mu\nu}\delta_{ip}.$$

If this is written down for all the possible pairs of values of i and p ($i = 1, \ldots, n_\mu$; $p = 1, \ldots, n_\nu$) and the resulting equations are added, one obtains

$$\sum_{i=1}^{n_\mu} \sum_{p=1}^{n_\nu} \sum_R [D^{(\mu)}(R)]_{ii}^* [D^{(\nu)}(R)]_{pp} = \frac{g}{n_\mu} \delta_{\mu\nu} \sum_{i=1}^{n_\mu} \sum_{p=1}^{n_\nu} \delta_{ip}. \tag{6.7}$$

We can perform the additions on the left-hand side of (6.7) by first fixing on a particular group element R and summing over i and p. This gives

$$\left(\sum_{i=1}^{n_\mu} [D^{(\mu)}(R)]_{ii}^* \right) \left(\sum_{p=1}^{n_\nu} [D^{(\nu)}(R)]_{pp} \right) = \chi^{*(\mu)}(R) \chi^{(\nu)}(R).$$

If we now sum over all the group elements R we obtain the left-hand side of (6.7) in the form

$$\sum_R \chi^{*(\mu)}(R) \chi^{(\nu)}(R) = \sum_{i=1}^{k} g_i \chi_i^{*(\mu)} \chi_i^{(\nu)},$$

since all the g_i elements R belonging to the same class $\mathscr{K}_i$ have the same character. Thus the left-hand side of (6.7) is the left-hand side of (6.2).

The right-hand side of (6.7) is zero if $\mu \neq \nu$, since then $\delta_{\mu\nu} = 0$. Thus if $\mu \neq \nu$, (6.7) is the same as (6.2').

In the case $\mu = \nu$, $\delta_{\mu\nu} = 1$, the right-hand side of (6.7) is $\dfrac{g}{n_\mu} \sum_{i=1}^{n_\mu} \sum_{p=1}^{n_\mu} \delta_{ip}$. For fixed i, $\sum_{p=1}^{n_\mu} \delta_{ip} = 1$ since $\delta_{ip} = 0$ except for the one term where $p = i$ and $\delta_{ip} = 1$.

The sum over i then contributes the number $+1$ for each value of $i = 1, 2, \ldots, n_\mu$ and is equal to n_μ. This cancels the n_μ in the denominator and so, if $\mu = \nu$, the right-hand side of (6.7) is g, and we have obtained (6.2'').

PROOF OF THEOREM I:

Consider the set of g numbers $[D^{(\mu)}(R)]_{ij}$, with fixed values of μ, i, j, as R runs through the g elements of the group. These may be regarded as the components of a vector in a space of g dimensions. Each IR Γ_μ of the group provides us with n_μ^2 such vectors corresponding to all the possible pairs of values of i and j from 1 to n_μ. If the group has altogether r IRs, the total number of vectors we can construct in this way is

$$n_1^2 + n_2^2 + \cdots + n_r^2.$$

If we regard the matrix elements of the IRs as components of g-dimensional vectors in this way, equations (6.6a,b) show that the vectors are all orthogonal to each other (compare (3.32)). Since, however, there cannot be more than g orthogonal vectors in a space of g dimensions it follows that

$$n_1^2 + n_2^2 + \cdots + n_r^2 \leqslant g. \tag{6.8}$$

Again, we may regard the sets of numbers $\sqrt{g_i} \chi_i^{(\mu)}$ for fixed μ as i runs over the k classes of the group as the components of a vector in a space of k dimensions. If the group has r IRs there are r such vectors, and (6.2') shows that they are all orthogonal to each other. But there cannot be more than k orthogonal vectors in a space of k dimensions and so

$$r \leqslant k. \tag{6.9}$$

Equations (6.8) and (6.9) partially prove Theorem I. The rest of the proof consists in showing that in both equations only the equality is allowed, but to prove this requires a sophisticated argument into which we shall not enter.

6.6 The Reduction of a Reducible Representation (ii)

The relations of Theorem III between matrix elements of the IRs of a group imply certain properties of the base vectors of these representations which can be used to solve the problem of finding a basis for a reducible representation in which the matrices have the completely reduced form (5.24).

Suppose that we have chosen orthonormal bases for all the IRs of the group and that we have found the matrices $D^{(v)}(R)$. Denote the n_v base vectors of Γ_v by $f_1^{(v)}, \ldots, f_{n_v}^{(v)}$. Then

$$O_R f_q^{(v)} = \sum_{p=1}^{n_v} [D^{(v)}(R)]_{pq} f_p^{(v)}.$$

Multiply this equation by $[D^{(\mu)}(R)]_{ij}^*$ and sum over all the group elements R to obtain

$$\sum_R [D^{(\mu)}(R)]_{ij}^* O_R f_q^{(v)} = \sum_{p=1}^{n_v} \sum_R [D^{(\mu)}(R)]_{ij}^* [D^{(v)}(R)]_{pq} f_p^{(v)}. \qquad (6.10)$$

The right-hand side of (6.10) is, by Theorem III, equal to

$$\sum_{p=1}^{n_v} \frac{g}{n_\mu} \delta_{\mu v} \, \delta_{ip} \, \delta_{jq} f_p^{(v)}.$$

It therefore vanishes if $\mu \neq v$, while, if $\mu = v$, it is equal to $(g/n_\mu) \, \delta_{jq} f_i^{(\mu)}$, since the only non-zero term in the summation over p is the one for which $p = i$. Consequently we can write (6.10) as

$$P_{ij}^{(\mu)} f_q^{(v)} = \frac{g}{n_\mu} \delta_{\mu v} \, \delta_{jq} f_i^{(\mu)}, \qquad (6.11)$$

where

$$P_{ij}^{(\mu)} = \sum_R [D^{(\mu)}(R)]_{ij}^* O_R. \qquad (6.12)$$

$P_{ij}^{(\mu)}$ is an operator which is a definite linear combination of the operators O_R with coefficients which depend on the matrices of Γ_μ.

Consider, in particular, the operators

$$P_{ii}^{(\mu)} = \sum_R [D^{(\mu)}(R)]_{ii}^* O_R; \quad i = 1, 2, \ldots, n_\mu.$$

If we write down these operators for all the values of i from 1 to n_μ and add them together we shall obtain an operator

$$P^{(\mu)} = \sum_{i=1}^{n_\mu} P_{ii}^{(\mu)} = \sum_R \sum_{i=1}^{n_\mu} [D^{(\mu)}(R)]_{ii}^* O_R = \sum_R \chi^{*(\mu)}(R) O_R \qquad (6.13)$$

in which the coefficient of O_R is the complex conjugate of the character of R in Γ_μ. Thus, whereas we cannot write down the operators $P_{ij}{}^{(\mu)}$ of (6.12) unless we have a complete set of matrices belonging to Γ_μ, the operator $P^{(\mu)}$ can be written down immediately from the character table of the group. This operator can be introduced into our equations by putting $j = i$ in (6.11) and summing over all values of i. This gives

$$P^{(\mu)}f_q{}^{(\nu)} = \sum_{i=1}^{n_\mu} \frac{g}{n_\mu}\, \delta_{\mu\nu}\, \delta_{iq} f_i{}^{(\mu)}.$$

This equation covers two cases:

$$\mu \neq \nu: \qquad\qquad P^{(\mu)}f_q{}^{(\nu)} = 0. \tag{6.14a}$$

$$\mu = \nu: \qquad\qquad P^{(\mu)}f_q{}^{(\mu)} = \frac{g}{n_\mu} f_q{}^{(\mu)}. \tag{6.14b}$$

Now any general vector in the space of Γ_ν is a linear combination of the base vectors $f_1{}^{(\nu)}, \ldots, f_{n_\nu}{}^{(\nu)}$. Let us denote such a vector by $f^{(\nu)}$. Then (6.14) shows that

$$P^{(\mu)}f^{(\nu)} = 0 \quad \text{if } \mu \neq \nu, \tag{6.15a}$$

and that, if $\nu = \mu$,

$$P^{(\mu)}f^{(\mu)} = \frac{g}{n_\mu} f^{(\mu)}. \tag{6.15b}$$

We have, therefore, found in $P^{(\mu)}$ an operator which annihilates any vector which does not belong to the Γ_μ space but which, when it is applied to a vector $f^{(\mu)}$ belonging to the Γ_μ space, simply produces a numerical multiple of $f^{(\mu)}$. An operator with this property is called a *projection operator*.

EXAMPLE

Take the irreducible matrix representations of $\mathscr{C}_{3v}$ shown in Table 6.5. Denote the base vectors of E by f_1, f_2; the base vector of A_2 by g; the base vector of A_1 by h. Then the results of applying the operators O_R to these base vectors are shown in the table below, in which the entries in the column headed R, where $R = E, C_3, \ldots, \sigma_c$, give the effects of O_R on the base vectors written down the left-hand column.

	E	C_3	$C_3{}^{-1}$	σ_a	σ_b	σ_c
h	h	h	h	h	h	h
g	g	g	g	$-g$	$-g$	$-g$
f_1	f_1	ϵf_1	$\epsilon^* f_1$	f_2	ϵf_2	$\epsilon^* f_2$
f_2	f_2	$\epsilon^* f_2$	ϵf_2	f_1	$\epsilon^* f_1$	ϵf_1

We use the character table of $\mathscr{C}_{3v}$ in conjunction with (6.13) to write down the projection operators for the IRs A_1, A_2 and E. They are

$$P^{(A_1)} = E + C_3 + C_3^{-1} + \sigma_a + \sigma_b + \sigma_c,$$

$$P^{(A_2)} = E + C_3 + C_3^{-1} - \sigma_a - \sigma_b - \sigma_c,$$

$$P^{(E)} = 2E - C_3 - C_3^{-1},$$

where, for simplicity, we have signified the operator O_R by the symbol R itself. The application of these operators to the base vectors h, g, f_1, f_2 gives the following equations, all of them in accord with (6.15). (In the last six equations we use $\epsilon + \epsilon^* = -1$.)

$$P^{(A_1)}h = h + h + h + h + h + h = 6h,$$

$$P^{(A_2)}h = h + h + h - h - h - h = 0,$$

$$P^{(E)}h = 2h - h - h = 0;$$

$$P^{(A_1)}g = g + g + g + (-g) + (-g) + (-g) = 0,$$

$$P^{(A_2)}g = g + g + g - (-g) - (-g) - (-g) = 6g,$$

$$P^{(E)}g = 2g - g - g = 0;$$

$$P^{(A_1)}f_1 = f_1 + \epsilon f_1 + \epsilon^* f_1 + f_2 + \epsilon f_2 + \epsilon^* f_2 = 0,$$

$$P^{(A_2)}f_1 = f_1 + \epsilon f_1 + \epsilon^* f_1 - f_2 - \epsilon f_2 - \epsilon^* f_2 = 0,$$

$$P^{(E)}f_1 = 2f_1 - \epsilon f_1 - \epsilon^* f_1 = 3f_1;$$

$$P^{(A_1)}f_2 = f_2 + \epsilon^* f_2 + \epsilon f_2 + f_1 + \epsilon^* f_1 + \epsilon f_1 = 0,$$

$$P^{(A_2)}f_2 = f_2 + \epsilon^* f_2 + \epsilon f_2 - f_1 - \epsilon^* f_1 - \epsilon f_1 = 0,$$

$$P^{(E)}f_2 = 2f_2 - \epsilon^* f_2 - \epsilon f_2 = 3f_2.$$

Let us now consider a reducible representation Γ. Its matrices will be defined with respect to a basis $g_1, \ldots, g_n$ in an n-dimensional space V. Since Γ is reducible, the arguments of Section 5.6 show that V consists of a number of invariant sub-spaces V_μ; each sub-space V_μ gives rise to an IR Γ_μ and the reduction of Γ is achieved by finding a new basis for V in which the base vectors are divided into independent sets forming bases for the separate invariant sub-spaces.

Suppose that the IRs that occur in Γ are $\Gamma_1, \Gamma_2, \ldots, \Gamma_\nu, \ldots$ and that *none of them occurs more than once*. Then the new basis for Γ will be a set of vectors

$$f_1^{(1)}, \ldots, f_{n_1}^{(1)}; \quad \ldots; \quad f_1^{(\nu)}, \ldots, f_{n_\nu}^{(\nu)}; \quad \ldots$$

in which the various sub-sets $f_1^{(\nu)}, \ldots, f_{n_\nu}^{(\nu)}$ serve as bases for the Γ_ν.

The transformation from the original basis $g_1, \ldots, g_n$ to this new basis will express each g_s as a linear combination of the $f_i^{(\nu)}$:

$$g_s = \sum_\nu \sum_{i=1}^{n_\nu} \beta_{\nu i}^{(s)} f_i^{(\nu)},$$

where the $\beta_{vi}^{(s)}$ are certain numerical coefficients. We write

$$F_s^{(v)} = \sum_{i=1}^{n_v} \beta_{vi}^{(s)} f_i^{(v)}.$$

Then $F_s^{(v)}$ is a vector which lies in the invariant sub-space V_v and each g_s can be expressed as a combination of such vectors, one from each invariant sub-space:

$$g_s = F_s^{(1)} + \cdots + F_s^{(v)} + \cdots \qquad (6.16)$$

Now choose one of the IRs that occur in Γ, Γ_μ say, and apply the corresponding projection operator $P^{(\mu)}$ to g_s. From (6.15) we see that

$$P^{(\mu)} g_s = (g/n_\mu) F_s^{(\mu)}, \qquad (6.17)$$

since the only term that survives from the right-hand side of (6.16) is the one in which $v = \mu$ and (6.15) shows that the effect of $P^{(\mu)}$ on this term is to multiply it by g/n_μ.

Now $P^{(\mu)}$ is a definite linear combination of the operators O_R. Since the original representation Γ was defined with respect to $g_1, \ldots, g_n$ as basis, $O_R g_s$ is a known linear combination of these base vectors. Hence $P^{(\mu)} g_s$ is a known linear combination of $g_1, \ldots, g_n$; (6.17) tells us that this linear combination is proportional to a vector $F_s^{(\mu)}$ which belongs to the invariant sub-space of the Γ_μ representation. If we apply $P^{(\mu)}$ to each of the base vectors $g_1, \ldots, g_n$ in turn, we shall in this way obtain n linear combinations of $g_1, \ldots g_n$ which belong to the invariant sub-space of Γ_μ. These cannot all be linearly independent but we shall be able to find amongst them n_μ linearly independent combinations of $g_1, \ldots, g_n$ which belong to the Γ_μ sub-space and which may be taken as a basis for this sub-space. In this fashion, we may use the projection operators $P^{(v)}$ belonging to the different IRs that occur in Γ to find bases for its invariant sub-spaces and so to effect the reduction.

The situation is more complicated if the same IR recurs in Γ. Suppose, for example, that Γ_μ occurs twice. Then (6.16) will have the form

$$g_s = \cdots + F_s^{(\mu)} + F_s'^{(\mu)} + \cdots,$$

where $F_s^{(\mu)}$ and $F_s'^{(\mu)}$ belong to *different* invariant sub-spaces. In this case

$$P^{(\mu)} g_s = (g/n_\mu)(F_s^{(\mu)} + F_s'^{(\mu)}),$$

and the result of applying $P^{(\mu)}$ to $g_1, \ldots, g_n$ in turn is to give us linear combinations of $g_1, \ldots, g_n$ which have components in two different invariant sub-spaces. There is no standard way of separating these two sub-spaces; one has to proceed as best one can, guided by a knowledge of the matrices of Γ.

EXAMPLE

Take the representation of $\mathscr{C}_{3v}$ given in column Γ_3 of Table 5.1. Application of (6.5) to the characters of these matrices shows that this is a reducible representation with irreducible components A_1 and E. (See Example (i) of Section 6.4.) In the notation used above, the base vectors of this representation are g_1, g_2, g_3; we shall suppose that they are orthonormal. The results of applying the operators O_R to these base vectors can be read off from the matrices of Table 5.1 and are given in the table below.

	E	C_3	C_3^{-1}	σ_a	σ_b	σ_c
g_1	g_1	g_2	g_3	g_1	g_3	g_2
g_2	g_2	g_3	g_1	g_3	g_2	g_1
g_3	g_3	g_1	g_2	g_2	g_1	g_3

The projection operators for $\mathscr{C}_{3v}$ were given in the previous example. Applying them to g_1, g_2, g_3 gives the following results:

Representation A_1:

$$P^{(A_1)}g_1 = P^{(A_1)}g_2 = P^{(A_1)}g_3 = 2(g_1+g_2+g_3).$$

Hence the one-dimensional basis for A_1 has a base vector proportional to $g_1+g_2+g_3$. Since g_1, g_2, g_3 are orthonormal, the scalar product of this vector with itself is $1^2+1^2+1^2 = 3$ so that a normalized base vector for A_1 is

$$f^{(A_1)} = \frac{1}{\sqrt{3}}(g_1+g_2+g_3).$$

Representation A_2:

$$P^{(A_2)}g_1 = P^{(A_2)}g_2 = P^{(A_2)}g_3 = 0.$$

This shows that there is no combination of g_1, g_2, g_3 that belongs to A_2 and that this IR does not occur. This verifies the result that we found from considering the characters.

Representation E:

$$P^{(E)}g_1 = 2g_1-g_2-g_3, \quad P^{(E)}g_2 = 2g_2-g_3-g_1, \quad P^{(E)}g_3 = 2g_3-g_1-g_2.$$

Here we have three different combinations of g_1, g_2, g_3. They are not, however, linearly independent since their sum is zero. (This must be the case since, as we have seen, $g_1+g_2+g_3$ belongs to A_1 and so $P^{(E)}(g_1+g_2+g_3)$ must vanish.) We can choose two linearly independent combinations from these three in many different ways. One choice would be to take $P^{(E)}g_1$ and the difference $P^{(E)}g_2 - P^{(E)}g_3$, which gives the combinations $(2g_1-g_2-g_3)$ and $3(g_2-g_3)$. If we normalize these combinations, they become

$$f_1^{(E)} = \frac{1}{\sqrt{6}}(2g_1-g_2-g_3) \quad \text{and} \quad f_2^{(E)} = \frac{1}{\sqrt{2}}(g_2-g_3).$$

Their scalar product is

$$(f_1^{(E)}, f_2^{(E)}) = \frac{1}{\sqrt{12}}\{2\cdot 0+(-1)\cdot 1+(-1)\cdot(-1)\} = 0,$$

and so they are orthogonal to each other. They must also be orthogonal to $f^{(A_1)}$ as is easily verified.

On the basis of these considerations we assert that a suitable orthonormal basis for the representation Γ_3 of Table 5.1, with respect to which its matrices will appear as direct sums of matrices belonging to the IRs E and A_1 of $\mathscr{C}_{3v}$ is

$$f_1^{(E)} = \frac{1}{\sqrt{6}}\,(2g_1 - g_2 - g_3), \quad f_2^{(E)} = \frac{1}{\sqrt{2}}\,(g_2 - g_3), \quad f^{(A_1)} = \frac{1}{\sqrt{3}}\,(g_1 + g_2 + g_3).$$

$$(6.18)$$

Compare this result with the way in which we originally found the matrices of Γ_3. They were defined with respect to a basis d_1, d_2, d_3 in physical space, and we saw that they were equivalent to the reduced matrices given in column Γ_1 of Table 5.1, whose basis was the set of vectors e_1, e_2, e_3. The relations between these two bases were given by equations (5.8). In the special case where d_1, d_2, d_3 are orthogonal, i.e. when, in (5.8), $\sin \lambda = \sqrt{(2/3)}$ and $\cos \lambda = \sqrt{(1/3)}$, it will be seen that (5.8b) is the same as (6.18) if we make e_1, e_2, e_3 correspond to $f_1^{(E)}$, $f_2^{(E)}$, $f^{(A_1)}$ and $-d_1$, $-d_2$, $-d_3$ correspond to g_1, g_2, g_3. It follows that the change of basis from g_1, g_2, g_3 to the combinations defined by (6.18) will indeed put the matrices with which we began into reduced form, specifically the form given in column Γ_1 of Table 5.1.

PROBLEMS

The results of this chapter that are of most importance in the applications of group theory to molecular problems are (i) the enumeration of the IRs contained in a reducible representation, with the help of equation (6.5) and the group character table, and (ii) the method of using projection operators to find a basis which reduces a given reducible representation.

The use of equation (6.5)

The following examples give the characters χ_i of a reducible representation Γ of the indicated point group $\mathscr{G}$ for the various classes of $\mathscr{G}$ in the order in which these classes appear in the character tables of Appendix H. The reader is asked to prove by the use of (6.5) and the character table of $\mathscr{G}$ that Γ can be reduced in the manner indicated.

6.1. $\mathscr{C}_{2v}$: $\chi_i = 4, -2, 0, -2$: $\Gamma = A_2 + 2B_1 + B_2$.

6.2. $\mathscr{C}_{4v}$: $\chi_i = 4, 0, 0, 0, -2$: $\Gamma = A_2 + B_1 + E$.

6.3. $\mathscr{C}_{3h}$: $\chi_i = 4, 1, 1, 2, -1, -1$: $\Gamma = A' + A'' + E'$.

6.4. $\mathscr{D}_{4h}$: $\chi_i = 4, 2, 0, -2, -2, 2, 0, -2, 0, 0$: $\Gamma = A_{2g} + A_{2u} + E_g$.

6.5. $\mathscr{D}_{4d}$: $\chi_i = 6, 0, -2, 0, -2, 0, 0$: $\Gamma = E_1 + E_2 + E_3$.

6.6. $\mathscr{T}_d$: $\chi_i = 9, 0, 1, -1, 3$: $\Gamma = A_1 + E + 2T_2$.

6.7. $\mathscr{O}_h$: $\chi_i = 15, 0, -1, 1, 1, -3, 0, 5, -1, 3$:

$$\Gamma = A_{1g} + E_g + T_{2g} + 2T_{1u} + T_{2u}.$$

6.8. $\mathscr{D}_{6h}$: $\chi_i = 30, -4, 0, 2, -2, 2, 0, 0, 0, 12, 0, 4$:

$$\Gamma = 2A_{1g} + A_{2g} + 2B_{2g} + E_{1g} + 4E_{2g} + A_{2u} + 2B_{1u} + 2B_{2u} + 3E_{1u} + 2E_{2u}.$$

Projection operators (Section 6.6)

6.9. Show that the projection operators, defined by (6.13), for the various IRs of $\mathscr{D}_4$ are

$$P^{(A_1)} = E + C_4 + C_4^{-1} + C_2 + C_{2a}' + C_{2b}' + C_{2a}'' + C_{2b}'',$$

$$P^{(A_2)} = E + C_4 + C_4^{-1} + C_2 - C_{2a}' - C_{2b}' - C_{2a}'' - C_{2b}'',$$

$$P^{(B_1)} = E - C_4 - C_4^{-1} + C_2 + C_{2a}' + C_{2b}' - C_{2a}'' - C_{2b}'',$$

$$P^{(B_2)} = E - C_4 - C_4^{-1} + C_2 - C_{2a}' - C_{2b}' + C_{2a}'' + C_{2b}'',$$

$$P^{(E)} = 2E - 2C_2,$$

where C_{2a}', C_{2b}' and C_{2a}'', C_{2b}'' are the pairs of operations belonging to the classes C_2' and C_2'' respectively.

6.10. The table below gives the effects of the symmetry operations of $\mathscr{D}_4$ on the orthonormal base vectors g_1, g_2, g_3, g_4 of a four-dimensional representation Γ of $\mathscr{D}_4$.

	E	C_4	C_4^{-1}	C_2	C_{2a}'	C_{2b}'	C_{2a}''	C_{2b}''
g_1	g_1	g_2	g_4	g_3	$-g_4$	$-g_2$	$-g_1$	$-g_3$
g_2	g_2	g_3	g_1	g_4	$-g_3$	$-g_1$	$-g_4$	$-g_2$
g_3	g_3	g_4	g_2	g_1	$-g_2$	$-g_4$	$-g_3$	$-g_1$
g_4	g_4	g_1	g_3	g_2	$-g_1$	$-g_3$	$-g_2$	$-g_4$

Show that $\Gamma = A_2 + B_1 + E$ and use the projection operators for $\mathscr{D}_4$ to prove that an orthonormal basis which reduces Γ is

$$f^{(A_2)} = \tfrac{1}{2}(g_1 + g_2 + g_3 + g_4),$$

$$f^{(B_1)} = \tfrac{1}{2}(g_1 - g_2 + g_3 - g_4),$$

$$f_1^{(E)} = (g_1 - g_3)/\sqrt{2}, \qquad f_2^{(E)} = (g_2 - g_4)/\sqrt{2}.$$

6.11. The effects of the symmetry operations of $\mathscr{C}_{3v}$ on the orthonormal base vectors $g_1, \ldots, g_6$ of a six-dimensional representation Γ of $\mathscr{C}_{3v}$ are given in the table below.

	E	C_3	C_3^{-1}	σ_a	σ_b	σ_c
g_1	g_1	$-\tfrac{1}{2}(g_3 - \sqrt{3}g_4)$	$-\tfrac{1}{2}(g_5 + \sqrt{3}g_6)$	$-g_1$	$\tfrac{1}{2}(g_5 + \sqrt{3}g_6)$	$\tfrac{1}{2}(g_3 - \sqrt{3}g_4)$
g_2	g_2	$-\tfrac{1}{2}(\sqrt{3}g_3 + g_4)$	$\tfrac{1}{2}(\sqrt{3}g_5 - g_6)$	g_2	$\tfrac{1}{2}(\sqrt{3}g_5 - g_6)$	$-\tfrac{1}{2}(\sqrt{3}g_3 + g_4)$
g_3	g_3	$-\tfrac{1}{2}(g_5 - \sqrt{3}g_6)$	$-\tfrac{1}{2}(g_1 + \sqrt{3}g_2)$	$-g_5$	$\tfrac{1}{2}(g_3 + \sqrt{3}g_4)$	$\tfrac{1}{2}(g_1 - \sqrt{3}g_2)$
g_4	g_4	$-\tfrac{1}{2}(\sqrt{3}g_5 + g_6)$	$\tfrac{1}{2}(\sqrt{3}g_1 - g_2)$	g_6	$\tfrac{1}{2}(\sqrt{3}g_3 - g_4)$	$-\tfrac{1}{2}(\sqrt{3}g_1 + g_2)$
g_5	g_5	$-\tfrac{1}{2}(g_1 - \sqrt{3}g_2)$	$-\tfrac{1}{2}(g_3 + \sqrt{3}g_4)$	$-g_3$	$\tfrac{1}{2}(g_1 + \sqrt{3}g_2)$	$\tfrac{1}{2}(g_5 - \sqrt{3}g_6)$
g_6	g_6	$-\tfrac{1}{2}(\sqrt{3}g_1 + g_2)$	$\tfrac{1}{2}(\sqrt{3}g_3 - g_4)$	g_4	$\tfrac{1}{2}(\sqrt{3}g_1 - g_2)$	$-\tfrac{1}{2}(\sqrt{3}g_5 + g_6)$

Show that $\Gamma = A_1 + A_2 + 2E$ and use the projection operators for $\mathscr{C}_{3v}$ to show that when Γ is reduced the normalized base vectors for A_1 and A_2 are

$$f^{(A_1)} = (2g_2 - \sqrt{3}g_3 - g_4 + \sqrt{3}g_5 - g_6)/2\sqrt{3},$$

$$f^{(A_2)} = (2g_1 - g_3 + \sqrt{3}g_4 - g_5 - \sqrt{3}g_6)/2\sqrt{3}.$$

By direct application of $P^{(E)}$ to the following expressions verify that they form a possible choice of orthonormal base vectors for the two distinct E representations:

$$f_1^{(E)} = (g_1 + g_3 + g_5)/\sqrt{3}, \qquad f_2^{(E)} = (g_2 + g_4 + g_6)/\sqrt{3};$$

$$f_1'^{(E)} = (2g_2 + \sqrt{3}g_3 - g_4 - \sqrt{3}g_5 - g_6)/2\sqrt{3},$$

$$f_2'^{(E)} = (2g_1 - g_3 - \sqrt{3}g_4 - g_5 + \sqrt{3}g_6)/2\sqrt{3}.$$

Chapter 7

REPRESENTATIONS AND QUANTUM MECHANICS

7.1 Symmetry Properties of the Potential Energy

The connection between physical problems concerning molecules and the representation theory that has been developed in the preceding chapters depends on certain symmetry properties of the Hamiltonian operator which appears in the Schrödinger equation for a molecule. The Hamiltonian is a sum of terms describing the potential and kinetic energies of the molecule and we begin by discussing the potential energy.

The Born–Oppenheimer approximation allows us to deal separately with the problems of the electronic structure and the vibrations of a molecule. In discussing *electronic structure* we assume that the electrons move with respect to a fixed framework formed by the nuclei of the molecule placed in their equilibrium positions; the potential energy of the electrons is the total Coulomb energy arising from their electrostatic attractions towards the fixed nuclei and from their mutual repulsions. When *molecular vibrations* are under discussion, we consider small motions of the nuclei about their equilibrium positions in the molecule. These equilibrium positions form a fixed reference framework and the potential energy is assumed to depend only on the displacements of the nuclei from their equilibrium positions.

In both cases we set up a configuration space with coordinates $x_1^{(1)}$, $x_2^{(1)}$, $x_3^{(1)}; \ldots; x_1^{(n)}$, $x_2^{(n)}$, $x_3^{(n)}$. In the electronic case, the variables $x_1^{(p)}$, $x_2^{(p)}$, $x_3^{(p)}$ are the coordinates of electron p relative to a chosen set of axes whose origin is at a point which is left unmoved by all the symmetry operations of the molecule, the same axes being used for all the electrons. In the vibrational case, the variables $x_1^{(p)}$, $x_2^{(p)}$, $x_3^{(p)}$ are the coordinates of nucleus p relative to a set of axes whose origin is at the equilibrium position of p. In this case a different set of axes is used for each nucleus.

Let X stand for a complete set of values of $x_1^{(1)}, \ldots, x_3^{(n)}$. Each such set describes a particular configuration of the electrons or the nuclei and in both approximations, that for the electronic structure and that for the vibrations, the assumptions described above mean that the potential energy is a function of the coordinates which associates a certain value $V(X)$ with each configuration X. Since the potential energy is intimately related to the framework formed by the nuclei of the molecule in their equilibrium positions, we may expect this function to have a simple connection with the point group which describes the symmetry of the molecular framework.

Suppose that R is one of the symmetry operations of the molecular framework, a reflection or rotation or a combination of these, which moves the framework into itself. We *define* the effect of R on the vectors of the configuration space by saying that when R is applied to the configuration X it produces a new configuration X' which is related to X as follows:

(*a*) *Electronic structure:* X' is the configuration produced from X by applying R to all the electrons simultaneously so that in going from X to X' each electron is rotated or reflected into a new position and all the electrons are moved in the same way. The nuclear framework, meanwhile, is not changed and each nucleus stays in its fixed position.

(*b*) *Vibrations:* X describes a configuration in which each nucleus has a definite displacement from its equilibrium position. This may be pictured geometrically by drawing an arrow from the equilibrium position of each

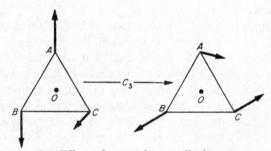

7.1 Effect of a rotation on displacements.

nucleus to the position it occupies in X. Then X' is the configuration which is produced by applying R to these arrows, leaving the equilibrium framework unchanged; if R, when it is applied to the framework, rotates or reflects nucleus p into the position of nucleus q, then, in the new configuration X', q is given the displacement which is obtained by applying R to the arrow which describes the displacement of p in X. (Figure 7.1 illustrates this for the rotation C_3 applied to displacements of three equivalent nuclei A, B, C which form an equilateral triangle.)

With these definitions of what is meant by applying R to a configuration, we can see that the potential energies of the configurations X and X' must be the same. For suppose that the molecule is frozen in the configuration X', whose potential energy is $V(X')$, and that the inverse operation R^{-1} is applied to the whole system including the nuclear framework. After this has been done, since everything has been moved together in the same way, the potential energy will be unaltered, and must still have the value $V(X')$. But the result of applying R^{-1} to the whole system will be to restore the electrons (or nuclei) to their original positions in X and at the same time to change round some physically identical points in the fixed molecular framework. This latter change can have no effect on the potential energy which must, therefore, have the value $V(X)$. It follows that the potential energy function has the property that if R changes X to X', where R is any symmetry operation of the molecular framework, then

$$V(X') = V(X). \tag{7.1}$$

We say that X and X' are *physically equivalent* configurations.

If we turn from the configurations themselves to a function $F(X)$ of the coordinates which specify a configuration, we can associate with each symmetry operation R an operator O_R, defined by (4.40), which turns F into a new function $O_R F$. If we apply this definition to the potential energy function we find, on using (7.1), that

$$(O_R V)(X') = V(X) = V(X').$$

This is true for any configuration X and so for any configuration X'. Hence, in any configuration, the transformed function $O_R V$ has the same value as V and

$$O_R V = V. \tag{7.2}$$

This equation, which is merely another way of writing (7.1), is valid when R is any symmetry operation belonging to the point group of the molecular framework. We say that V possesses the complete symmetry of the molecular framework and that it is *invariant* under all the operations of the point group of the molecule.

The property (7.2) may be expressed in a slightly different way. Suppose that F is any function of the coordinates, and consider the product function VF. From the definition of O_R it is clear that $O_R(VF)=(O_R V)\cdot(O_R F)$. Then (7.2) shows that, for any function F,

$$O_R(VF) = V(O_R F). \tag{7.3}$$

7.2 Symmetry Properties of the Kinetic Energy

The kinetic energy of the electrons (or nuclei) of a molecule is represented in the Hamiltonian by the differential operator

$$T = -\frac{h^2}{8\pi^2} \sum_{p=1}^{n} \frac{1}{m^{(p)}} \nabla_p^2, \tag{7.4}$$

where $\nabla_p{}^2 = \sum_{k=1}^{3} \partial^2/\partial x_k{}^{(p)2}$. The summation in (7.4) runs over all the n particles; $m^{(p)}$ is the mass of particle p and $x_1{}^{(p)}$, $x_2{}^{(p)}$, $x_3{}^{(p)}$ are its coordinates referred to a set of mutually perpendicular axes. The operator T becomes meaningful when it is applied to a function $F(X)$ of all the coordinates $x_1{}^{(1)}, \ldots, x_3{}^{(n)}$: TF is another function of the coordinates which is obtained from F by differentiation. We may apply O_R to this function so as to form the function $O_R(TF)$. The important result that we wish to prove is that $O_R(TF)$ is the same as the function formed by applying T to $O_R F$;

$$O_R(TF) = T(O_R F), \qquad (7.5)$$

an equation analogous to (7.3).

PROOF OF (7.5)

The truth of (7.5) is a consequence of the particular way in which a symmetry operation acts on the coordinates. Consider first a single point with coordinates (x_1, x_2, x_3). Under the operation R this point moves to (x_1', x_2', x_3') where

$$x_i' = \sum_{j=1}^{3} r_{ij} x_j. \qquad (7.6)$$

Compare equation (4.6').) The coefficients r_{ij} depend on the nature of R and its relation to the chosen coordinate system but, as we saw in Section 4.8, equation (4.51), they must satisfy the orthogonality relations

$$\sum_{k=1}^{3} r_{ik} r_{jk} = \delta_{ij}. \qquad (7.7)$$

Now take a function $f(x_1, x_2, x_3)$ of position. The effect of O_R on f is to change it into the function $O_R f$ where

$$(O_R f)(x_1', x_2', x_3') = f(x_1, x_2, x_3).$$

From f we can form a new function $\nabla^2 f$, and the effect of O_R on this function is to change it into $O_R(\nabla^2 f)$ where

$$[O_R(\nabla^2 f)](x_1', x_2', x_3') = \nabla^2 f(x_1, x_2, x_3) = \nabla^2\{(O_R f)(x_1', x_2', x_3')\}. \qquad (7.8)$$

The right-hand side of this equation has the form $\nabla^2 g'$, where g' is a function of the variables x_1', x_2', x_3' and ∇^2 refers to differentiation with respect to x_1, x_2, x_3. From the rule for differentiating a function of a function we have, for any function $g'(x_1', x_2', x_3')$,

$$\frac{\partial g'}{\partial x_k} = \frac{\partial g'}{\partial x_1'} \cdot \frac{\partial x_1'}{\partial x_k} + \frac{\partial g'}{\partial x_2'} \cdot \frac{\partial x_2'}{\partial x_k} + \frac{\partial g'}{\partial x_3'} \cdot \frac{\partial x_3'}{\partial x_k} = \sum_{i=1}^{3} r_{ik} \frac{\partial g'}{\partial x_i'},$$

since (7.6) shows that $\partial x_i'/\partial x_k = r_{ik}$. Differentiating once more with respect to x_k gives

$$\frac{\partial^2 g'}{\partial x_k{}^2} = \sum_{j=1}^{3} \sum_{i=1}^{3} r_{jk} r_{ik} \frac{\partial}{\partial x_j'}\left(\frac{\partial g'}{\partial x_i'}\right),$$

and summing this equation over the three values of k gives

$$\nabla^2 g' = \sum_{k=1}^{3} \frac{\partial^2 g'}{\partial x_k^2} = \sum_{j=1}^{3} \sum_{i=1}^{3} \sum_{k=1}^{3} r_{jk} r_{ik} \frac{\partial}{\partial x_j'} \left(\frac{\partial g'}{\partial x_i'} \right).$$

The summation over k can be carried out by using the orthogonality relations (7.7); the result is

$$\nabla^2 g' = \sum_{j=1}^{3} \sum_{i=1}^{3} \delta_{ij} \frac{\partial}{\partial x_j'} \left(\frac{\partial g'}{\partial x_i'} \right) = \sum_{j=1}^{3} \frac{\partial^2 g'}{\partial x_j'^2} = \nabla'^2 g', \tag{7.9}$$

where $\nabla'^2 = \sum\limits_{j=1}^{3} \partial^2/\partial x_j'^2$.

If we put $g' = O_R f$ in (7.9), we see that (7.8) becomes

$$[O_R(\nabla^2 f)](x_1', x_2', x_3') = \nabla'^2 \{(O_R f)(x_1', x_2', x_3')\}.$$

Since the same variables x_1', x_2', x_3' occur throughout this equation, we conclude that $O_R(\nabla^2 f)$ is the same function as $\nabla^2(O_R f)$,

i.e. $$O_R(\nabla^2 f) = \nabla^2(O_R f). \tag{7.10}$$

The proof of (7.5) follows from an application of this result. The proof is slightly different in the two cases that we need to consider.

(a) *Electron motions:* The effect of R on the coordinates of electon p is given by equations of the form of (7.6). We may, therefore, apply (7.10) directly and say that, if F is any function of all the coordinates,

$$O_R(\nabla_p^2 F) = \nabla_p^2(O_R F).$$

There is one such equation for each electron. Equation (7.5) follows on multiplying the equation for electron p by $h^2/8\pi^2 m$, where m is the electron mass, and adding all the equations together.

(b) *Vibrations:* In general, let us suppose that R, when it is applied to the equilibrium molecular framework, moves nucleus p into the position of nucleus q. Our definition of the effect of R in changing a configuration X of the displaced nuclei into a configuration X' then says that the displacement of q in X' is obtained by rotating or reflecting the displacement of p in X into the position of q, without changing its magnitude; accordingly, the coordinates of q in X' will be orthogonal linear combinations of the coordinates of p in X of the form

$$x_i'^{(q)} = \sum_{j=1}^{3} r_{ij} x_j^{(p)}, \tag{7.11}$$

where the coefficients r_{ij} form an orthogonal matrix. A slight modification of the derivation of (7.10) then shows that, for a function F of all the coordinates,

$$O_R(\nabla_p^2 F) = \nabla_q^2(O_R F).$$

But if R moves p to q, p and q must be physically identical nuclei with the same mass so that

$$O_R\left(\frac{1}{m^{(p)}} \nabla_p^2 F \right) = \frac{1}{m^{(q)}} \nabla_q^2(O_R F),$$

and (7.5) follows by addition.

7.3 Representations and the Schrödinger Equation

The Hamiltonian H which appears in the Schrödinger equation for the electrons (or nuclei) of a molecule represents their total energy, kinetic and potential:

$$H = T + V,$$

where T is the operator defined by (7.4) and V is the potential energy. It follows from (7.3) and (7.5) that

$$O_R(HF) = H(O_R F), \qquad (7.12)$$

where F is any function of the coordinates and R is any symmetry operation belonging to the point group of the molecular framework. Thus H is invariant under all the operations of the point group of the molecule; it is this property of *invariance of the Hamiltonian*, coupled with some properties of the Schrödinger equation, that enables us to apply the theory of group representations to molecular problems.

The Schrödinger equation for a system of particles is

$$H\psi = E\psi, \qquad (7.13)$$

where E is the total energy of the system when it is in the state described by the wave function ψ. This is a partial differential equation for ψ, which is a function of the coordinates of all the particles of the system. Physically possible bound states of the system correspond to those solutions of (7.13) which satisfy certain *boundary conditions*; roughly speaking, these conditions are that ψ should vanish for large separations of the particles and that any singularities in ψ should not be too violent. These conditions can only be satisfied for certain special values of E in (7.13), say $E_1, E_2, \ldots, E_\nu, \ldots$ and these values define the various possible *energy levels* of the system.

There may be several different allowable solutions of (7.13) for a given energy level E_ν. Suppose that ψ_1 and ψ_2 are two such solutions; they both satisfy the boundary conditions and also

$$H\psi_1 = E_\nu\psi_1, \qquad H\psi_2 = E_\nu\psi_2.$$

Then, since H is a linear operator with the property that

$$H(a\psi_1 + b\psi_2) = a(H\psi_1) + b(H\psi_2)$$

for any pair of numbers a and b, it follows that the function $(a\psi_1 + b\psi_2)$ is also a solution of (7.13) with $E = E_\nu$ which satisfies the boundary conditions. This means that all the allowable solutions of (7.13) with $E = E_\nu$, taken together, form a definite function space associated with the energy level E_ν. If this space has dimension n_ν, we may choose n_ν linearly independent functions $\psi_1^{(\nu)}, \ldots, \psi_{n_\nu}^{(\nu)}$ as a basis for the space. Each of them satisfies the boundary conditions and the equation

$$H\psi_j^{(\nu)} = E_\nu\psi_j^{(\nu)}, \quad j = 1, 2, \ldots, n_\nu, \qquad (7.14)$$

and any solution of (7.13) with $E = E_v$ which satisfies the boundary conditions may be written as a linear combination of $\psi_1^{(v)}, \ldots, \psi_{n_v}^{(v)}$. The dimension n_v of the function space associated with the energy level E_v is called its *degeneracy*. (In discussions of electronic structure this is sometimes referred to as *orbital degeneracy* to distinguish it from the degeneracy which arises from the spins of the electrons.)

The link between the wave functions of a molecule and its symmetry depends on the invariance property (7.12) of the Hamiltonian. The operators O_R which satisfy (7.12) are those which correspond to the symmetry operations of the point group of the molecule. If we could show that, for these operators, the functions $O_R \psi_j^{(v)}$, with $j = 1, 2, \ldots, n_v$, all belonged to the function space of the energy level E_v and so could be expressed as linear combinations of $\psi_1^{(v)}, \ldots, \psi_{n_v}^{(v)}$ of the form

$$O_R \psi_j^{(v)} = \sum_{i=1}^{n_v} [D^{(v)}(R)]_{ij} \psi_i^{(v)}, \qquad (7.15)$$

this would prove that the $\psi_j^{(v)}$ formed a basis for a representation of the molecular point group, the matrices of this representation being formed from the coefficients $[D^{(v)}(R)]_{ij}$ which appear in (7.15). But this result is easily established. For, in the first place, from the way in which O_R is defined, it is clear that $O_R \psi_j^{(v)}$ satisfies the same boundary conditions as $\psi_j^{(v)}$; and, in the second place, by combining (7.12) and (7.14) we see that

$$H(O_R \psi_j^{(v)}) = O_R(H \psi_j^{(v)}) = O_R(E_v \psi_j^{(v)}) = E_v(O_R \psi_j^{(v)}).$$

Thus $O_R \psi_j^{(v)}$ is a solution of (7.13) with $E = E_v$ which satisfies the boundary conditions. It must, therefore, belong to the function space associated with the energy level E_v and be expressible in the form (7.15) as a linear combination of the base functions of this space.

In this way we establish the fundamental relation between the solutions of the Schrödinger equation for a molecule and its symmetry: *the wave functions which belong to the energy level E_v of a molecule form a function space and this function space gives rise to a representation Γ_v of the point group of the molecule*. The theory is silent on the question as to whether Γ_v is reducible or irreducible. In applying the theory, *we make the assumption that Γ_v is irreducible*. If, in a particular case, it happened that the representation associated with a given energy level was, in fact, reducible, we would think of this as a numerical coincidence of a number of different energy levels, each with its own IR, and we would speak of an *accidental degeneracy*.

There is an exception to the assumption that Γ_v is irreducible that may occur for molecules whose point groups possess one-dimensional IRs with complex characters. In general, since H is a real operator and the energy values E_v are real, the complex conjugates of the base functions $\psi_j^{(v)}$ also belong to the function space associated with E_v and they may equally well be taken as a basis for this space. They will be transformed by the operators O_R according to equations which are complex conjugate to (7.15) and so they will give rise to a representation Γ_v^* whose matrices are the complex conjugates of the matrices defined by (7.15). No difficulty arises if the characters of Γ_v are all real numbers, since then Γ_v and Γ_v^* have the same characters and are equivalent representations. Taking the complex conjugate base functions makes no essential difference; indeed, in this case, we may, if we wish, choose the $\psi_j^{(v)}$ to be real functions.

If, however, we find that a molecule has an energy level whose associated wave function serves as the basis of a one-dimensional IR Γ_c with *complex characters*, the above argument shows that this level must be degenerate with another whose wave function forms a basis for the complex conjugate IR Γ_c^*. These representations, therefore, always appear together in pairs; that is why they are bracketed together in the character tables and given a single Mulliken symbol E, the symbol appropriate to a doubly-degenerate IR.

The importance of the connection between the Schrödinger equation and representation theory is that we know all about the IRs of the molecular point groups and that we can use this information to tell us a great deal about the possible wave functions of a molecule and their properties, without having to find detailed solutions of the Schrödinger equation. In fact, of course, we cannot hope to solve the Schrödinger equation exactly, except in rather simple cases, and in many applications we make do with approximate solutions. Group theory is of great help in forming and handling these approximate wave functions since, like the exact wave functions, they must give rise to IRs of the point group of the molecule.

7.4 Perturbations

Although in most cases the Schrödinger equation for a system of particles is too complicated for the exact wave functions and energy levels to be found, it very often happens that one can write the exact Hamiltonian in the form

$$H = H_0 + H_1$$

where H_0 is a simpler Hamiltonian that gives rise to a Schrödinger equation whose solutions can be found, at least in principle, and H_1 is a correction term, called the *perturbation*, which turns H_0 into the correct Hamiltonian. In the case of the electrons of a molecule, for example, H_1 might be the potential energy due to the repulsions between the electrons; then H_0 would be the Hamiltonian for a system of non-interacting electrons moving in the electrostatic field of the nuclei.

In order to see what kind of relation there will be between the solutions of the Schrödinger equation with Hamiltonian H_0 and the exact solutions we consider a fictitious Hamiltonian of the form

$$H(s) = H_0 + sH_1;$$

$s=1$ corresponds to the correct Hamiltonian H, $s=0$ corresponds to the unperturbed Hamiltonian H_0, and we can make a continuous transformation from H to H_0 by letting s change continuously from 1 to 0.

For any intermediate value of s, the Schrödinger equation

$$H(s)\psi = E\psi$$

will have solutions ψ_s belonging to energy levels E_s and a small change in the value of s must give rise to correspondingly small changes in E_s and the wave functions ψ_s. Thus, by letting s decrease continuously from 1 to 0, we can achieve a continuous change from the exact wave functions and energy levels to the approximate wave functions and energy levels that arise from assuming H_0 to be the Hamiltonian.

At each stage in the change from H to H_0, the Hamiltonian $H(s)$ will have the point group $\mathscr{G}$ of the original Hamiltonian H and the energy levels and wave functions of $H(s)$ can be classified according to the IRs of $\mathscr{G}$. If we fix our attention on a particular energy level of H whose wave functions form a basis for a particular IR of $\mathscr{G}$ it is clear that, by a continuous change from $s=1$ to $s=0$, this energy level will turn into an energy level of H_0 whose wave functions form a basis for the *same* IR of $\mathscr{G}$; one cannot have a sudden change in the IR during a smooth transition from one Hamiltonian to the other.

The reverse process, i.e. the change from the energy levels and wave functions of H_0 to those of H, is straightforward for any energy level of H_0 whose wave functions are found to generate a definite *irreducible* representation of $\mathscr{G}$; this level must become an energy level of H whose wave functions belong to the same IR. This means, in particular, that the degeneracy of the level remains unchanged and that the perturbation that changes H_0 to H does not split the level.

It very often happens, however, that an accidental degeneracy is created by the process of simplifying the Hamiltonian, and that the wave functions that belong to a given energy level of H_0 form the basis for a *reducible* representation, say Γ_0, of $\mathscr{G}$. It is clear that in this case the process of making s become zero has led to the coalescence of a number of distinct energy levels of H to form a single level of H_0. The reverse process will then have the effect of splitting the accidentally degenerate level of H_0 into a number of distinct levels, one for each IR of $\mathscr{G}$ that is contained in Γ_0; the perturbation that changes H_0 into H splits the unperturbed level and the way in which this level is split can be found by identifying the IRs that are contained in Γ_0.

There are two cases to be considered here. The simpler case is that in which H and H_0 both have the same point group. This is the case, for instance, in the example mentioned above where H_0 is the Hamiltonian for a system of non-interacting electrons and H_1 is the potential energy of their interactions. Then H_1 is invariant under any symmetry operation and H_0 and H

both have the full symmetry of the point group of the molecule. In a case such as this all that it is necessary to do when an unperturbed level gives rise to a reducible representation Γ_0 is to use the character table of the point group to find the IRs that are contained in Γ_0.

The second case to be considered is that in which H and H_1 both have the full symmetry of the molecular point group $\mathcal{G}$ but in which H_0 has higher symmetry, i.e. the point group $\mathcal{G}_0$ of H_0 contains, as it must, all the symmetry operations of $\mathcal{G}$ but contains some other symmetry operations as well. In such a case, $\mathcal{G}$ is a *sub-group* of the larger group $\mathcal{G}_0$ and the accidental degeneracy with which we are concerned arises because a set of functions which forms a basis for an IR of $\mathcal{G}_0$ may form a basis for a *reducible* representation of $\mathcal{G}$.

For example, $\mathcal{G}_0$ might be the point group of a molecule and $\mathcal{G}$ the point group of the same molecule after it has been slightly distorted, say by introducing it into a site in a crystal lattice. Or one might deliberately choose to imagine the molecule to be more symmetrical than it really is, say by ignoring small differences between certain bond lengths. In cases such as this the perturbation which represents the distortion of the molecule may result in a splitting of the unperturbed levels.

A set of wave functions which belongs to an unperturbed energy level of H_0 and which forms a basis for an IR Γ_0 of $\mathcal{G}_0$ must, at the same time, form a basis for a representation, say Γ_0', of $\mathcal{G}$. If Γ_0' is an IR of $\mathcal{G}$ then the perturbation which represents the distortion cannot split the unperturbed level; if Γ_0' is a reducible representation of $\mathcal{G}$, the unperturbed level will be split by the perturbation and the way in which it is split can be found by using the character table of $\mathcal{G}$ to reduce Γ_0'. To do this we need to know the characters of Γ_0'; these are simply the characters of Γ_0 for those symmetry operations of $\mathcal{G}_0$ which also belong to $\mathcal{G}$ and these can be read off from the character table of $\mathcal{G}_0$.

EXAMPLE

Consider an octahedral MX_6 molecule with point group $\mathcal{G}_0 = \mathcal{O}_h = \mathcal{O} \times i$. We take the x, y, z axes to point along the M—X bond directions and consider a distortion in which the two bonds along the positive and negative directions of the z axis are symmetrically lengthened, the other bonds remaining unchanged; see Fig. 7.2. The distorted molecule has the symmetry operations of $\mathcal{G} = \mathcal{D}_{4h} = \mathcal{D}_4 \times i$, namely rotations C_4 and C_2 about the z axis, rotations C_2' about the x and y axes, rotations C_2'' about axes in the xy plane which bisect the angles between the x and y axes, together with the operations that are obtained from these by multiplying them by the inversion i in the centre of symmetry. If an IR Γ_0 of $\mathcal{O}$ is a representation Γ_0' of $\mathcal{D}_4$, the IRs Γ_{0g} or Γ_{0u} of $\mathcal{O}_h$ will become the corresponding representations Γ_{0g}' or Γ_{0u}' of $\mathcal{D}_{4h}$; thus all the information we require can be obtained by considering $\mathcal{O}$ and $\mathcal{D}_4$ rather than the complete groups $\mathcal{O}_h$ and $\mathcal{D}_{4h}$. In considering the relation between the two groups, note that the C_2' rotations about the x and y axes in $\mathscr{D}_4$ correspond to the C_2 rotations of $\mathcal{O}$ while the C_2'' rotations of $\mathscr{D}_4$ correspond to the C_2' rotations of $\mathcal{O}$.

The way in which an IR of $\mathcal{O}$ becomes a representation of $\mathscr{D}_4$ is shown in Table 7.1. The characters set out in this table are the characters, for the symmetry operations of $\mathscr{D}_4$, of the IRs of $\mathcal{O}$ that are listed down the left-hand column; these are obtained from the character table of $\mathcal{O}$. The character table of $\mathscr{D}_4$ then allows us to find the IRs of $\mathscr{D}_4$ that are contained in representations of $\mathscr{D}_4$ that have these characters and these IRs of $\mathscr{D}_4$ are listed down the right-hand column.

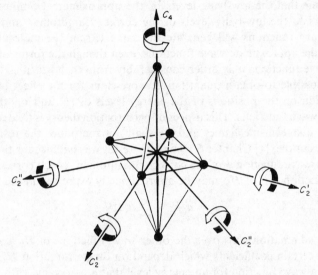

7.2 An MX$_6$ molecule with point group $\mathscr{D}_{4h}$.

TABLE 7.1. *Correlations between $\mathcal{O}$ and $\mathscr{D}_4$*

IRs of $\mathcal{O}$	Classes of $\mathscr{D}_4$					IRs of $\mathscr{D}_4$
	E	$2C_4$	C_2	$2C_2'$	$2C_2''$	
A_1	1	1	1	1	1	A_1
A_2	1	-1	1	1	-1	B_1
E	2	0	2	2	0	$A_1 + B_1$
T_1	3	1	-1	-1	-1	$A_2 + E$
T_2	3	-1	-1	-1	1	$B_2 + E$

Suppose, for instance, that a certain energy level of H_0 was found to belong to the representation $\Gamma_0 = T_2$ of $\mathcal{O}$. The Table shows that this corresponds to the representation $\Gamma_0' = B_2 + E$ of $\mathscr{D}_4$. Consequently, a distortion which reduces the symmetry from $\mathcal{O}$ to $\mathscr{D}_4$ will split a T_2 level of $\mathcal{O}$ into a non-degenerate level described by the B_2 representation of $\mathscr{D}_4$ and a doubly degenerate level described by the E representation of $\mathscr{D}_4$. Similarly, the distortion will split a T_1 level of $\mathcal{O}$ into an A_2 and an E level of $\mathcal{D}_4$ and it will split an E level of $\mathcal{O}$ into two non-degenerate levels of $\mathcal{D}_4$ described by the IRs A_1 and B_1 of $\mathcal{D}_4$. The only levels which are not split by the distortion are the non-degenerate A_1 and A_2 levels of $\mathcal{O}$ which become the equivalent non-degenerate A_1 and B_1 levels of $\mathcal{D}_4$.

The simple qualitative connection between the IRs of the exact energy levels of H and the IRs of the levels of the approximate Hamiltonian H_0 forms the background to the applications of the theory that are discussed in the succeeding chapters. Given that the perturbation H_1 is not too large, one may assume that the low-lying levels of the approximate Hamiltonian will correspond to the low-lying levels of the correct Hamiltonian and that the correct wave functions will generate the same IRs of the molecular point group as the approximate wave functions, even though the forms of the two sets of wave functions may differ considerably from each other.

It is possible to obtain quantitative expressions for the effect of a small perturbation on the positions of the energy levels of H_0 and on the corresponding wave functions. This aspect of perturbation theory is treated in most books on quantum mechanics and we shall not reproduce the results here. (See, for example, [1] Chapter 6.) The only result we shall need is the general one that a wave function ψ of the correct Hamiltonian, which corresponds to a wave function $\psi^{(0)}$ of H_0, may be approximately expressed in the form

$$\psi = a_0 \psi^{(0)} + \sum_k a_k \psi^{(k)} \qquad (7.16)$$

where the summation runs over the other wave functions of H_0 and a_0 and the a_k are certain coefficients which depend on the perturbation H_1.

If ψ is a wave function for an energy level that is associated with a certain IR of the molecular point group, there will be one expression of this kind for each basis function of the IR. The sets of functions ψ and $\psi^{(0)}$ that are linked by (7.16) must form bases for the same IR and so the other wave functions of H_0 that appear in the summation must also belong to this IR. The effect of the perturbation is, therefore, to mix the wave functions of H_0 that belong to levels with the same IR. If the level in which we are interested is far removed in energy from other levels of H_0 that belong to the same IR the amount of mixing will be small and the coefficients a_k in (7.16) will be small compared to a_0. If, however, two or more levels of H_0 with the same IR happen to be rather close together, the perturbation may produce a strong mixing of the unperturbed wave functions and the coefficients a_0 and a_k in (7.16) may be of comparable size.

7.5 Product Wave Functions

It very often happens that the variables X which describe configurations of a system with Hamiltonian H can be separated into two sets, X' and X'', in such a way that the Hamiltonian becomes

$$H = H' + H'' + H_1$$

where H' depends only on the variables in X' and H'' depends only on the variables in X'', while H_1 is an interaction term which depends on both sets of variables. In many cases of this kind it is a reasonable starting approximation to neglect H_1 and to describe the system by the Hamiltonian

$$H_0 = H' + H''.$$

We then have the situation discussed in the preceding section, with a particular form for H_0 which gives rise to the approximate Schrödinger equation

$$H_0 \Psi(X) = (H' + H'')\Psi(X) = E\Psi(X). \tag{7.17}$$

The important result that we wish to establish is that the solutions of (7.17) can be found by combining together solutions $\psi(X')$ and $\phi(X'')$ of the independent Schrödinger-like equations

$$H'\psi(X') = E'\psi(X'), \quad H''\phi(X'') = E''\phi(X''). \tag{7.18}$$

In fact, if $\psi(X')$ and $\phi(X'')$ satisfy these equations, a possible solution of (7.17) is the product function

$$\Psi(X) = \psi(X')\phi(X'')$$

and the energy of the state described by Ψ is $E = E' + E''$. This follows from (7.18) since

$$H_0\psi(X')\phi(X'') = (H' + H'')\psi(X')\phi(X'')$$
$$= [H'\psi(X')]\phi(X'') + \psi(X')[H''\phi(X'')] = (E' + E'')\psi(X')\phi(X'').$$

In the cases that are of most interest to us, the operators H_0, H' and H'' are all invariant under the symmetry operations of the same molecular point group $\mathscr{G}$ and the division of the configuration space variables into the sets X' and X'' is a division of the configuration space into two invariant subspaces which are not mixed together by any of the symmetry operations of $\mathscr{G}$. The arguments of Section 7.3 then apply to the solutions of (7.18). E' will have one of a definite set of values $E'_1, \ldots, E'_\rho, \ldots$ and E'' will have one of a definite set of values $E''_1, \ldots, E''_\sigma, \ldots$. A function $\psi(X')$ which satisfies (7.18) with $E' = E'_\rho$ can be expressed in terms of n_ρ linearly independent functions $\psi_i^{(\rho)}(X')$ and a function $\phi(X'')$ which satisfies (7.18) with $E'' = E''_\sigma$ can be expressed in terms of n_σ linearly independent functions $\phi_j^{(\sigma)}(X'')$:

$$\psi(X') = \sum_{i=1}^{n_\rho} a_i\psi_i^{(\rho)}(X') \quad \text{where} \quad H'\psi_i^{(\rho)}(X') = E'_\rho\psi_i^{(\rho)}(X');$$

$$\phi(X'') = \sum_{j=1}^{n_\sigma} b_j\phi_j^{(\sigma)}(X'') \quad \text{where} \quad H''\phi_j^{(\sigma)}(X'') = E''_\sigma\phi_j^{(\sigma)}(X'').$$

The functions $\psi_i^{(\rho)}$ form a basis for a representation Γ_ρ, and the functions $\phi_j^{(\sigma)}$ form a basis for a representation Γ_σ, of the molecular point group $\mathcal{G}$.

A product function $\Psi(X) = \psi(X')\phi(X'')$ then has the form

$$\Psi(X) = \sum_{i=1}^{n_\rho} \sum_{j=1}^{n_\sigma} a_i b_j \psi_i^{(\rho)}(X') \phi_j^{(\sigma)}(X''), \qquad (7.19)$$

and it is a solution of (7.17) belonging to the energy level $E = E_\rho' + E_\sigma''$. Equation (7.19) shows that wave functions belonging to this energy level may be expressed as linear combinations of the $n_\rho n_\sigma$ linearly independent products $\psi_i^{(\rho)}(X') \phi_j^{(\sigma)}(X'')$, where the suffixes i and j run independently through the values $i = 1, \ldots, n_\rho$, $j = 1, \ldots, n_\sigma$.

These products form a basis for the function space associated with the energy level $E_\rho' + E_\sigma''$ and so they form a basis for some representation of $\mathcal{G}$. This representation is called the *direct product* (or the Kronecker product) of Γ_ρ and Γ_σ, and we denote it by $\Gamma_\rho \times \Gamma_\sigma$.

It may happen that the variables in X' and X'' can themselves be further separated into smaller invariant sub-sets. The same general arguments will still apply, so that one will be led to consider wave functions which are products of several factors and thus to consider direct product representations which are formed by multiplying together base functions from several different representations. The way in which these direct product representations may be analyzed is discussed in the next section.

EXAMPLE: *Electronic structure*

Since a symmetry operation moves an electron into a new position which is quite independent of the coordinates of the other electrons, the configuration space of the n electrons may be divided into n invariant sub-spaces, one sub-space for the coordinates of each electron. *If we neglect the mutual repulsions of the electrons*, each electron moves independently of the others in the electrostatic field of the nuclei, and the Hamiltonian has the form

$$H_0 = \sum_{p=1}^{n} H_p,$$

where H_p is the Hamiltonian for a single electron moving in the field of the nuclei. H_p depends only on the coordinates of electron p and it is invariant under the operations of the molecular point group.

We indicate that a function f depends on the coordinates of p by writing it as $f(p)$. We may then write a wave function for the system of n electrons as the product

$$\Psi(1, 2, \ldots, n) = \psi_i^{(\rho)}(1) \psi_j^{(\sigma)}(2) \cdots \psi_k^{(\mu)}(n),$$

where the functions $\psi_i^{(\rho)}, \psi_j^{(\sigma)}, \ldots, \psi_k^{(\mu)}$ form bases for IRs of the point group of the molecule.

In the particular case of an atom, for example, the point group is the rotation group $\mathcal{R}_3$ and the functions $\psi_i^{(\rho)}, \ldots$ are the $s, p, d, \ldots$ atomic orbitals which form bases for the IRs of $\mathcal{R}_3$ (see Section 6.3). The product function then corresponds to the idea of building up the system of n electrons by placing them in individual atomic orbitals. The extension of these ideas to molecules leads to the concept of molecular orbitals.

This over-simplified description of electronic structure needs to be modified in order to incorporate the spins of the electrons and the Pauli exclusion principle, and also to take some account of the electron repulsions, but it contains, nevertheless, the fundamental ideas on which more elaborate discussions of electronic structure are based.

7.6 Direct Product Representations

Suppose that Γ_μ and Γ_ν are two representations of a group, with base functions $\psi_i^{(\mu)}$ and $\phi_j^{(\nu)}$ which satisfy

$$O_R \psi_i^{(\mu)} = \sum_{p=1}^{n_\mu} [D^{(\mu)}(R)]_{pi} \psi_p^{(\mu)}, \qquad O_R \phi_j^{(\nu)} = \sum_{q=1}^{n_\nu} [D^{(\nu)}(R)]_{qj} \phi_q^{(\nu)}. \quad (7.20)$$

Then the $n_\mu n_\nu$ products $\psi_i^{(\mu)} \phi_j^{(\nu)}$ $(i=1,\ldots,n_\mu; j=1,\ldots,n_\nu)$ form a basis for the direct product representation $\Gamma_\mu \times \Gamma_\nu$. The effect of O_R on these products can be calculated from (7.20). One has

$$O_R(\psi_i^{(\mu)} \phi_j^{(\nu)}) = (O_R \psi_i^{(\mu)})(O_R \phi_j^{(\nu)}) = \sum_{p=1}^{n_\mu} \sum_{q=1}^{n_\nu} [D^{(\mu)}(R)]_{pi} [D^{(\nu)}(R)]_{qj} \psi_p^{(\mu)} \phi_q^{(\nu)}.$$
$$(7.21)$$

Suppose that we form all the products $\psi_i^{(\mu)} \phi_j^{(\nu)}$ and write them down in a definite order. We can number them from 1 to $n_\mu n_\nu$ and designate them by a symbol with a single suffix r:

$$\Psi_r = \psi_i^{(\mu)} \phi_j^{(\nu)},$$

where $r=1, 2, \ldots, n_\mu n_\nu$ and there is a fixed relation between each r and the pair of suffixes i and j to which it corresponds. Then we can write (7.21) as

$$O_R \Psi_r = \sum_{s=1}^{n_\mu n_\nu} [D^{(\mu \times \nu)}(R)]_{sr} \Psi_s, \quad (7.22)$$

where, if r corresponds to the pair of suffixes (i, j) and s to the pair (p, q),

$$[D^{(\mu \times \nu)}(R)]_{sr} = [D^{(\mu)}(R)]_{pi} [D^{(\nu)}(R)]_{qj}. \quad (7.23)$$

These equations show how the matrix $D^{(\mu \times \nu)}(R)$ which represents the group operation R in the direct product representation is related to the matrices which represent R in Γ_μ and Γ_ν. The relation between these matrices is complicated, but the relation between their characters, which are the quantities of most interest to us, is simple. The character of R in $\Gamma_\mu \times \Gamma_\nu$ is

$$\chi^{(\mu \times \nu)}(R) = \sum_{r=1}^{n_\mu n_\nu} [D^{(\mu \times \nu)}(R)]_{rr}.$$

Putting $s=r$ in (7.23) means putting $p=i$ and $q=j$; summing over all values of r means summing independently over all the values of i from 1 to n_μ and all the values of j from 1 to n_ν. Thus

$$\chi^{(\mu \times \nu)}(R) = \sum_{i=1}^{n_\mu} \sum_{j=1}^{n_\nu} [D^{(\mu)}(R)]_{ii}[D^{(\nu)}(R)]_{jj} = \chi^{(\mu)}(R)\chi^{(\nu)}(R), \quad (7.24)$$

i.e. the character of R in $\Gamma_\mu \times \Gamma_\nu$ is the product of its characters in Γ_μ and Γ_ν. Since (7.24) is symmetrical between μ and ν, we see that the order of Γ_μ and Γ_ν in the direct product is immaterial; $\Gamma_\mu \times \Gamma_\nu$ and $\Gamma_\nu \times \Gamma_\mu$ have the same characters and are equivalent to each other.

We can extend these arguments to form the direct product of three or more representations. Suppose we have formed $\Gamma_\mu \times \Gamma_\nu$ with characters $\chi^{(\mu \times \nu)}=\chi^{(\mu)}\chi^{(\nu)}$. We can then form the direct product of $\Gamma_\mu \times \Gamma_\nu$ with a third representation Γ_σ to obtain the product representation $\Gamma_\sigma \times (\Gamma_\mu \times \Gamma_\nu)$. The characters of this representation will be

$$\chi^{(\sigma)}\chi^{(\mu \times \nu)} = \chi^{(\sigma)}\chi^{(\mu)}\chi^{(\nu)}.$$

This result is independent of the order of σ, μ, ν so that the representations $\Gamma_\sigma \times (\Gamma_\mu \times \Gamma_\nu)$, $\Gamma_\mu \times (\Gamma_\sigma \times \Gamma_\nu)$ and $\Gamma_\nu \times (\Gamma_\sigma \times \Gamma_\mu)$ are all equivalent and may be denoted indifferently by $\Gamma_\sigma \times \Gamma_\mu \times \Gamma_\nu$ without any need for introducing brackets. One can proceed in this way to form the direct product of any number of representations.

Our arguments apply whether the representations used to form direct products are reducible or irreducible, but their usual application is to direct products of IRs. The characters of Γ_μ and Γ_ν are then contained in the character table of the group concerned and it is a simple matter to use this table in (7.24) to calculate the characters of $\Gamma_\mu \times \Gamma_\nu$. Even though Γ_μ and Γ_ν are IRs, their direct product may be a reducible representation; if so, we can use (6.5) to find the irreducible components of $\Gamma_\mu \times \Gamma_\nu$. The results of such calculations for many of the point groups are summarized in Appendix I.

The reduction of direct products like $\Gamma_\sigma \times \Gamma_\mu \times \Gamma_\nu$ is straightforward. If the reduction of $\Gamma_\mu \times \Gamma_\nu$ gives

$$\Gamma_\mu \times \Gamma_\nu = a_1\Gamma_1 + a_2\Gamma_2 + \cdots + a_k\Gamma_k,$$

then

$$\chi^{(\mu \times \nu)} = a_1\chi^{(1)} + a_2\chi^{(2)} + \cdots + a_k\chi^{(k)}.$$

The character of $\Gamma_\sigma \times (\Gamma_\mu \times \Gamma_\nu)$ is thus

$$\chi^{(\sigma)}\chi^{(\mu \times \nu)} = a_1\chi^{(\sigma)}\chi^{(1)} + a_2\chi^{(\sigma)}\chi^{(2)} + \cdots + a_k\chi^{(\sigma)}\chi^{(k)}.$$

But this is the character of a partially reduced representation whose matrices are expressed as a direct sum of a_1 sub-matrices whose characters $\chi^{(\sigma)}\chi^{(1)}$

show that they belong to the direct product representation $\Gamma_\sigma \times \Gamma_1$, a_2 submatrices belonging to the representation $\Gamma_\sigma \times \Gamma_2$, etc. We may, therefore, write

$$\Gamma_\sigma \times (\Gamma_\mu \times \Gamma_\nu) = \Gamma_\sigma \times (a_1\Gamma_1 + \cdots + a_k\Gamma_k) = a_1\Gamma_\sigma \times \Gamma_1 + \cdots + a_k\Gamma_\sigma \times \Gamma_k,$$

treating the '$\times$' sign according to the distributive law for ordinary multiplication, and all we then need to do is to reduce direct products with just two factors.

EXAMPLE: *Direct products for $\mathcal{T}_d$*

TABLE 7.2. *Character table of $\mathcal{T}_d$*

$\mathcal{T}_d$	E	$8C_3$	$3C_2$	$6S_4$	6σ
A_1	1	1	1	1	1
A_2	1	1	1	-1	-1
E	2	-1	2	0	0
T_1	3	0	-1	1	-1
T_2	3	0	-1	-1	1
$T_1 \times T_2$	9	0	1	-1	-1

The character table of $\mathcal{T}_d$ is given in Table 7.2. The characters of the direct product $T_1 \times T_2$ are given in the bottom line of the table; these are obtained, using (7.24), by multiplying the corresponding characters of T_1 and T_2. The rule (6.5) applied to this set of characters gives

$$a_{A_1} = 0, \quad a_{A_2} = 1, \quad a_E = 1, \quad a_{T_1} = 1, \quad a_{T_2} = 1,$$

so that the reduction of $T_1 \times T_2$ is

$$T_1 \times T_2 = A_2 + E + T_1 + T_2.$$

In similar fashion, the reader may verify the following results:

$$T_1 \times T_1 = T_2 \times T_2 = A_1 + E + T_1 + T_2,$$

$$E \times T_1 = E \times T_2 = T_1 + T_2,$$

$$E \times E = A_1 + A_2 + E,$$

$$A_i \times E = E, \quad \text{for } i = 1 \text{ or } 2,$$

$$A_i \times T_j = T_k, \qquad A_i \times A_j = A_k,$$

where, in the last two equations, $k = 1$ if $i = j = 1$ or 2 but $k = 2$ if $i \neq j$.

We may use these results to reduce direct products containing more than two factors. Consider, for example, the representation $E \times T_1 \times T_2$. Doing the reduction in one order, we find

$$E \times (T_1 \times T_2) = E \times (A_2 + E + T_1 + T_2) = E \times A_2 + E \times E + E \times T_1 + E \times T_2$$

$$= E + (A_1 + A_2 + E) + (T_1 + T_2) + (T_1 + T_2)$$

$$= A_1 + A_2 + 2E + 2T_1 + 2T_2.$$

Reducing the same representation in another order gives the identical result:

$$(E \times T_1) \times T_2 = (T_1 + T_2) \times T_2 = T_1 \times T_2 + T_2 \times T_2$$
$$= (A_2 + E + T_1 + T_2) + (A_1 + E + T_1 + T_2)$$
$$= A_1 + A_2 + 2E + 2T_1 + 2T_2.$$

7.7 Vanishing Integrals

In many applications of quantum mechanics one comes across integrals of the form

$$\int \Psi_\sigma^*(X) F_\lambda(X) \Psi_\rho(X) \, d\tau, \tag{7.25}$$

where Ψ_σ and Ψ_ρ are wave functions which belong to energy levels E_σ and E_ρ of a molecule, $F_\lambda(X)$ is a given function of the configuration space variables X, and the integration extends over the whole range of these variables. Very often it is not so much the numerical value of an integral like this that is of interest but, rather, the general conditions which the factors in the integral must satisfy if it is not to vanish. For example, as we shall see in the following chapters, the intensity of a line in the spectrum of a molecule caused by a transition between the levels E_ρ and E_σ depends upon the values of integrals like (7.25) in which F_λ is a component of the electric dipole moment of the molecule. If these integrals are zero, the transition between E_ρ and E_σ is forbidden and the conditions under which the integrals will necessarily vanish determine the selection rules for the spectrum of the molecule.

The condition that an integral like (7.25) should vanish depends upon the symmetry properties of the functions Ψ_σ^*, Ψ_ρ, F_λ in its integrand. As we saw in Section 7.3, the wave functions Ψ_σ and Ψ_ρ belong to the function spaces of the energy levels E_σ and E_ρ and they may be expressed as linear combinations of suitable basis functions which generate definite IRs Γ_σ and Γ_ρ of the point group of the molecule. The complex conjugate functions Ψ_σ^* are then associated with the IR Γ_σ^*. (For point groups with real characters, Γ_σ and Γ_σ^* are equivalent representations and it is only necessary to distinguish between them for the relatively unimportant point groups which possess IRs with complex characters.) In our applications, F_λ will be a function from a function space whose basis generates an IR Γ_λ of the point group. It follows that a product of the form $\Psi_\sigma^* F_\lambda \Psi_\rho$ may be expressed as a linear combination of the base functions of the direct product representation $\Gamma_\sigma^* \times \Gamma_\lambda \times \Gamma_\rho$. If, by a suitable change of basis, this product representation is reduced into the form

$$\Gamma_\sigma^* \times \Gamma_\lambda \times \Gamma_\rho = \Gamma_\alpha + \cdots + \Gamma_\nu + \cdots, \tag{7.26}$$

where $\Gamma_\alpha, \ldots, \Gamma_\nu, \ldots$ are IRs of the molecular point group, it will, correspondingly, be possible to express $\Psi_\sigma^* F_\lambda \Psi_\rho$ in the form

$$\Psi_\sigma^* F_\lambda \Psi_\rho = f^{(\alpha)} + \cdots + f^{(\nu)} + \cdots, \tag{7.27}$$

where $f^{(v)}$ is a function which belongs to a function space whose basis generates the IR Γ_v.

The functions $f^{(v)}$ may be found by using the projection operators $P^{(v)}$, defined by (6.13), which have the properties described in (6.15). We apply (6.15) in a negative fashion and say that if a particular IR Γ_μ does *not* appear in (7.26), so that there is *no* function $f^{(\mu)}$ in (7.27), then certainly

$$P^{(\mu)}(\Psi_\sigma^* F_\lambda \Psi_\rho) = 0$$

for any arbitrary choice of the functions Ψ_σ, F_λ and Ψ_ρ from their respective function spaces. In particular, if $\Gamma_\sigma^* \times \Gamma_\lambda \times \Gamma_\rho$ does not contain the identical representation Γ_1, in which $\chi^{(1)}(R) = 1$ for all R so that $P^{(1)} = \sum_R O_R$, we shall have

$$P^{(1)}(\Psi_\sigma^* F_\lambda \Psi_\rho) = \sum_R O_R(\Psi_\sigma^* F_\lambda \Psi_\rho) = 0. \qquad (7.28)$$

The relevance of these considerations to the problem of deciding when the integral (7.25) will vanish lies in the fact that, as we saw in Section 4.8, the operators O_R are such that, for any function $Q(X)$,

$$\int Q(X)\, d\tau = \int (O_R Q)(X')\, d\tau' = \int (O_R Q)(X)\, d\tau$$

since $(O_R Q)(X') = Q(X)$ and we integrate over all possible configurations X. If we sum over all the g elements of the molecular point group, it follows that

$$\int Q\, d\tau = (1/g) \int \left(\sum_R O_R Q \right) d\tau,$$

and, therefore, that the integral must vanish if

$$\sum_R O_R Q = 0. \qquad (7.29)$$

If we apply this result with $Q = \Psi_\sigma^* F_\lambda \Psi_\rho$ we see that if $\Gamma_\sigma^* \times \Gamma_\lambda \times \Gamma_\rho$ does not contain the identical representation, so that (7.28) is satisfied, then the integral (7.25) must be zero. Notice that we have here established a *sufficient condition* for the vanishing of (7.25). *It is not a necessary condition* for one cannot rule out the possibility that in a particular case the functions Ψ_σ^*, F_λ, Ψ_ρ might be such that $f^{(1)}$ in (7.27) was zero and that (7.28) was satisfied even though $\Gamma_\sigma^* \times \Gamma_\lambda \times \Gamma_\rho$ did contain the identical representation.

The condition that $\Gamma_\sigma^* \times \Gamma_\lambda \times \Gamma_\rho$ does not contain the identical representation Γ_1 may be expressed in the following way. Consider the direct product $\Gamma_\sigma^* \times \Gamma_\mu$ where Γ_σ and Γ_μ are two IRs of a point group. Take a symmetry operation R from a class $\mathcal{K}_i$ of the group. The character of R in Γ_σ^* is $\chi_i^{*(\sigma)}$, the complex conjugate of its character in Γ_σ and the character of R in Γ_μ is $\chi_i^{(\mu)}$; thus the character of R in $\Gamma_\sigma^* \times \Gamma_\mu$ is, by (7.24),

$$\chi_i^{(\sigma^* \times \mu)} = \chi_i^{*(\sigma)} \chi_i^{(\mu)}.$$

Also, for any class of the group, the identical representation has character $\chi_i^{(1)} = 1$. Thus (6.5) shows that the number of times that the identical representation will appear in the reduction of $\Gamma_\sigma^* \times \Gamma_\mu$ is

$$a_1 = \frac{1}{g} \sum_{i=1}^{k} g_i \chi_i^{*(1)} \chi_i^{(\sigma^* \times \mu)} = \frac{1}{g} \sum_{i=1}^{k} g_i \chi_i^{*(\sigma)} \chi_i^{(\mu)}.$$

But the sum over the classes on the right-hand side of this equation is precisely the sum that appears in (6.2), and substituting from (6.2) gives

$$a_1 = \delta_{\sigma\mu},$$

i.e. the identical representation appears once in $\Gamma_\sigma^* \times \Gamma_\mu$ if $\mu = \sigma$ but not at all if $\mu \neq \sigma$.

We may apply this result to $\Gamma_\sigma^* \times \Gamma_\lambda \times \Gamma_\rho$ if we let Γ_μ run over the various IRs that appear in the reduction of $\Gamma_\lambda \times \Gamma_\rho$. The conclusion of this argument may be stated thus: *if Ψ_σ, F_λ, and Ψ_ρ are functions from spaces whose bases generate the IRs Γ_σ, Γ_λ and Γ_ρ, and if $\Gamma_\lambda \times \Gamma_\rho$ does not contain Γ_σ, then*

$$\int \Psi_\sigma^* F_\lambda \Psi_\rho \, d\tau = 0.$$

PROBLEMS

Perturbations (Section 7.4)

7.1. A distorted octahedral molecule with point group $\mathscr{D}_4$ has four energy levels which belong respectively to the IRs A_1, B_1, B_2 and E of $\mathscr{D}_4$. If the distortion is removed and the molecule regains pure octahedral symmetry with point group $\mathcal{O}$, use Table 7.1 to show that the undistorted levels, classified according to the IRs of $\mathcal{O}$ could be either A_1, A_2, T_2 or E, T_2.

7.2. If CH_4 is changed to CH_3D the symmetry is reduced from $\mathscr{T}_d$ to $\mathscr{C}_{3v}$. Construct the correlation table, analogous to Table 7.1, which gives the relations between the IRs of $\mathscr{T}_d$ and $\mathscr{C}_{3v}$ and show that the IRs A_1, A_2, E, T_1 and T_2 of $\mathscr{T}_d$ give rise respectively to the representations A_1, A_2, E, A_2+E and A_1+E of $\mathscr{C}_{3v}$.

7.3. There are several other sub-groups of $\mathcal{O}_h$ besides $\mathscr{D}_{4h}$. For example, $\mathcal{O}_h$ contains the sub-group $\mathscr{D}_{3d} = \mathscr{D}_3 \times i$ obtained by singling out one of the three-fold axes of $\mathcal{O}$ and the three C_2' axes at right-angles to this axis. Another sub-group of $\mathcal{O}_h$ is $\mathscr{T}_d$. Construct the correlation tables which give the relations between the IRs of $\mathcal{O}$ and $\mathscr{D}_3$ and the relations between the IRs of $\mathcal{O}_h$ and $\mathscr{T}_d$. (These are Tables G.2 and G.3 of Appendix G.)

Direct Products (Section 7.6)

7.4. Show that, for $\mathscr{C}_{3v}$, $A_1 \times A_1 = A_2 \times A_2 = A_1$, $A_1 \times A_2 = A_2$,

$$A_1 \times E = A_2 \times E = E, \quad E \times E = A_1 + A_2 + E.$$

7.5. Show that, for $\mathscr{D}_3$, $E \times E = A_1 + A_2 + E$ while, for $\mathscr{D}_4$,

$$E \times E = A_1 + A_2 + B_1 + B_2.$$

7.6. Show that, for $\mathscr{C}_{5v}$, $E_1 \times E_1 = A_1 + A_2 + E_2$, $E_2 \times E_2 = A_1 + A_2 + E_1$, $E_1 \times E_2 = E_1 + E_2$. (*Note:* when $\alpha = 72° = 2\pi/5$, $2\cos^2\alpha = \cos 2\alpha + 1$, $2\cos^2 2\alpha = \cos 4\alpha + 1 = \cos\alpha + 1$, $2\cos\alpha\cos 2\alpha = \cos 2\alpha + \cos\alpha$.)

Vanishing Integrals (Section 7.7)

Integrals of the form (7.25) must vanish unless $\Gamma_\lambda \times \Gamma_\rho$ contains Γ_σ. In the following examples Γ_λ and Γ_ρ are given: prove that the only possibly non-vanishing integrals are those in which Γ_σ is as indicated.

7.7. $\mathscr{C}_{4v}$: $\Gamma_\lambda = E$, $\quad \Gamma_\rho = E$; $\quad \Gamma_\sigma = A_1, A_2, B_1, B_2$.

7.8. $\mathscr{D}_{3d}$: $\Gamma_\lambda = E_u$, $\quad \Gamma_\rho = E_u$; $\quad \Gamma_\sigma = A_{1g}, A_{2g}, E_g$.

7.9. $\mathscr{D}_{6h}$: $\Gamma_\lambda = E_{1u}$, $\quad \Gamma_\rho = B_{2g}$; $\quad \Gamma_\sigma = E_{2u}$.

$\qquad\quad \Gamma_\lambda = E_{1u}$, $\quad \Gamma_\rho = E_{2g}$; $\quad \Gamma_\sigma = B_{1u}, B_{2u}, E_{1u}$.

7.10. $\mathscr{T}_d$: $\Gamma_\lambda = T_2$, $\quad \Gamma_\rho = E$; $\quad \Gamma_\sigma = T_1, T_2$.

$\qquad\quad \Gamma_\lambda = T_2$, $\quad \Gamma_\rho = T_1$; $\quad \Gamma_\sigma = A_2, E, T_1, T_2$.

Chapter 8

MOLECULAR VIBRATIONS

8.1 Normal Coordinates

In Section 7.1 we set up a coordinate system for the displacements of the n nuclei of a molecule from their equilibrium positions. In this system the position of nucleus p is specified by its coordinates $x_1^{(p)}$, $x_2^{(p)}$, $x_3^{(p)}$ relative to three mutually perpendicular axes whose origin is at the equilibrium position of p, and a general configuration of the nuclei is specified by the $3n$ coordinates $x_1^{(1)}, \ldots, x_3^{(n)}$ of a point in the $3n$-dimensional configuration space of the nuclei. For convenience in writing out expressions involving the coordinates we shall number them in sequence from 1 to $3n$ and write

$$x_1 = x_1^{(1)}, \quad x_2 = x_2^{(1)}, \quad \ldots, \quad x_{3n} = x_3^{(n)}.$$

Then the coordinates which refer to nucleus p are

$$x_{3p-2} = x_1^{(p)}, \quad x_{3p-1} = x_2^{(p)}, \quad x_{3p} = x_3^{(p)}.$$

We also associate a mass m_k with each coordinate x_k by writing

$$m_{3p-2} = m_{3p-1} = m_{3p} = m^{(p)},$$

where $m^{(p)}$ is the mass of nucleus p.

Our first problem is to write down expressions for the kinetic and potential energies of the nuclei and to put them into a form which enables us to solve the Schrödinger equation for the vibrations of the molecule. The definitions made above allow us to write the kinetic energy operator T of (7.4) as

$$T = -\frac{h^2}{8\pi^2} \sum_{k=1}^{3n} \frac{1}{m_k} \frac{\partial^2}{\partial x_k^2}. \tag{8.1}$$

This expression may be simplified by introducing what are called *mass-weighted* coordinates; these are quantities $y_1, y_2, \ldots, y_{3n}$ which are related to the coordinates x_k by the equations

$$y_k = x_k \sqrt{m_k}. \tag{8.2}$$

In terms of these new variables, the kinetic energy (8.1) becomes

$$T = -\frac{h^2}{8\pi^2} \sum_{k=1}^{3n} \frac{\partial^2}{\partial y_k{}^2}. \tag{8.3}$$

Since the masses m_k are all known constants, the mass-weighted coordinates provide just as good a description of the configuration of a molecule as the original coordinates. Their introduction merely corresponds to a change of the scale with which we measure the displacement of a nucleus by a factor which depends on its mass.

The potential energy, V, of the molecule will have its minimum possible value when all the nuclei are in their equilibrium positions and all the coordinates x_k are zero. We choose this minimum value to be the zero of the potential energy scale. Then any departure of the coordinates from zero will produce a configuration in which the potential energy cannot be negative, i.e. $V \geqslant 0$ in any configuration.

In a general configuration, various bond lengths and angles will be changed from their equilibrium values. We make the assumption that, for small changes in these quantities, the forces that act to bring the molecule back to equilibrium are proportional to the changes; the appropriate constants of proportionality are called *force constants*. This assumption means that the potential energy will be a function of the squares of the changes in bond lengths and angles. These changes may, in first approximation, be expressed as linear combinations of the coordinates $x_1, \ldots, x_{3n}$ describing the configuration, and so our assumption means that the potential energy will be a quadratic function of the coordinates of the general form

$$V = \tfrac{1}{2} \sum_{i,j=1}^{3n} V_{ij} x_i x_j, \tag{8.4}$$

where the coefficients V_{ij} depend on the force constants of the molecule. If we introduce the mass-weighted coordinates defined by (8.2), this becomes a quadratic function of $y_1, \ldots, y_{3n}$:

$$V = \tfrac{1}{2} \sum_{i,j=1}^{3n} V'_{ij} y_i y_j, \tag{8.5}$$

where $V'_{ij} = V_{ij}/\sqrt{(m_i m_j)}$.

We may regard $y_1, \ldots, y_{3n}$ as the coordinates of a point in the mass-weighted configuration space of the molecule relative to a certain orthonormal basis. Suppose that we change from this basis to some other orthonormal basis. A configuration of the nuclei will be specified, in the new basis, by $3n$ coordinates which we call $Q_1, \ldots, Q_{3n}$. The new coordinates are related to the original coordinates by linear equations of the form

$$Q_k = \sum_{l=1}^{3n} a_{kl} y_l; \qquad y_i = \sum_{j=1}^{3n} b_{ij} Q_j. \tag{8.6}$$

The matrices A and B which are formed by the coefficients a_{kl} and b_{ij} are inverse to each other and, since we have restricted ourselves to orthonormal bases, they will be orthogonal matrices whose elements satisfy orthogonality relations like

$$\sum_{k=1}^{3n} a_{ik}a_{jk} = \delta_{ij}. \tag{8.7}$$

(Equations (8.6) and (8.7) extend to the coordinates the considerations which in Sections 4.8 and 5.1 were applied to the base vectors.)

We may use (8.6) to change the variables in the kinetic energy (8.3) from the y_k to the Q_k. A straightforward generalization of the argument that led to (7.9) shows that, in terms of the new coordinates,

$$T = -\frac{h^2}{8\pi^2} \sum_{k=1}^{3n} \frac{\partial^2}{\partial Q_k^2}. \tag{8.8}$$

For the potential energy, we may substitute (8.6) into (8.5) to obtain

$$V = \tfrac{1}{2} \sum_{r,s=1}^{3n} V_{rs}'' Q_r Q_s, \tag{8.9}$$

where $\qquad V_{rs}'' = \sum_{i,j=1}^{3n} V_{ij}' b_{ir} b_{js}.$

Thus, in general, a change of coordinates gives us expressions for T and V of the same form as in the original mass-weighted coordinate system. It is, however, possible to choose the new coordinates in such a way as to simplify the expression for V. The theory here makes use of a theorem (which we shall state without proof) that it is always possible to find coefficients b_{ij} in (8.6) which make $V_{rs}''=0$ if $r \neq s$; i.e. it is always possible to find new coordinates $Q_1, \ldots, Q_{3n}$ which are orthogonal linear combinations of the original coordinates $y_1, \ldots, y_{3n}$ and which are such that the potential energy has the simple form

$$V = \tfrac{1}{2} \sum_{r=1}^{3n} \lambda_r Q_r^2, \tag{8.10}$$

where we have written $V_{rr}'' = \lambda_r$.

Coordinates for which V has the form (8.10) are called *normal coordinates*; we shall henceforth reserve the symbols $Q_1, \ldots, Q_{3n}$ to designate such coordinates. The theorem quoted above guarantees that, for any molecule, it will always be possible to find a set of normal coordinates. The importance of normal coordinates lies in the fact that their introduction enables us to solve the Schrödinger equation for the molecular vibrations, as we shall see below in Section 8.3.

8.2 Translations, Rotations, Vibrations

There will always be a number of displaced configurations of a molecule in which the bond lengths and angles are not changed from their equilibrium values and in which the potential energy has the same value, $V=0$, as it has in the equilibrium configuration. These are configurations in which the molecule has moved from its equilibrium position as a rigid whole. They may be achieved by giving the molecule a *translation* along some given direction, so that each nucleus has a displacement which is parallel and equal to the displacement of every other nucleus, or by *rotating* the molecule as a rigid whole about some axis, or by combining translations with rotations.

If the molecule is non-linear, a rigid displacement of the molecule as a whole may be expressed as a combination of translations along three independent axes and of rotations about these three axes. Any other kind of displacement of the nuclei must result in changes in bond lengths and angles and must give rise to a configuration in which $V>0$. If we express displacements of the nuclei in terms of the normal coordinates, this means that there must be precisely six linearly independent combinations of $Q_1, \ldots, Q_{3n}$, in which not all the Q_k are zero, which make $V=0$ (these correspond to the three translations and the three rotations) and that any other combinations of $Q_1, \ldots, Q_{3n}$ in which not all the Q_k are zero must give configurations in which $V>0$.

Now the expression (8.10) for V in terms of normal coordinates shows (i) that, since $V \geqslant 0$, every one of the λ_k must satisfy $\lambda_k \geqslant 0$, and (ii) that the only way in which V may be made to vanish for a set of values of the Q_k not all of which are zero is for some of the λ_k themselves to vanish. On the basis of these facts and the remarks made in the paragraph above, we conclude that six of the coefficients λ_k in (8.10) must be zero and that the remaining $3n-6$ coefficients must be positive.

Let us number the normal coordinates in such a way that $\lambda_k > 0$ for $k=1$, $2, \ldots, 3n-6$ while $\lambda_k=0$ for $k=3n-5, \ldots, 3n$. Then

$$V = \tfrac{1}{2} \sum_{k=1}^{3n-6} \lambda_k Q_k^2 \qquad (8.11)$$

and the normal coordinates may be divided into two sets $Q_1, \ldots, Q_{3n-6}$ and $Q_1''=Q_{3n-5}, \ldots, Q_6''=Q_{3n}$. Any configuration in which all the normal coordinates in the first set are zero corresponds to a combination of rigid translations and rotations of the molecule, and $V=0$ whatever the values of $Q_1'', \ldots, Q_6''$. Any configuration in which $Q_1''=Q_2''=\cdots=Q_6''=0$ is one in which the molecule as a whole has suffered no resultant translation or rotation. The $3n-6$ coordinates $Q_1, \ldots, Q_{3n-6}$ are normal coordinates which describe *pure vibrations* of the molecule; we shall call them *vibrational coordinates*.

The case of a linear molecule is slightly different for, if the molecule is linear, a rotation about the molecular axis gives a zero displacement to the nuclei. Consequently, any rigid displacement of a linear molecule may be analysed in terms of three translations but only two rotations. Only five of the λ_k will vanish, corresponding to five normal coordinates which represent rigid displacements of the molecule. The remaining $3n-5$ normal coordinates are vibrational coordinates with $\lambda_k > 0$, and the sum in (8.11) runs from $k=1$ to $k=3n-5$.

8.3 Vibrational Energy Levels and Wave Functions

When we are concerned with the pure vibrations of a molecule the only configurations that are of interest to us are those in which there is no resultant translation or rotation of the molecule as a whole so that the normal coordinates which describe translations and rotations are all zero. A vibrational state of the molecule is described by a wave function Ψ which is a function of the vibrational coordinates $Q_1, \ldots, Q_s$, where $s=3n-6$ or $3n-5$ according as the molecule is non-linear or linear. Ψ is a solution of the Schrödinger equation

$$H\Psi = E\Psi,$$

and (8.8) and (8.11) show that the Hamiltonian, expressed in terms of the vibrational coordinates, is

$$H = T+V = \sum_{k=1}^{s} H_k \quad \text{with} \quad H_k = -\frac{h^2}{8\pi^2}\frac{\partial^2}{\partial Q_k{}^2} + \frac{1}{2}\lambda_k Q_k{}^2. \quad (8.12)$$

Since H is a sum of terms each of which involves only one of the normal coordinates, the arguments of Section 7.5 show that Ψ may be written as a product function:

$$\Psi(Q_1, \ldots, Q_s) = \psi(Q_1)\psi(Q_2)\ldots\psi(Q_s), \quad (8.13)$$

where the functions $\psi(Q_k)$ are solutions of the equations

$$H_k\psi(Q_k) = E_k\psi(Q_k), \quad k = 1, 2, \ldots, s. \quad (8.14)$$

The energy of the state described by the wave function (8.13) is the sum of the energy values E_k belonging to the various $\psi(Q_k)$ of (8.14):

$$E = E_1 + E_2 + \cdots + E_s. \quad (8.15)$$

The equations (8.14) all have the same form and differ from each other only in that they involve different normal coordinates and have different numerical values of the coefficients λ_k. As we have seen, all the λ_k must be positive. We may, therefore, express them in terms of new quantities ν_k defined by

$$\lambda_k = (2\pi\nu_k)^2. \quad (8.16)$$

Equations (8.14) may then be simplified by writing

$$\alpha_k = 4\pi^2 \nu_k / h, \qquad \varepsilon_k = 8\pi^2 E_k / h^2 \tag{8.17}$$

when they all take on the form

$$\frac{d^2 \psi}{dQ^2} + (\varepsilon - \alpha^2 Q^2)\psi = 0. \tag{8.18}$$

(We shall, for the moment, discard the distinguishing suffix k.)

Equation (8.18) is a standard form for the Schrödinger equation of a *harmonic oscillator*. This equation is discussed in most texts on quantum mechanics and we shall here merely quote the relevant results. (For a proof, see, for example, [1], Section 11.) The allowable solutions of (8.18) are characterized by a quantum number v which may have any positive integral value, $v = 0, 1, 2, \ldots$. For a given v, the energy E is

$$E(v) = (v + \tfrac{1}{2})h\nu, \tag{8.19}$$

where ν, defined in (8.16), is the *frequency* of the harmonic oscillator. The corresponding function $\psi(Q)$ is

$$\psi_v(Q) = N_v \exp\left(-\tfrac{1}{2}\alpha Q^2\right) H_v(\sqrt{\alpha} Q) \tag{8.20}$$

where N_v is a normalizing factor which does not concern us, α is the quantity defined in (8.17), and H_v is a polynomial. In particular,

$$H_0(\sqrt{\alpha} Q) = 1, \qquad H_1(\sqrt{\alpha} Q) = 2\sqrt{\alpha} Q. \tag{8.21}$$

The solutions of (8.18) with the two lowest energies are given by $v = 0$ and 1. Their energies are $\tfrac{1}{2}h\nu$ and $(1 + \tfrac{1}{2})h\nu$ and, by (8.20) and (8.21), their wave functions, apart from constant factors, are proportional to

$$\exp\left(-\tfrac{1}{2}\alpha Q^2\right) \quad \text{and} \quad Q \exp\left(-\tfrac{1}{2}\alpha Q^2\right) \tag{8.22}$$

respectively.

We use the solutions of (8.18), one solution with quantum number v_k for each normal coordinate Q_k, to form the product functions (8.13) which represent vibrational states of the whole molecule. These states are characterized by the set of s quantum numbers $v_1, \ldots, v_s$ and may be classified in the following manner.

(i) The ground state

The lowest vibrational state occurs when every $v_k = 0$. It has energy

$$E_0 = \sum_{k=1}^{s} \tfrac{1}{2}h\nu_k,$$

the 'zero-point energy' of the molecular vibrations, and its wave function, apart from a normalizing factor, is

$$\Psi_0 = \exp\left(-\tfrac{1}{2}\alpha_1 Q_1{}^2\right)\cdots\exp\left(-\tfrac{1}{2}\alpha_s Q_s{}^2\right) = \exp\left(-\tfrac{1}{2}\sum_{k=1}^{s}\alpha_k Q_k{}^2\right). \quad (8.23)$$

(ii) The fundamental levels

This set of levels occurs when all the v_k are zero except for one which has the value unity. If the non-zero quantum number is v_p, the energy of the corresponding fundamental level is

$$E_p = \sum_{k \neq p}\tfrac{1}{2}h\nu_k + (1+\tfrac{1}{2})h\nu_p = E_0 + h\nu_p,$$

so that it lies above the ground state by an amount $h\nu_p$. The wave function of this level is, by (8.22), proportional to

$$\Psi_p = Q_p \Psi_0, \quad (8.24)$$

where Ψ_0 is the ground state wave function (8.23).

(iii) Overtone and combination levels

These are the more complicated energy levels in which some of the v_k may have values greater than one and in which more than one of the v_k may be non-zero.

The infra-red and Raman spectra of a molecule are dominated by the lines which arise from transitions between the ground state and the fundamental levels and we shall confine our attention to these. In order to make a transition from the ground state to a fundamental level E_p the molecule must absorb energy of amount $h\nu_p$. This is the energy of a photon of frequency ν_p and so one would expect to observe the *fundamental frequencies* $\nu_1, \ldots, \nu_s$ (which are defined by (8.16) in terms of the coefficients λ_k which appear in the expression (8.11) for the potential energy) in the spectrum of the molecule.

The number of fundamentals that will actually be observed in the spectrum of a given molecule is not, however, in general equal to the number s of its vibrational coordinates. In the first place, some of the λ_k, and so the corresponding ν_k, may well be equal to each other which means that the corresponding fundamental levels are *degenerate*; and, in the second place, there are certain *selection rules* which may forbid the occurrence of an energetically possible transition.

It is here that group theory comes into the discussion of molecular vibrations. We shall see that the possible degeneracies of the energy levels and the form of the selection rules are determined by the symmetry of the molecule and that they may be discussed in terms of the IRs of the point group to which the molecule belongs. These matters are discussed in Section 8.5, but before passing on to them we shall pause to consider an example which illustrates the theory that has been developed above.

8.4 An Illustrative Example

Consider a hypothetical molecule which consists of three identical nuclei a, b, c whose equilibrium positions are at the vertices of an equilateral triangle ABC of side l (Fig. 8.1). We restrict ourselves, for simplicity, to a discussion of the

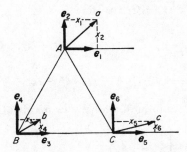

8.1 Coordinates for an X_3 molecule.

motions of these nuclei in the plane of the triangle. We set up a coordinate system with base vectors $e_1, \ldots, e_6$ as shown in Fig. 8.1; a displaced configuration of the nuclei is specified by the coordinates (x_1, x_2) of a, the coordinates (x_3, x_4) of b and the coordinates (x_5, x_6) of c.

When the nuclei are all displaced from their equilibrium positions, the ab, bc and ca bond lengths change from l to $l+\delta r_{ab}$, $l+\delta r_{bc}$ and $l+\delta r_{ca}$ respectively, and we assume that the potential energy has the form

$$V = \tfrac{1}{2}F\{(\delta r_{ab})^2 + (\delta r_{bc})^2 + (\delta r_{ca})^2\}, \qquad (8.25)$$

where F is the force constant governing stretching of the ab, bc and ca bonds.

For small displacements, the first approximation to δr_{ab} is

$$\delta r_{ab} = x_a - x_b$$

where x_a and x_b are the components of the displacements of a and b along the side AB of the equilibrium triangle:

$$x_a = (x_1 + \sqrt{3}x_2)/2; \qquad x_b = (x_3 + \sqrt{3}x_4)/2.$$

Similar expressions hold for δr_{bc} and δr_{ca}. If we introduce the mass-weighted coordinates $y_i = x_i\sqrt{m}$ where m is the mass of a nucleus, we find

$$\delta r_{ab} = (y_1 + \sqrt{3}y_2 - y_3 - \sqrt{3}y_4)/2\sqrt{m},$$

$$\delta r_{bc} = (y_5 - y_3)/\sqrt{m}, \qquad (8.26)$$

$$\delta r_{ca} = (y_5 - \sqrt{3}y_6 - y_1 + \sqrt{3}y_2)/2\sqrt{m}.$$

Substitution of these expressions into (8.25) will give us the potential energy expressed in the form (8.5) as a function of $y_1, \ldots, y_6$.

Now introduce new variables $Q_1, \ldots, Q_6$ by means of the relations

$$y_1 = \frac{1}{\sqrt{3}} (Q_2 + Q_4 + Q_6),$$

$$y_2 = \frac{1}{\sqrt{3}} (Q_1 + Q_3 + Q_5),$$

$$y_3 = \frac{1}{2\sqrt{3}} (-\sqrt{3}Q_1 - Q_2 + \sqrt{3}Q_3 + 2Q_4 - Q_6),$$

$$y_4 = \frac{1}{2\sqrt{3}} (-Q_1 - \sqrt{3}Q_2 - Q_3 + 2Q_5 + \sqrt{3}Q_6),$$

$$y_5 = \frac{1}{2\sqrt{3}} (\sqrt{3}Q_1 - Q_2 - \sqrt{3}Q_3 + 2Q_4 - Q_6),$$

$$y_6 = \frac{1}{2\sqrt{3}} (-Q_1 + \sqrt{3}Q_2 - Q_3 + 2Q_5 - \sqrt{3}Q_6).$$

(8.27)

These are equations of the form (8.6) where the matrix of the coefficients b_{ij} is

$$\mathbf{B} = \frac{1}{2\sqrt{3}} \begin{bmatrix} 0 & 2 & 0 & 2 & 0 & 2 \\ 2 & 0 & 2 & 0 & 2 & 0 \\ -\sqrt{3} & -1 & \sqrt{3} & 2 & 0 & -1 \\ -1 & -\sqrt{3} & -1 & 0 & 2 & \sqrt{3} \\ \sqrt{3} & -1 & -\sqrt{3} & 2 & 0 & -1 \\ -1 & \sqrt{3} & -1 & 0 & 2 & -\sqrt{3} \end{bmatrix}$$

(8.28)

It is readily verified that this is an orthogonal matrix, so that (8.27) is an orthogonal transformation of the kind required for the introduction of normal coordinates.

If we substitute (8.27) into (8.26) we find

$$\delta r_{ab} = (2Q_1 + \sqrt{3}Q_2 + Q_3)/2\sqrt{m},$$

$$\delta r_{bc} = (Q_1 - Q_3)/\sqrt{m},$$

$$\delta r_{ca} = (2Q_1 - \sqrt{3}Q_2 + Q_3)/2\sqrt{m},$$

and substitution of these expressions into (8.25) gives V as a function of $Q_1, \ldots, Q_6$:

$$V = \tfrac{1}{2}(3F/2m)(2Q_1{}^2 + Q_2{}^2 + Q_3{}^2).$$

(8.29)

Thus V, expressed as a function of the Q_k, has the form (8.10) with

$$\lambda_1 = 3F/m, \quad \lambda_2 = \lambda_3 = 3F/2m, \quad \lambda_4 = \lambda_5 = \lambda_6 = 0,$$

(8.30)

and the variables defined by (8.27) are indeed normal coordinates.

The fact that three of the λ_k are zero follows from the fact that any rigid displacement of the triangle ABC which occurs in the plane of ABC may be regarded as a combination of translations along two independent directions in the plane and a rotation about an axis perpendicular to the plane. There must, accordingly, be three normal coordinates to describe these rigid displacements and three of the λ_k must vanish. The equations (8.30) show that these normal coordinates are Q_4, Q_5 and Q_6, and that Q_1, Q_2 and Q_3 are the vibrational coordinates.

It is instructive to consider the relations (8.27) between the normal coordinates and the displacements of the individual nuclei a little more closely. When we are thinking in terms of normal coordinates we regard a general configuration of the nuclei, which is specified by definite numerical values $Q_k = d_k$ of the normal coordinates, as made up from a superposition of the six particular configurations in which $Q_1 = d_1$, $Q_i = 0$ for $i \neq 1$; ...; $Q_6 = d_6$, $Q_i = 0$ for $i \neq 6$. The mass-weighted coordinates of the three nuclei in these particular configurations may be calculated from (8.27) and they are shown in Table 8.1: row k of the table gives the values of $y_1, \ldots, y_6$ in the configuration in which $Q_k = 2\sqrt{3}d$, where d is a constant, while all the other $Q_i = 0$. The corresponding displacements of the nuclei are shown in Fig. 8.2.

TABLE 8.1. *Relations between the Q_k and y_i*

	y_1	y_2	y_3	y_4	y_5	y_6
$Q_1 \neq 0$	0	$2d$	$-\sqrt{3}d$	$-d$	$\sqrt{3}d$	$-d$
$Q_2 \neq 0$	$2d$	0	$-d$	$-\sqrt{3}d$	$-d$	$\sqrt{3}d$
$Q_3 \neq 0$	0	$2d$	$\sqrt{3}d$	$-d$	$-\sqrt{3}d$	$-d$
$Q_4 \neq 0$	$2d$	0	$2d$	0	$2d$	0
$Q_5 \neq 0$	0	$2d$	0	$2d$	0	$2d$
$Q_6 \neq 0$	$2d$	0	$-d$	$\sqrt{3}d$	$-d$	$-\sqrt{3}d$

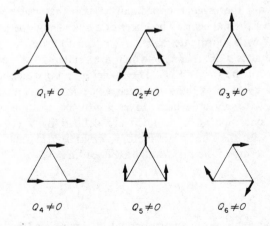

$Q_1 \neq 0$ $Q_2 \neq 0$ $Q_3 \neq 0$

$Q_4 \neq 0$ $Q_5 \neq 0$ $Q_6 \neq 0$

8.2 Displacements of the nuclei in which all the Q_k save one are zero.

From the figure we see that Q_4 and Q_5 describe translations of the molecule along two perpendicular directions in its plane and Q_6 describes a rotation of the molecule about an axis through its centre perpendicular to its plane. The normal coordinates Q_1, Q_2, Q_3, on the other hand, describe deformations of the molecule in which the bond lengths are changed but the molecule as a whole has no resultant translation or rotation.

If we remove the restriction to motion in the plane of the molecule we shall have to introduce nine coordinates to describe a general configuration. Six of these will be required to deal with translations and rotations and the molecule will still have just three vibrational coordinates. A little thought shows that in this more general case the potential energy is still given correctly by (8.29) where Q_1, Q_2 and Q_3 are the vibrational coordinates pictured in Fig. 8.2. This must be so since any general configuration of the three nuclei may be achieved by first of all deforming the triangle into its final shape in its own plane and then bringing the deformed triangle into its final position by suitable translations and rotations.

If we now apply the considerations of Section 8.3, we see that although the molecule has three vibrational coordinates it has only two different fundamentals. These are related to the λ_k of (8.30) by (8.16) and are:

$$\nu = (3F/m)^{\frac{1}{2}}/2\pi \quad \text{associated with } Q_1;$$

$$\nu' = (3F/2m)^{\frac{1}{2}}/2\pi \quad \text{associated with } Q_2 \text{ and } Q_3.$$

We say that the normal coordinate Q_1 is *non-degenerate* while Q_2 and Q_3 form a *doubly-degenerate pair* of normal coordinates.

8.5 The Configuration Space Representation

The point of departure for the introduction of group theory into the discussion of the vibrations of a molecule is the representation of the molecular point group that is provided by the configuration space of the molecule.

We begin with the original coordinate system that we used to describe configurations of the molecule. The effect of a symmetry operation R on the configuration X with coordinates $x_1^{(1)}, \ldots, x_3^{(n)}$ is to produce a configuration X' with coordinates $x_1'^{(1)}, \ldots, x_3'^{(n)}$ which are related to the coordinates of X by equations of the form (7.11). The nuclei p and q which are related by these equations must have the same mass since R is a symmetry operation of the molecular framework which moves p into the position of q. Thus the mass-weighted coordinates of p and q are defined by $y_i^{(p)} = x_i^{(p)}\sqrt{m}$ and $y_i^{(q)} = x_i^{(q)}\sqrt{m}$ with the same scale factor $\sqrt{m}$, and (7.11) may be expressed equally well in terms of the mass-weighted coordinates:

$$y_i'^{(q)} = \sum_{j=1}^{3} r_{ij} y_j^{(p)}, \tag{8.31}$$

where the coefficients r_{ij} form an orthogonal 3×3 matrix of the kind discussed in Section 4.2.

If we renumber the coordinates from 1 to $3n$, these equations may be combined into a single set of equations of the form

$$y'_i = \sum_{j=1}^{3n} [D_0(R)]_{ij} y_j, \tag{8.32}$$

where the coefficients $[D_0(R)]_{ij}$ define an orthogonal matrix of $3n$ rows and columns. There is one such matrix for each symmetry operation of the point group of the molecule, and the set of matrices $D_0(R)$ forms a certain representation, Γ_0, say, of the point group.

The matrices of Γ_0 are defined by (8.32) with respect to an orthonormal basis for the mass-weighted configuration space of the molecule. Any other basis will give rise to an equivalent set of matrices belonging to the same representation. In particular, the change from mass-weighted coordinates to normal coordinates corresponds to a change from one orthonormal basis to another. The matrix which represents R with respect to the normal coordinate basis is defined by

$$Q'_k = \sum_{r=1}^{3n} [D_n(R)]_{kr} Q_r, \tag{8.33}$$

where the normal coordinates $(Q'_1, \ldots, Q'_{3n})$ describe the configuration which is obtained by applying R to the configuration $(Q_1, \ldots, Q_{3n})$. $D_n(R)$ will be an orthogonal matrix and it may be obtained from $D_0(R)$ by a transformation of the form (5.5) where A is the matrix, defined in (8.6), which describes the change of basis from the mass-weighted to the normal coordinates.

EXAMPLE

Take the three nuclei of Fig. 8.1 and consider a rotation C_3 about the axis of symmetry. Figure 8.3(a) shows three general displacements of the nuclei and Fig.

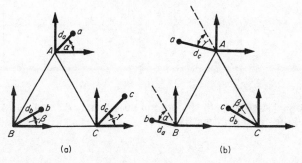

(a)   (b)

8.3 Displaced configurations of an X_3 molecule. (a) a general configuration; (b) the effect of C_3 on (a).

8.3(b) shows the effect of C_3 on these displacements. In the original configuration the nuclei have coordinates

$$x_1 = d_a \cos \alpha, \ x_2 = d_a \sin \alpha; \quad x_3 = d_b \cos \beta, \ x_4 = d_b \sin \beta;$$

$$x_5 = d_c \cos \gamma, \ x_6 = d_c \sin \gamma.$$

In the rotated configuration the coordinates are:

$$x_1' = -d_c \sin (\gamma + 30^\circ) = -(1/2)x_5 - (\sqrt{3}/2)x_6,$$

$$x_2' = d_c \cos (\gamma + 30^\circ) \ = (\sqrt{3}/2)x_5 - (1/2)x_6;$$

$$x_3' = -d_a \sin (\alpha + 30^\circ) = -(1/2)x_1 - (\sqrt{3}/2)x_2,$$

$$x_4' = d_a \cos (\alpha + 30^\circ) \ = (\sqrt{3}/2)x_1 - (1/2)x_2;$$

$$x_5' = -d_b \sin (\beta + 30^\circ) = -(1/2)x_3 - (\sqrt{3}/2)x_4,$$

$$x_6' = d_b \cos (\beta + 30^\circ) \ = (\sqrt{3}/2)x_3 - (1/2)x_4.$$

Since all the nuclei have the same mass, the mass-weighted coordinates are given by $y_i = x_i \sqrt{m}$ with a common scale factor $\sqrt{m}$; the above equations may be written in terms of the mass-weighted coordinates as

$$y_i' = \sum_{j=1}^{6} [D_0(C_3)]_{ij} y_j,$$

where $D_0(C_3)$ is the matrix

$$D_0(C_3) = \begin{bmatrix} 0 & 0 & 0 & 0 & -\dfrac{1}{2} & -\dfrac{\sqrt{3}}{2} \\[2mm] 0 & 0 & 0 & 0 & \dfrac{\sqrt{3}}{2} & -\dfrac{1}{2} \\[2mm] -\dfrac{1}{2} & -\dfrac{\sqrt{3}}{2} & 0 & 0 & 0 & 0 \\[2mm] \dfrac{\sqrt{3}}{2} & -\dfrac{1}{2} & 0 & 0 & 0 & 0 \\[2mm] 0 & 0 & -\dfrac{1}{2} & -\dfrac{\sqrt{3}}{2} & 0 & 0 \\[2mm] 0 & 0 & \dfrac{\sqrt{3}}{2} & -\dfrac{1}{2} & 0 & 0 \end{bmatrix} \tag{8.34}$$

If we now change over to the normal coordinates defined by (8.27), $D_0(C_3)$ changes into the equivalent matrix

$$D_n(C_3) = A D_0(C_3) A^{-1},$$

where $A^{-1} = B$ is given by (8.28). Noting that $A = B^{-1} = \tilde{B}$ since A and B are orthogonal matrices, we find on multiplying the matrices together that

$$
\mathbf{D}_n(C_3) = \begin{bmatrix}
1 & 0 & 0 & 0 & 0 & 0 \\
0 & -\dfrac{1}{2} & \dfrac{\sqrt{3}}{2} & 0 & 0 & 0 \\
0 & -\dfrac{\sqrt{3}}{2} & -\dfrac{1}{2} & 0 & 0 & 0 \\
0 & 0 & 0 & -\dfrac{1}{2} & -\dfrac{\sqrt{3}}{2} & 0 \\
0 & 0 & 0 & \dfrac{\sqrt{3}}{2} & -\dfrac{1}{2} & 0 \\
0 & 0 & 0 & 0 & 0 & 1
\end{bmatrix}
\tag{8.35}
$$

A striking feature of $\mathbf{D}_n(C_3)$ is that it has the diagonal block form of a re-duced matrix. The matrix shows that the effect of C_3 on a configuration $(Q_1, \ldots, Q_6)$ is to produce a configuration $(Q'_1, \ldots, Q'_6)$ in which $Q'_1 = Q_1$, Q'_2 and Q'_3 are linear combinations of Q_2 and Q_3, Q'_4 and Q'_5 are linear combinations of Q_4 and Q_5, and $Q'_6 = Q_6$. This result might have been obtained directly from the pictorial representations of the normal coordinates given in Fig. 8.2. For from this figure we see that C_3 has no effect on the vibrational coordinate Q_1 or on the rotational coordinate Q_6; that C_3 applied to Q_4 or Q_5 produces a translation which may be resolved into component Q_4 and Q_5 translations; and, less obviously, that C_3 applied to the vibrational coordinates Q_2 and Q_3 produces displacements which may be expressed as linear combinations of the displacements corre-sponding to Q_2 and Q_3.

This example suggests that the change to normal coordinates is a change of basis which reduces the configuration space representation. We shall see in the next section that this is indeed the case.

8.6 The Reduction of Γ_0

The configuration space representation Γ_0 is reducible since its dimension, $3n$, is certainly greater than the dimension of any IR of any molecular point group. The important result that we shall now establish is that the change of basis from the original coordinates to normal coordinates serves to reduce Γ_0.

In order to see how the reduction occurs we shall first introduce a new notation for the normal coordinates. Some of the coefficients λ_r which occur in the expression (8.10) for the potential energy may be equal to each other. (We know, for example, that the value $\lambda = 0$ will occur six times for a non-linear molecule.) Suppose that there are altogether N distinct numerical values $\lambda^{(1)}, \ldots, \lambda^{(N)}$ of these coefficients. Then we group together the normal coordinates associated with $\lambda^{(v)}$ and denote them by $Q_{v1}, \ldots, Q_{vn_v}$, where n_v is the number of times that $\lambda^{(v)}$ occurs in (8.10). In this way we divide the set of $3n$ normal coordinates into N sub-sets, one sub-set for each value of ν from 1 to N. With this change of notation (8.10) becomes

$$V = \tfrac{1}{2} \sum_{\rho=1}^{N} \lambda^{(\rho)} \{Q_{\rho 1}{}^2 + \cdots + Q_{\rho n_\rho}{}^2\} = \tfrac{1}{2} \sum_{\rho=1}^{N} \sum_{l=1}^{n_\rho} \lambda^{(\rho)} Q_{\rho l}{}^2 \qquad (8.36)$$

and the equations (8.33) which express the effect of a symmetry operation on the normal coordinates become

$$Q_{\mu i} = \sum_{\sigma=1}^{N} \sum_{j=1}^{n_\sigma} [D_n(R)]_{\mu i,\, \sigma j} Q_{\sigma j}. \qquad (8.37)$$

(Note that it is now necessary to label the rows and columns of $D_n(R)$ by two symbols each.)

The division of the normal coordinates into N sub-sets, one sub-set for each value of $\lambda^{(\nu)}$, divides the total configuration space into N sub-spaces; the sub-space associated with $\lambda^{(\nu)}$ consists of all configurations in which $Q_{\sigma k} = 0$ for $\sigma \neq \nu$ and in which some or all of the $Q_{\nu j}$ have non-zero values. The result that we wish to establish is that these sub-spaces are *invariant* under the symmetry operations of the molecular point group, i.e. the effect of applying a symmetry operation to a configuration which belongs to the $\lambda^{(\nu)}$ sub-space, so that $Q_{\nu j} \neq 0$, $Q_{\sigma k} = 0$ for $\sigma \neq \nu$, is to produce a configuration in which $Q'_{\nu j} \neq 0$, $Q'_{\sigma k} = 0$ for $\sigma \neq \nu$ and which, therefore, also belongs to the $\lambda^{(\nu)}$ sub-space. If the reader refers back to Section 5.6 he will see that, if we succeed in proving this result, we may conclude that the invariant sub-space associated with $\lambda^{(\nu)}$ generates by itself a representation, Γ_ν say, of the molecular point group and that the introduction of normal coordinates, grouped together in the way we have described, reduces the configuration space representation Γ_0 into N component representations $\Gamma_1, \ldots, \Gamma_N$.

If we apply a symmetry operation to a configuration which belongs to the $\lambda^{(\nu)}$ sub-space, so that $Q_{\sigma k} = 0$ for $\sigma \neq \nu$, (8.37) shows that

$$Q'_{\mu i} = \sum_{j=1}^{n_\nu} [D_n(R)]_{\mu i,\, \nu j} Q_{\nu j}, \qquad (8.38)$$

and the result we wish to prove is that, in (8.38), $Q'_{\mu i} = 0$ if $\mu \neq \nu$, whatever the values of the $Q_{\nu j}$ may be. It follows from (8.38) that what we want to prove is that the elements of $D_n(R)$ are such that

$$[D_n(R)]_{\mu i,\, \nu j} = 0 \quad \text{if} \quad \mu \neq \nu, \qquad (8.39)$$

for any symmetry operation R which belongs to the point group of the molecule.

The proof of (8.39) makes use of the facts that the potential energy is invariant under the symmetry operations of the molecular point group and that the matrices $D_n(R)$ are orthogonal. Details of the proof are given in

Appendix D; we shall here continue the argument on the assumption that (8.39) is true.

Equation (8.39) shows that $D_n(R)$ has the diagonal block form of a reduced matrix with N sub-matrices down its diagonal, one sub-matrix for each $\lambda^{(\nu)}$ in (8.36):

$$D_n(R) = \begin{bmatrix} D^{(1)}(R) & & & \\ & D^{(2)}(R) & & \\ & & \ddots & \\ & & & D^{(N)}(R) \end{bmatrix} \qquad (8.40)$$

The sub-matrix $D^{(\rho)}(R)$, whose elements are

$$[D^{(\rho)}(R)]_{ij} = [D_n(R)]_{\rho i, \rho j}, \quad i, j = 1, \ldots, n_\rho,$$

is the $n_\rho \times n_\rho$ matrix which represents R in the representation Γ_ρ associated with $\lambda^{(\rho)}$.

EXAMPLE

In the example of Section 8.4, the values of the coefficients λ_r are given in (8.30). There are three different values,

$$\lambda^{(1)} = \lambda_1 = 3F/m; \quad \lambda^{(2)} = \lambda_2 = \lambda_3 = 3F/2m; \quad \lambda^{(3)} = \lambda_4 = \lambda_5 = \lambda_6 = 0.$$

The six-dimensional configuration space is consequently divided into three invariant sub-spaces of dimensions 1, 2 and 3 respectively with coordinates $Q_{\nu j}$ defined by

$$Q_{11} = Q_1; \quad Q_{21} = Q_2, \ Q_{22} = Q_3; \quad Q_{31} = Q_4, \ Q_{32} = Q_5, \ Q_{33} = Q_6.$$

These three sub-spaces give rise to representations Γ_1, Γ_2 and Γ_3 respectively and the configuration space representation is reduced to the form

$$\Gamma_0 = \Gamma_1 + \Gamma_2 + \Gamma_3$$

by the introduction of the normal coordinates.

The reduction is illustrated by the matrix $D_n(C_3)$ given by (8.35) which has the correct diagonal block form. The reader may verify that the matrices representing the other symmetry operations of the point group $\mathscr{D}_{3h}$ of the equilateral triangle have the same block form. Notice that, in this example, the representation Γ_3 which is associated with $\lambda^{(3)} = 0$ and the translation and rotation coordinates Q_4, Q_5, Q_6 is itself a reducible representation.

8.7 Classification of the Normal Coordinates

The fact that the introduction of normal coordinates reduces the configuration space representation enables us to infer a great deal about the normal coordinates of any given molecule by using the methods for reducing representations that were described in Chapter 6. In particular, these methods allow us, by simple calculations based on characters, to decide how many different fundamentals a molecule of given symmetry will possess, to determine the symmetry species of the sets of normal coordinates associated with the fundamentals, and to find out which of these are infra-red active and which are Raman active.

We begin the discussion of these matters by noting that six of the normal coordinates of a non-linear molecule, or five of the normal coordinates of a linear molecule, describe rigid translations and rotations of the molecule as a whole and that these coordinates are associated with a vanishing coefficient, say $\lambda^{(N)}$, in (8.36). The other coefficients $\lambda^{(1)}, \ldots, \lambda^{(N-1)}$ are positive and are associated with the normal coordinates that describe pure vibrations of the molecule.

It follows that, in the reduction of Γ_0 by the introduction of normal coordinates, the translation-rotation coordinates are grouped together and give rise to a certain representation, say $\Gamma_{t,r}$, of the point group of the molecule. $\Gamma_{t,r}$ must be reducible since its dimension is greater than that of any IR of any molecular point group. Thus as a first step in the reduction of Γ_0 we have

$$\Gamma_0 = \Gamma_{vib} + \Gamma_{t,r}, \tag{8.41}$$

where Γ_{vib} is the representation which arises from the vibrational coordinates. This representation is reducible in its turn, and we may write

$$\Gamma_{vib} = \Gamma_1 + \cdots + \Gamma_{N-1} \tag{8.42}$$

where $\Gamma_1, \ldots, \Gamma_{N-1}$ are the representations which are generated by the sets of vibrational coordinates associated with the non-zero coefficients $\lambda^{(1)}, \ldots, \lambda^{(N-1)}$ in (8.36).

There are two general points one may make about the reduction of Γ_{vib}. The first is that there is no reason for the representations in (8.42) to be all different; it may very well happen that different sets of normal coordinates, associated with different values of $\lambda^{(\rho)}$ in (8.36), give rise to the same representation. The second point is that the theory tells us nothing about the reducibility or otherwise of $\Gamma_1, \ldots, \Gamma_{N-1}$. On the analogy with $\Gamma_{t,r}$, it might well seem that we should proceed on the basis that they should be regarded as possibly reducible representations, but we shall instead adopt the contrary hypothesis: *we assume that $\Gamma_1, \ldots, \Gamma_{N-1}$ are irreducible representations.* As we shall see in Section 8.11 this assumption means that we disregard the possible occurrence of accidental degeneracies.

Now as we shall see below, it is quite easy to determine the characters of Γ_0 and of $\Gamma_{t,r}$. By subtracting these we obtain the characters of Γ_{vib} and we may apply the results of Chapter 6, in particular equation (6.5), to determine the IRs which Γ_{vib} contains. The assumption made above means that these IRs must be the IRs associated with the different non-zero values of the $\lambda^{(\rho)}$ in (8.36). Thus by purely group-theoretical methods it is possible to determine the number of different non-zero coefficients $\lambda^{(\rho)}$ that will appear in (8.36) and to classify the set of normal coordinates associated with each $\lambda^{(\rho)}$ according to the IR of the molecular point group which it generates. This can be done from a knowledge of the character table of the point group of the molecule and of the characters of Γ_0 and of $\Gamma_{t,r}$; there is no need to find the actual transformation (8.6) from the original coordinate system to normal coordinates, nor is it necessary to write down an explicit expression for V and to transform it into the form (8.36).

Since the fundamental frequencies of a molecule are, by (8.16), directly related to the λ coefficients in its potential energy, it is clear that the reduction of Γ_{vib} immediately tells us the number of distinct fundamentals in the molecule and their degeneracies, i.e. the number n_ρ of normal coordinates with the same fundamental frequency $\nu^{(\rho)} = \sqrt{\lambda^{(\rho)}}/2\pi$. The IR Γ_ρ which is generated by the normal coordinates $Q_{\rho i}$, $i = 1, \ldots, n_\rho$, with the same fundamental frequency $\nu^{(\rho)}$ is called their *symmetry species* (i.e. we say that $Q_{\rho i}$ belongs to the symmetry species Γ_ρ) and we shall see in Sections 8.12 and 8.13 how the symmetry species of the normal coordinates determine the selection rules for the infra-red and Raman spectra. But before we pass on to a discussion of the vibrational spectrum of the molecule we must show how it is possible to effect the reduction (8.42) of Γ_{vib}.

8.8 Determination of the Characters

(a) The character of Γ_0

The character of a symmetry operation R in Γ_0 is

$$\chi_0(R) = \sum_{i=1}^{3n} [D_0(R)]_{ii}$$

where $D_0(R)$ is defined by (8.32). In calculating $\chi_0(R)$ we need to know the coefficient $[D_0(R)]_{ii}$ of y_i on the right-hand side of (8.32); the other coefficients $[D_0(R)]_{ij}$ with $i \neq j$ are of no interest in this connexion. Now $D_0(R)$ is made up from the 3×3 matrices with elements r_{ij} defined by equations (8.31) and we may use these equations to find the contribution to $\chi_0(R)$ from the coordinates of each nucleus. These contributions are of two kinds depending on whether or not R moves a nucleus away from its original position in the molecule.

If q is a nucleus which is shifted by R, $q \neq p$ in (8.31). The coordinates of q on the left-hand side of (8.32) are y'_{3q-2}, y'_{3q-1}, y'_{3q} and, from (8.31) with $q \neq p$, we see that the right-hand sides of the equations for these coordinates depend on the coordinates y_{3p-2}, y_{3p-1}, y_{3p} of p and not at all on the coordinates of q. Thus the diagonal elements $[D_0(R)]_{ii}$ with $i = 3q-2, 3q-1, 3q$ are all zero and the coordinates of any nucleus which is shifted by R give a zero contribution to $\chi_0(R)$.

If q is a nucleus which is not shifted by R, $q=p$ in (8.31). It is then clear from these equations that the diagonal elements of $D_0(R)$ with $i=3p-2$, $3p-1$, $3p$ are r_{11}, r_{22} and r_{33} respectively, so that an unshifted nucleus gives a contribution to $\chi_0(R)$ of amount

$$\chi_R = r_{11}+r_{22}+r_{33}. \tag{8.43}$$

Now χ_R is the character of R in a representation whose basis consists of three mutually perpendicular unit vectors in physical space with origin at a point which is left unmoved by R. This representation was discussed in Section 4.2 and typical matrices for the different types of symmetry operation are given by equations (4.8, 10, 13, 14, 15 and 16). Although these matrices were obtained for rather special choices of the directions of the base vectors relative to the particular symmetry operation being considered, their characters are, of course, independent of the choice of base vectors. From the matrices given in the equations listed above, we find the following values for χ_R:

$R =$	E	$C(\alpha)$	σ	$S(\alpha)$	i
$\chi_R =$	3	$1+2\cos\alpha$	1	$-1+2\cos\alpha$	-3

One may note that the identical operation E is equivalent to a rotation through angle 2π and that the character $\chi_E=3$ of E is a special case of the result for the character of $C(\alpha)$ with $\alpha=2\pi$. Similarly, $\sigma=S(2\pi)$, with character $\chi_\sigma=-1+2\cos 2\pi=1$, and $i=S(\pi)$, with character $\chi_i=-1+2\cos\pi=-3$, are special cases of the general result for $S(\alpha)$. It is, therefore, only necessary to consider two kinds of symmetry operation, *proper rotations* $C(\alpha)$ and *improper rotations* $S(\alpha)$.

If the contributions to $\chi_0(R)$ from all the nuclei are added together, the results above show that each nucleus which is left unmoved when R is applied to the molecular framework gives the same contribution χ_R to $\chi_0(R)$ and that each nucleus which is shifted by R gives a zero contribution. Consequently, if n_R is the number of nuclei that are left in their original positions when R is applied to the molecular framework,

$$\chi_0(R) = n_R\chi_R, \tag{8.44}$$

where

$$\chi_R = 1+2\cos\alpha \text{ for } R = C(\alpha); \quad \chi_R = -1+2\cos\alpha \text{ for } R = S(\alpha). \tag{8.45}$$

(b) The character of $\Gamma_{t,r}$

We discuss here the case of a non-linear molecule with three translational and three rotational normal coordinates; linear molecules will be dealt with separately below. The six translational and rotational coordinates define an invariant sub-space of the total configuration space, but it is clear that this sub-space in its turn consists of two three-dimensional invariant sub-spaces, one for the translational coordinates and one for the rotational coordinates. This is so because a symmetry operation, applied to a configuration in which all the nuclei have suffered the same given translation from their equilibrium positions, will produce a configuration which corresponds to another pure translation; similarly, the effect of a symmetry operation on a pure rotated configuration will be to produce another rotated configuration. Thus $\Gamma_{t,r}$ is a reducible representation and we may write

$$\Gamma_{t,r} = \Gamma_t + \Gamma_r,$$

where Γ_t is the representation associated with the translational coordinates and Γ_r is the representation associated with the rotational coordinates.

In any configuration which is a pure translation, the displacements of the nuclei are all equal to a certain displacement vector $\mathbf{p}$, and the effect of R on the configuration is completely described by its effects on $\mathbf{p}$. Thus the three translational coordinates must generate exactly the same representation as that generated by position vectors in physical space. This is the representation described in Section 4.2; it follows that the character of R in Γ_t is

$$\chi_t(R) = \chi_R, \tag{8.46}$$

where χ_R is defined by (8.45).

The 'space' of Γ_r consists of all possible rotations about all possible axes of rotation. We introduce a coordinate system into this space by associating a rotation through an angle ϕ *in the right-handed screw sense* about the direction of a unit vector $\mathbf{e}$ with the vector $\phi\mathbf{e}$. If we resolve this rotation vector into its components along three mutually perpendicular axes specified by unit vectors $\mathbf{e}_1$, $\mathbf{e}_2$, $\mathbf{e}_3$ we may use these as a basis to calculate the matrices of Γ_r.

Consider first a proper rotation $R = C(\alpha)$. The effect of $C(\alpha)$ on a rotation vector $\phi\mathbf{e}$ is to change the direction of $\mathbf{e}$ in exactly the same way as it changes the direction of an ordinary position vector; further, $C(\alpha)$ does not affect the right-handed screw relation between the sense of the rotation ϕ and the direction of $\mathbf{e}$. The matrix which represents $C(\alpha)$ in Γ_r is, therefore, the same as the matrix which represents $C(\alpha)$ in the physical space of the position vectors or the space of Γ_t. Consequently, the character of $C(\alpha)$ in Γ_r is the same as its character in Γ_t:

$$\chi_r[C(\alpha)] = \chi_t[C(\alpha)]. \tag{8.47a}$$

Now consider an improper rotation $S(\alpha) = \sigma_h C(\alpha)$, where σ_h is a reflection in a plane perpendicular to the rotation axis. The effect of $S(\alpha)$ on a rotation vector $\phi\mathbf{e}$ may be described as follows: $C(\alpha)$ rotates $\mathbf{e}$ to a new direction $\mathbf{e}'$; then σ_h reflects $\mathbf{e}'$ into the position $\mathbf{e}''$ and *at the same time* σ_h changes the right-handed screw rotation about $\mathbf{e}'$ into a left-handed screw rotation about $\mathbf{e}''$, as illustrated in Fig. 8.4. But a left-handed screw rotation about the direction of $\mathbf{e}''$ is exactly the same as a right-handed screw rotation about the direction of $-\mathbf{e}''$. It follows that, if $S(\alpha)$ changes the position vector $\mathbf{e}$ into e″, it changes the rotation vector ϕe into $-\phi e''$, and that the matrix which represents $S(\alpha)$ in the rotation space is the negative of the matrix which represents $S(\alpha)$ in the space of the position vectors or the space of Γ_t. The characters of $S(\alpha)$ in Γ_r and Γ_t are, therefore, equal in magnitude but opposite in sign:

$$\chi_r[S(\alpha)] = -\chi_t[S(\alpha)]. \tag{8.47b}$$

Combining (8.46) with (8.47a,b) gives the character $\chi_{t,r}(R)$ of R in $\Gamma_{t,r}$:

$$\chi_{t,r}(R) = 2\chi_R \text{ for } R = C(\alpha); \quad \chi_{t,r}(R) = 0 \text{ for } R = S(\alpha), \tag{8.48}$$

where the χ_R are defined in (8.45).

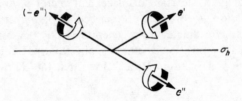

8.4 The effect of a reflection on a rotation vector.

For all the point groups, except $\mathcal{T}_d$ and $\mathcal{O}_h$, Γ_t and Γ_r are themselves reducible representations. They may be reduced by computing the appropriate characters from (8.46) and (8.47a,b) and then using (6.5) and the character table of the molecular point group concerned. We denote the normal coordinates which describe translations along three mutually perpendicular x, y, z axes by T_x, T_y, T_z and the normal coordinates which describe rotations about these axes by R_x, R_y, R_z. The IRs to which these coordinates belong are shown in the character tables of Appendix H, which also explains the relation of the x, y, z axes to the axes and planes of symmetry of the molecular point groups.

(c) The character of Γ_{vib}

We are now in a position to write down the characters of Γ_{vib}. From (8.41), the character $\chi_{vib}(R)$ of R in Γ_{vib} is $\chi_{vib}(R) = \chi_0(R) - \chi_{t,r}(R)$. Using (8.44) and (8.48), this gives

$$\chi_{vib}(R) = (n_R - 2)\chi_R \text{ for } R = C(\alpha); \quad \chi_{vib}(R) = n_R\chi_R \text{ for } R = S(\alpha). \tag{8.49}$$

For the molecular point groups, we are interested in rotations C_n^k and improper rotations S_n^k through angles $\alpha = 2\pi k/n$. The corresponding values of χ_R, calculated from (8.45), are listed in Table 8.2. We may use this table in conjunction with (8.49) to compute the characters $\chi_{vib}(R)$ of the symmetry operations belonging to the point group of any given non-linear molecule.

Then equation (6.5) enables us to find the IRs into which Γ_{vib} may be decomposed.

TABLE 8.2. *Values of* χ_R

$R = C_n^{\ k}$	χ_R	$R = S_n^{\ k}$	χ_R
$E \equiv C_1$	3	$\sigma \equiv S_1$	1
C_2	-1	$i \equiv S_2$	-3
$C_3, C_3^{\ 2}$	0	$S_3, S_3^{\ 5}$	-2
$C_4, C_4^{\ 3}$	1	$S_4, S_4^{\ 3}$	-1
$C_5, C_5^{\ 4}$	$1 + 2 \cos 72°$	$S_5, S_5^{\ 9}$	$-1 + 2 \cos 72°$
$C_5^{\ 2}, C_5^{\ 3}$	$1 + 2 \cos 144°$	$S_5^{\ 3}, S_5^{\ 7}$	$-1 + 2 \cos 144°$
$C_6, C_6^{\ 5}$	2	$S_6, S_6^{\ 5}$	0

EXAMPLES

(i) *Equilateral triangular* X_3: *point group* $\mathscr{D}_{3h}$

This molecule is shown in Fig. 8.1. Its point group $\mathscr{D}_{3h}$ contains the following classes of symmetry operations: E; rotations C_3, C_3^{-1} about the threefold symmetry axis perpendicular to the molecular plane; three rotations C_2' about the three twofold axes lying in the molecular plane; a reflection σ_h in the molecular plane; improper rotations S_3, $S_3^{\ 5} = S_3^{-1}$ about the threefold axis; three reflections σ_v in the three vertical symmetry planes. Of these operations, E and σ_h leave all the nuclei in position and have $n_R = 3$; the rotations and improper rotations about the threefold axis move all the nuclei and have $n_R = 0$; the C_2' rotations and σ_v reflections each leave one nucleus in position and interchange the other two giving $n_R = 1$.

The characters of Γ_{vib} for this molecule can be calculated from (8.49) using the above values for n_R and the appropriate χ_R taken from Table 8.2. The calculation is conveniently set out in tabular form:

	Proper Rotations			Improper Rotations		
	E	$2C_3$	$3C_2'$	σ_h	$2S_3$	$3\sigma_v$
n_R	3	0	1	3	0	1
χ_R	3	0	-1	1	-2	1
χ_{vib}	3	0	1	3	0	1

The reduction of Γ_{vib} can be effected by substituting its characters and those of the IRs of $\mathscr{D}_{3h}$, taken from the character table in Appendix H, into (6.5). The calculation gives

$$\Gamma_{vib} = A_1' + E'. \tag{8.50}$$

We thus verify the result of Section 8.4. The molecule has two fundamentals: one of these is non-degenerate with a normal coordinate of symmetry species A_1' while the other is doubly degenerate with a pair of normal coordinates of symmetry species E'. These normal coordinates are the vibrational coordinates illustrated in Fig. 8.2. In this figure Q_1 is unchanged by any of the symmetry operations of $\mathscr{D}_{3h}$ and generates the identical representation A_1', while the pair of coordinates Q_2 and Q_3 are transformed among themselves by the operations of $\mathscr{D}_{3h}$ and generate the IR E'.

(ii) *Methane: point group* $\mathscr{T}_d$

We imagine the methane tetrahedron inscribed into a cube as in Fig. 2.1. The symmetry operations of $\mathscr{T}_d$ all leave the carbon nucleus unmoved but may shift varying numbers of the protons from their original positions. The classes of $\mathscr{T}_d$ are: E, for which $n_R = 5$; rotations C_3 about the body diagonals of the cube which leave just one proton in position and for which $n_R = 2$; rotations C_2 about the twofold axes which move all the protons and for which $n_R = 1$; improper rotations S_4 about the twofold axes for which also $n_R = 1$; reflections σ_d in planes containing two CH bonds which leave two protons in position and for which $n_R = 3$.

The characters χ_{vib} for symmetry operations of these various types are given below.

	E	$8C_3$	$3C_2$	$6S_4$	$6\sigma_d$
n_R	5	2	1	1	3
χ_R	3	0	-1	-1	1
χ_{vib}	9	0	1	-1	3

The reduction of Γ_{vib} gives

$$\Gamma_{vib} = A_1 + E + 2F_2. \tag{8.51}$$

Thus the nine vibrational coordinates give rise to four different fundamentals; these are a non-degenerate fundamental of species A_1, a doubly-degenerate fundamental of species E, and two distinct triply-degenerate fundamentals with the same symmetry species F_2.

8.9 Internal Coordinates

The reduction of Γ_{vib} in the manner outlined above allows us to determine the number of different fundamentals that are possessed by a given molecule and to classify the fundamentals according to the symmetry species of the corresponding sets of normal coordinates. The reduction as such tells us nothing about the nature of the displaced configurations that are associated with the various fundamentals, but some qualitative information bearing on this topic may be obtained by using another method of reducing Γ_{vib}.

Instead of using mass-weighted coordinates for the nuclear displacements and then removing the pure translations and rotations, one may specify a deformed configuration of a molecule by detailing the changes that occur in a suitably chosen set of bond lengths and bond angles when the molecule is deformed from its equilibrium configuration. Such a set of changes in bond lengths and angles may be taken as a set of coordinates, called *internal coordinates*, for the configuration space of Γ_{vib}.

Let us denote these internal coordinates, of which there will be $s = 3n - 6$ for a non-linear molecule containing n nuclei, by $q_1, \ldots, q_s$. Then the effect of a symmetry operation R on a configuration X defined by a certain set of values $(q_1, \ldots, q_s)$ of the internal coordinates is to change it into a configuration X' with coordinates $(q'_1, \ldots, q'_s)$ where the q'_i are expressible as linear combinations of the q_j of the form

$$q'_i = \sum_{j=1}^{s} [D_q(R)]_{ij} q_j. \qquad (8.52)$$

The matrices $D_q(R)$ defined in this way provide a set of matrices belonging to Γ_{vib} and the reduction of Γ_{vib} may be achieved by examining their characters. The result, of course, must be identical with the result that would be obtained by using the method discussed in the previous section but the point of introducing internal coordinates lies in the fact that they provide a basis for Γ_{vib} in which the matrices $D_q(R)$ are already partially reduced. The way in which this partial reduction of Γ_{vib} occurs and the kind of information that can be derived from it are best illustrated by an example.

EXAMPLE: *Methane*

We choose the set of $3 \times 5 - 6 = 9$ internal coordinates for methane to be the changes from equilibrium in the four CH bond lengths and in five of the HCH bond angles (the sixth bond angle is determined by the other five) and we denote these by $s_1, \ldots, s_4$ (for the bond lengths) and $\beta_1, \ldots, \beta_5$ (for the bond angles).

The effect of a symmetry operation R on a configuration X with coordinates $(s_1, \ldots, s_4; \beta_1, \ldots, \beta_5)$ is to produce a new configuration X' with coordinates $(s'_1, \ldots, s'_4; \beta'_1, \ldots, \beta'_5)$. The bond lengths in X' will be some permutation of the bond lengths in X; in fact, if R is such that it moves bond j into the position of bond i when it is applied to the equilibrium molecular framework, the extension of bond i in X' will be equal to the extension of bond j in X and $s'_i = s_j$. Similarly, the bond angles $\beta'_1, \ldots, \beta'_5$ in X' will be expressible in terms of the bond angles $\beta_1, \ldots, \beta_5$ in X. Thus the internal coordinates for methane are such that the general equations (8.52) divide into two independent sets of the form

$$s'_i = \sum_{j=1}^{4} [D_s(R)]_{ij} s_j; \qquad \beta'_i = \sum_{m=1}^{5} [D_\beta(R)]_{lm} \beta_m, \qquad (8.53)$$

and the matrix $D_q(R)$ that represents R with respect to this set of coordinates has the diagonal block form

$$D_q(R) = \left[\begin{array}{c|c} D_s(R) & 0 \\ \hline 0 & D_\beta(R) \end{array} \right]$$

Thus the choice of internal coordinates that we have made allows us to write

$$\Gamma_{vib} = \Gamma_s + \Gamma_\beta \tag{8.54}$$

where Γ_s is a four-dimensional representation of the molecular point group $\mathcal{T}_d$ with matrices $D_s(R)$ and Γ_β is a five-dimensional representation of $\mathcal{T}_d$ with matrices $D_\beta(R)$.

The next step is to identify the IRs contained in Γ_s and Γ_β. The reduction of Γ_s is straightforward. As we have seen, $s'_i = s_j$ if R is such that it moves bond j into the position of bond i. It follows that, in (8.53), $[D_s(R)]_{ii} = 0$ if i refers to a bond that is moved by R and that $[D_s(R)]_{ii} = 1$ if i is a bond that is left in position by R. Thus the character

$$\chi_s(R) = \sum_{i=1}^{4} [D_s(R)]_{ii}$$

of R in Γ_s is simply equal to the number of bonds left in position by R. For the various classes of symmetry operations in $\mathcal{T}_d$ this rule gives

$$
\begin{array}{cccccc}
 & E & 8C_3 & 3C_2 & 6S_4 & 6\sigma_d \\
\chi_s = & 4 & 1 & 0 & 0 & 2
\end{array}
$$

and from these characters and the character table of $\mathcal{T}_d$ we see that

$$\Gamma_s = A_1 + F_2. \tag{8.55}$$

It is not so easy to find the characters of Γ_β for here we must deal with the effects of R on six bond angles only five of which are independent. We may, however, avoid this problem altogether and find the IRs contained in Γ_β by making use of the known result (8.51) for the IRs contained in Γ_{vib}. The IRs of Γ_β must be those that survive when the IRs belonging to Γ_s are struck out from (8.51); thus from (8.51) and (8.55) we deduce that

$$\Gamma_\beta = E + F_2. \tag{8.56}$$

We are now in a position to see how the introduction of internal coordinates gives us qualitative information about the nature of the deformations of the molecule that are associated with its different fundamentals. Since A_1 occurs in Γ_s but not in Γ_β, it follows that the normal coordinate of the A_1 fundamental is independent of changes in the bond angles and depends only on changes in the bond lengths. This fundamental is, therefore, associated with vibrations of the molecule in which the bond lengths change while the bond angles remain fixed at their equilibrium values. Similarly, since E occurs in Γ_β but not in Γ_s, it follows that the E fundamental is associated with vibrations in which the bond angles change while the bond lengths stay fixed.

If we now consider the F_2 fundamentals, we cannot say that because F_2 occurs in both Γ_s and Γ_β it follows that one of the F_2 fundamentals is associated with pure bond stretching vibrations while the other is associated with vibrations in which only the bond angles change. Rather, we must conclude that both these fundamentals depend on simultaneous changes in bond lengths and bond angles, the relative importance of which can be discovered only by finding those particular combinations of $s_1, \ldots, s_4; \beta_1, \ldots, \beta_5$ which form bases for F_2 and which put the potential energy into the normal coordinate form (8.36). The solution of this problem requires an explicit knowledge of the potential energy and takes us beyond the purely qualitative results that are provided by a consideration of symmetry alone.

This example illustrates the sort of information that is given by the introduction of internal coordinates. A further example will be found in Section 8.15. The reader is referred to [12] or [15] for a full discussion of the methods used to obtain explicit expressions for the normal coordinates.

8.10 Linear Molecules

A linear molecule may be unsymmetrical with point group $\mathscr{C}_{\infty v}$, or it may be symmetrical, with a centre of symmetry, and have the point group $\mathscr{D}_{\infty h}$. In either case, we choose a definite set of mutually perpendicular base-vectors e_1, e_2, e_3 with origin at a point in the line of the molecule and with the e_3 axis pointing along this line. For unsymmetrical molecules the choice of origin in the molecule is immaterial; for symmetrical molecules we take the origin at the centre of symmetry. We then erect parallel sets of axes $e_1^{(p)}$, $e_2^{(p)}$, $e_3^{(p)}$ at the equilibrium positions of the nuclei and refer the displacements of the nuclei from their equilibrium positions to these axes with appropriately mass-weighted coordinates $y_1^{(p)}$, $y_2^{(p)}$, $y_3^{(p)}$.

The $3n$-dimensional configuration space of the molecule, including translations and rotations, is divided by this choice of coordinates into an n-dimensional invariant sub-space, with basis $e_3^{(1)}, \ldots, e_3^{(n)}$, consisting of all configurations in which the nuclei have suffered longitudinal displacements along the line of the molecule and a $2n$-dimensional invariant sub-space, with basis $e_1^{(1)}, e_2^{(1)}, \ldots, e_1^{(n)}, e_2^{(n)}$, consisting of all the configurations in which the nuclei have transverse displacements perpendicular to the line of the molecule. Accordingly, the configuration space representation may be reduced into the form

$$\Gamma_0 = \Gamma_\parallel + \Gamma_\perp \qquad (8.57)$$

where $\Gamma_\parallel$ is an n-dimensional representation associated with the longitudinal displacements and $\Gamma_\perp$ is a $2n$-dimensional representation associated with the transverse displacements.

The symmetry operations that we need to consider are rotations $C(\alpha)$ about e_3 and reflections σ_v in planes containing e_3; in addition, for $\mathscr{D}_{\infty h}$, there is the inversion in the centre of symmetry. The effects of $C(\alpha)$ and σ_v on e_1, e_2, e_3 are described by the matrices (4.10) and (4.13). These matrices are already in reduced form, containing a one-dimensional IR of $\mathscr{C}_{\infty v}$ generated by e_3 and a two-dimensional IR generated by e_1 and e_2. The characters of the e_3 IR are $+1$ for both $C(\alpha)$ and σ_v so that it is the identical IR Σ^+ (or A_1)

of $\mathscr{C}_{\infty v}$. The characters of the (e_1, e_2) IR are $2 \cos \alpha$ for $C(\alpha)$ and 0 for σ_v; this is the IR Π (or E_1) of $\mathscr{C}_{\infty v}$. If we enlarge $\mathscr{C}_{\infty v}$ to $\mathscr{D}_{\infty h} = \mathscr{C}_{\infty v} \times i$ by the inclusion of a centre of symmetry, these representations are further characterized by their g or u behaviour under inversion. Since inversion changes the sign of all three base vectors e_1, e_2, e_3, they are in fact the odd representations Σ_u^+ and Π_u of $\mathscr{D}_{\infty h}$.

(a) Unsymmetrical molecules

We turn now to the configuration space of the molecule and consider first unsymmetrical molecules with point group $\mathscr{C}_{\infty v}$. The effects of $C(\alpha)$ and σ_v on the coordinates $y_i^{(p)}$ are described by equations of the form (8.31) with $p = q$, since neither of these operations moves any of the nuclei to other positions in the molecule. The matrix $[r_{ij}]$ that appears in (8.31) is the matrix (4.10) for $C(\alpha)$ and the matrix (4.13) for σ_v and the matrices $D_0(R)$ which represent $C(\alpha)$ and σ_v in the configuration space representation consist simply of these matrices repeated n times down the diagonal. Consequently, Γ_0 contains the identical representation Σ^+ and the two-dimensional IR Π repeated n times each:

$$\Gamma_\parallel = n\Sigma^+; \qquad \Gamma_\perp = n\Pi.$$

Now one of the IRs contained in $\Gamma_\parallel$ will correspond to a translation along the e_3 axis. If we remove the corresponding normal coordinate we are left with $n-1$ normal coordinates, all with symmetry species Σ^+, which describe longitudinal vibrations of the molecule. Again, $\Gamma_\perp$ will contain IRs which arise from translations along the e_1 and e_2 axes and from rotations about these axes. These IRs must both be of species Π, since $\Gamma_\perp$ consists wholly of Π representations; when they are removed, we are left with the $2n-4$ transverse vibrational coordinates divided into $n-2$ pairs of symmetry species Π. Thus an unsymmetrical molecule has $n-1$ non-degenerate fundamentals of symmetry species Σ^+ arising from the longitudinal vibrations and $n-2$ doubly-degenerate fundamentals of species Π arising from the transverse vibrations.

(b) Symmetrical molecules

The results for a symmetrical molecule depend on whether it has an even or an odd number of nuclei. If $n = 2m$, the nuclei are placed symmetrically on either side of the centre of symmetry, while if $n = 2m+1$, the odd nucleus is at the centre of symmetry. The inversion moves every nucleus except one that is at the centre of symmetry; consequently if $n = 2m$, the inversion has the character $\chi_0(i) = 0$ while if $n = 2m+1$, the odd nucleus contributes -3 to the character and $\chi_0(i) = -3$.

The matrices which represent $C(\alpha)$ and σ_v are the same as those described above for $\mathscr{C}_{\infty v}$. We may, therefore, divide Γ_0 into n IRs of species Σ^+ and n IRs of species Π relative to $C(\alpha)$ and σ_v. If $n=2m$, the fact that $\chi_0(i)=0$ shows that these must divide into equal numbers of g and u types with respect to inversion. Hence

for $n=2m$, $\qquad \Gamma_\| = m\Sigma_g{}^+ + m\Sigma_u{}^+ ; \qquad \Gamma_\perp = m\Pi_g + m\Pi_u.$

If $n=2m+1$, the fact that $\chi_0(i)=-3$ shows that there must be one extra $\Sigma_u{}^+$ and one extra Π_u representation, so that

for $n=2m+1$, $\quad \Gamma_\| = m\Sigma_g{}^+ + (m+1)\Sigma_u{}^+ ; \qquad \Gamma_\perp = m\Pi_g + (m+1)\Pi_u.$

To find the species of the vibrational coordinates we must remove the IRs of the translations and rotations from $\Gamma_\|$ and $\Gamma_\perp$. A translation along $\mathbf{e}_3$ has its sign reversed by i and belongs to the species $\Sigma_u{}^+$. Translations along the $\mathbf{e}_1$ and $\mathbf{e}_2$ axes are also of type u under inversion and belong to the species Π_u. Rotations are of type g under inversion since the inversion of a right-handed rotation about a given direction changes it into a left-handed rotation through the same angle about the opposite direction, and these two rotations are identical. Thus the pair of rotations about the $\mathbf{e}_1$ and $\mathbf{e}_2$ axes generates the IR Π_g of $\mathscr{D}_{\infty h}$. If these translational and rotational IRs are removed from $\Gamma_\|$ and $\Gamma_\perp$, we obtain the results set out in Table 8.3 for the numbers of fundamentals which belong to the different symmetry species.

TABLE 8.3. *Fundamentals of a $\mathscr{D}_{\infty h}$ molecule with n nuclei*

	Longitudinal species		Transverse species	
	$\Sigma_g{}^+$	$\Sigma_u{}^+$	Π_g	Π_u
$n=2m$	m	$m-1$	$m-1$	$m-1$
$n=2m+1$	m	m	$m-1$	m

EXAMPLES

(1) CO_2: $n=2m+1$ with $m=1$.

The molecule must have two non-degenerate fundamentals, of species $\Sigma_g{}^+$ and $\Sigma_u{}^+$ respectively, which arise from the longitudinal vibrations, and one doubly-degenerate fundamental, of species Π_u, which arises from the transverse vibrations. The g suffix means that any pure $\Sigma_g{}^+$ configuration is left unchanged by i; the u suffix means that the displacements of the nuclei in pure $\Sigma_u{}^+$ or Π_u configurations have their directions reversed by i. Configurations with these symmetries are shown in Fig. 8.5(a).

(2) Linear HCCH: $n = 2m$ with $m = 2$.

This molecule has one non-degenerate Σ_u^+ fundamental and two non-degenerate Σ_g^+ fundamentals arising from its longitudinal vibrations. Its transverse vibrations give rise to two doubly-degenerate fundamentals, one of species Π_u and the other of species Π_g. Typical configurations with these symmetries are shown in Fig. 8.5(b).

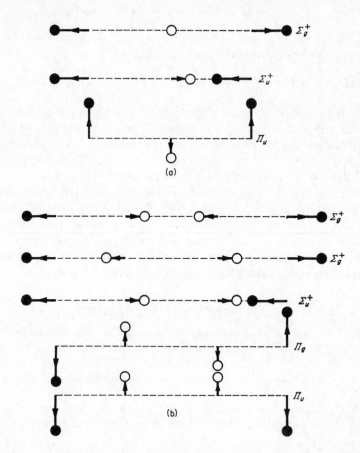

8.5 Longitudinal and transverse vibrations of (a) CO_2, (b) HCCH. (Displacements not to scale.)

8.11 Classification of the Vibrational Levels

The wave functions which belong to the various vibrational energy levels of a molecule are functions of the normal coordinates and we may use the symmetry properties of the normal coordinates to classify the wave functions. We shall deal with the ground state and the fundamental levels only.

(a) The ground state

The vibrationless ground state has a wave function which is proportional to the function Ψ_0 defined in (8.23). If the normal coordinates which belong to the various fundamentals of the molecule are grouped together in the way that we described in Section 8.6 when we were discussing the potential energy, Ψ_0 may be written in the form

$$\Psi_0(Q) = \exp\{-\Phi(Q)\} \quad \text{with} \quad \Phi(Q) = \tfrac{1}{2}\sum_{\rho}\sum_{l}\alpha^{(\rho)}Q_{\rho l}{}^2, \qquad (8.58)$$

where, by (8.17) and (8.16),

$$\alpha^{(\rho)} = 4\pi^2\nu^{(\rho)}/h = 2\pi\sqrt{\lambda^{(\rho)}}/h.$$

The expression (8.58) for $\Phi(Q)$ is the same as the expression (8.36) for the potential energy V with the replacement of $\lambda^{(\rho)}$ by $\alpha^{(\rho)}$, and it is evident that the wave function Ψ_0, like V, will be invariant under all the operations of the point group of the molecule. Thus, if the symmetry operation R changes the configuration Q to Q', we shall have

$$\Psi_0(Q') = \Psi_0(Q) \quad \text{and} \quad O_R\Psi_0 = \Psi_0. \qquad (8.59)$$

It follows that Ψ_0 generates the identical representation of the point group of the molecule.

(b) The fundamental levels

Each fundamental frequency $\nu^{(\rho)}$ has associated with it a set of normal coordinates $Q_{\rho l}$, where $l = 1, 2, \ldots, n_\rho$. The corresponding fundamental level lies at an energy $h\nu^{(\rho)}$ above the ground state and it has degeneracy n_ρ. By (8.24), we can take the n_ρ base functions for the function space belonging to this energy level to be proportional to

$$\Psi_l^{(\rho)}(Q) = Q_{\rho l}\Psi_0(Q), \quad l = 1, \ldots, n_\rho. \qquad (8.60)$$

Now a symmetry operation R changes the coordinates $Q_{\rho l}$ to $Q'_{\rho l}$ where

$$Q'_{\rho k} = \sum_{m=1}^{n_\rho} [D^{(\rho)}(R)]_{km}Q_{\rho m}; \qquad (8.61)$$

here $D^{(\rho)}(R)$ is the appropriate sub-matrix which appears in the reduction (8.40) of the configuration space representation. It is a matrix belonging to the IR of the molecular point group that determines the symmetry species of the set of normal coordinates $Q_{\rho l}$. $D^{(\rho)}(R)$ is orthogonal and so (8.61) gives

$$Q_{\rho l} = \sum_{k=1}^{n_\rho} [D^{(\rho)}(R)]_{kl}Q'_{\rho k}. \qquad (8.62)$$

(This result follows by multiplying (8.61) by $[D^{(\rho)}(R)]_{kl}$, summing over k, and using the orthogonality relation

$$\sum_{k=1}^{n_\rho} [D^{(\rho)}(R)]_{km}[D^{(\rho)}(R)]_{kl} = \delta_{ml}.)$$

We may use (8.62) and (8.59) to evaluate the effect of O_R on the wave functions defined in (8.60):

$$(O_R\Psi_l^{(\rho)})(Q') = \Psi_l^{(\rho)}(Q) = Q_{\rho l}\Psi_0(Q) = \sum_{k=1}^{n_\rho} [D^{(\rho)}(R)]_{kl}Q'_{\rho k}\Psi_0(Q').$$

Since this equation must hold in every configuration Q and so in every configuration Q', we deduce that

$$O_R\Psi_l^{(\rho)} = \sum_{k=1}^{n_\rho} [D^{(\rho)}(R)]_{kl}\Psi_k^{(\rho)}.$$

This shows that the functions $\Psi_l^{(\rho)}$ form a basis for the IR Γ_ρ, the same IR that describes the symmetry species of the normal coordinates $Q_{\rho l}$ that are associated with the fundamental $\nu^{(\rho)}$.

This result is the reason for the assumption made in Section 8.7 that the set of vibrational coordinates associated with the same fundamental frequency gives rise to an *irreducible* representation. It might conceivably happen that two fundamental frequencies associated with different IRs were, in fact, equal. This would give an extra degeneracy to the corresponding fundamental level beyond that demanded by the symmetry of the molecule. This extra degeneracy would, however, be accidental in that it could be removed by a small change in the numerical values of the force constants of the molecule which determine the values of the fundamental frequencies. Such an accidental degeneracy is extremely unlikely to occur in practice and its possibility may usually be ignored. The exception, as usual, occurs for those point groups whose IRs have complex characters; two complex one-dimensional IRs Γ_c and Γ_c^* must necessarily occur together and be associated with the same fundamental frequency.

8.12 The Infra-red Spectrum

In the infra-red absorption spectrum of a molecule one observes the absorption of energy from an incident beam of radiation. If the incident radiation contains photons of a frequency which coincides with one of the fundamentals of the molecule, the molecule may absorb a photon and make a transition from its ground state to the appropriate fundamental level. The probability that this transition will occur depends upon the relation between the electric dipole moment of the molecule and the wave functions of its ground state and fundamental level.

Suppose that we choose a set of mutually perpendicular axes, specified by the unit vectors e_1, e_2, e_3, with origin at a point which is left unmoved by the symmetry operations of the molecule, and that we refer the displacements of the nuclei to parallel sets of axes erected at their equilibrium positions. Then the dipole moment due to the displacements of the nuclei in a configuration X is defined to be the vector

$$\mu_1(X)\mathbf{e}_1 + \mu_2(X)\mathbf{e}_2 + \mu_3(X)\mathbf{e}_3 \tag{8.63}$$

with components which are definite functions of the coordinates of the nuclei in the configuration X:

$$\mu_k(X) = \sum_{p=1}^{n} e^{(p)} x_k{}^{(p)}, \tag{8.64}$$

where $e^{(p)}$ is an effective charge associated with the nucleus p.

The probability that the molecule will absorb a photon of frequency $\nu^{(\rho)}$ and make a transition from its ground state with wave function Ψ_0 to a fundamental level with wave function $\Psi_l{}^{(\rho)}$ is proportional to the quantity

$$\sum_{k=1}^{3} \left\{ \int \Psi_l{}^{(\rho)} \mu_k \Psi_0 \, d\tau \right\}^2,$$

where the integrations extend over all configurations. *The transition is forbidden and will not occur if all the integrals of the form*

$$\int \Psi_l{}^{(\rho)} \mu_k \Psi_0 \, d\tau \tag{8.65}$$

with $l = 1, \ldots, n_\rho$ and $k = 1, 2,$ or 3, are zero.

The conditions under which integrals like this must vanish were discussed in Section 7.7. In order to use the results obtained in that section we must investigate the effect of a symmetry operation on the functions $\mu_k(X)$. To do this we note, first of all, that the vectors $\mathbf{e}_1$, $\mathbf{e}_2$, $\mathbf{e}_3$ generate the representation of the molecular point group whose matrices were discussed in Section 4.2 and that this representation is the same as the representation Γ_t which is generated by the translational coordinates of the molecule. The second point to note is that if R, when it is applied to the framework of the molecule, moves nucleus p into the position of q, then its effect on the coordinates of these nuclei in changing the configuration X to X' is given by equations of the form (7.11). The matrix whose elements r_{ij} occur in these equations is identical with the matrix that represents R in Γ_t since we have chosen all our axes to be parallel. It is an orthogonal matrix and so, by a similar argument to that which led to (8.62), we may write (7.11) in the form

$$x_k{}^{(p)} = \sum_{i=1}^{3} r_{ik} x_i'{}^{(q)}.$$

But if R moves p into the position of q, p and q must be physically equivalent nuclei with the same effective charge and $e^{(p)} = e^{(q)}$. Hence we obtain the relation between the components of the dipole moment in the two configurations X and X':

$$\mu_k(X) = \sum_{p=1}^{n} e^{(p)} x_k{}^{(p)} = \sum_{i=1}^{3} r_{ik} \left\{ \sum_{q=1}^{n} e^{(q)} x_i'^{(q)} \right\} = \sum_{i=1}^{3} r_{ik}\mu_i(X'). \quad (8.66)$$

Since $\mu_k(X) = (O_R\mu_k)(X')$, it follows that

$$O_R\mu_k = \sum_{i=1}^{3} r_{ik}\mu_i,$$

and hence that the functions $\mu_k(X)$ form a basis for the representation Γ_t of the molecular point group. Except for $\mathscr{T}_d$ and $\mathcal{O}_h$ in which it is an IR, Γ_t is a reducible representation which can be reduced by a suitable choice of the directions of $\mathbf{e}_1$, $\mathbf{e}_2$, $\mathbf{e}_3$ relative to the axes and planes of symmetry of the molecule. The particular axes which reduce Γ_t are generally called the x, y, z axes of the molecule and the symbols T_x, T_y and T_z in the character tables show the IRs, or symmetry species, to which the corresponding components μ_x, μ_y and μ_z of the dipole moment belong.

If we now return to the integrals (8.65), the considerations of Section 7.7 show that, since Ψ_0 belongs to the identical representation and since the functions $\Psi_l^{(\rho)}$ are all real, these integrals will all vanish if Γ_t does not contain the IR Γ_ρ to which the functions $\Psi_l^{(\rho)}$ belong. In other words, *the fundamental $\nu^{(\rho)}$ can appear in the absorption spectrum (i.e. $\nu^{(\rho)}$ is infra-red active) only if its species coincides with one of the IRs that is contained in Γ_t.* This is the selection rule which governs the fundamental transitions from the ground state of a molecule.

8.13 The Raman Spectrum

When an incident beam of radiation of given frequency ν falls on a molecule, some of the radiation is scattered. If one observes the scattered radiation, one finds, in general, that as well as the incident frequency ν (Rayleigh scattering) the scattered radiation also contains frequencies of the form $\nu \pm \nu^{(\rho)}$ where $\nu^{(\rho)}$ is a fundamental of the molecule. This is the Raman effect and a fundamental which appears in the Raman spectrum of a molecule is called Raman active.

The theory of the Raman effect is based on the fact that an incident radiation field with electric vector $\mathbf{E}$ induces a dipole moment $\mathbf{M}$ in the molecule. If we set up a coordinate system in the molecule with unit vectors $\mathbf{e}_1$, $\mathbf{e}_2$, $\mathbf{e}_3$, the components of the induced dipole moment in a configuration X are given by

$$M_k(X) = \sum_{j=1}^{3} \alpha_{kj}(X)E_j, \quad (8.67)$$

where E_1, E_2, E_3 are the components of the electric field vector **E** and the coefficients α_{kj} are functions of the configuration space variables X. These coefficients have the property that $\alpha_{kj} = \alpha_{jk}$, so that there are, in fact, only six independent functions α_{11}, α_{22}, α_{33}, α_{12}, α_{23}, α_{13} to be considered. These functions define the *polarizability* of the molecule.

It is shown in Appendix E that these six functions are transformed by the symmetry operations of the point group of the molecule in exactly the same way as the functions x_1^2, x_2^2, x_3^2, $x_1 x_2$, $x_2 x_3$, $x_1 x_3$ which can be formed from the coordinates (x_1, x_2, x_3) of a general point. The six functions generate a reducible representation of the point group which we shall call Γ_α and which we shall discuss further below.

The probability that a Raman scattering involving the fundamental $\nu^{(\rho)}$ will occur depends upon the values of the integrals

$$\int \Psi_l^{(\rho)} \alpha_{ij} \Psi_0 \, d\tau, \quad i,j = 1, 2, 3; \; l = 1, \ldots, n_\rho,$$

where the $\Psi_l^{(\rho)}$ are wave functions of the fundamental level associated with $\nu^{(\rho)}$ and Ψ_0 is the ground state wave function. If $\nu^{(\rho)}$ is to be Raman active, at least one of these integrals must be non-zero. But, since Ψ_0 belongs to the identical representation and the wave functions $\Psi_l^{(\rho)}$ are all real, the considerations of Section 7.7 show that all the integrals will vanish if Γ_α does not contain the IR Γ_ρ to which the functions $\Psi_l^{(\rho)}$ belong. This gives the selection rule for Raman scattering: *the fundamental $\nu^{(\rho)}$ is Raman active only if its symmetry species Γ_ρ coincides with one of the IRs contained in Γ_α.*

In order to use this selection rule it is necessary to carry out the reduction of Γ_α; to do this we consider the functions $x_i x_j$ which transform in the same way as the polarizability coefficients α_{ij}. Consider the following linearly independent combinations of these functions:

$$r^2 = x_1^2 + x_2^2 + x_3^2,$$

$$d_1 = \tfrac{1}{2}(x_1^2 - x_2^2), \quad d_2 = x_1 x_2, \quad d_3 = x_1 x_3, \quad d_4 = x_2 x_3, \quad d_5 = (3x_3^2 - r^2)/2\sqrt{3}.$$

These functions may be taken as a basis for the six-dimensional function space of Γ_α. It will be seen that r^2 is invariant under any symmetry operation so that it generates the identical representation while the functions $d_1, \ldots, d_5$ will be transformed amongst themselves by a symmetry operation in exactly the same way as the d atomic orbitals that were discussed in Example 2 of Section 4.7.

The matrix which represents a rotation $C(\alpha)$ about the $\mathbf{e}_3$ axis in the function space of $d_1, \ldots, d_5$ is given by (4.42a); the character of this matrix is

$$1 + 2\cos\alpha + 2\cos 2\alpha = 4\cos^2\alpha + 2\cos\alpha - 1.$$

If we add to this the character $+1$ of r^2, we obtain the character of $C(\alpha)$ in Γ_α:

$$\chi_\alpha[C(\alpha)] = 2\cos\alpha(1 + 2\cos\alpha).$$

For an improper rotation $S(\alpha) = \sigma_h C(\alpha)$ about the $\mathbf{e}_3$ axis we note that σ_h reverses the signs of d_3 and d_4 but leaves d_1, d_2 and d_5 unchanged. The inclusion of these effects in the equations that led to (4.42a) shows that the character of $S(\alpha)$ in the space of $d_1, \ldots, d_5$ is

$$1 - 2 \cos \alpha + 2 \cos 2\alpha = 4 \cos^2 \alpha - 2 \cos \alpha - 1.$$

Adding the character $+1$ of r^2, we obtain the character of $S(\alpha)$ in Γ_α:

$$\chi_\alpha[S(\alpha)] = 2 \cos \alpha(-1 + 2 \cos \alpha).$$

These general expressions may be used to determine the characters of Γ_α for any point group and then the IRs that are contained in Γ_α may be found by applying (6.5).

The reduction of Γ_α has been carried out for all of the point groups. In the reduction, a particular set of axes, related in a simple way to the axes and planes of symmetry of the point group, is picked out. These are called the x, y, z axes (in place of x_1, x_2, x_3) and the character tables in Appendix H show the IRs whose bases are formed by the indicated combinations of the functions x^2, y^2, z^2, xy, xz, and yz. These IRs are precisely those which appear in Γ_α.

EXAMPLES OF THE SELECTION RULES

(i) *Equilateral triangular* X_3: *point group* $\mathscr{D}_{3h}$

From the character table of $\mathscr{D}_{3h}$ we find

$$\Gamma_t = A_2'' + E' \quad \text{and} \quad \Gamma_\alpha = 2A_1' + E' + E''.$$

Our discussion of the X_3 molecule, summarized in (8.50), showed that it has two fundamental of species A_1' and E' respectively. The selection rules for $\mathscr{D}_{3h}$ show that both of these are Raman active, since A_1' and E' are both contained in Γ_α, but that only the E' fundamental is infra-red active, since Γ_t contains E' but not A_1'.

An interesting application of this result is to ozone. Ozone certainly has more than one infra-red active fundamental. It cannot, therefore, have an equilateral triangular structure with point group $\mathscr{D}_{3h}$.

(ii) *Methane: point group* $\mathscr{T}_d$

From the character table of $\mathscr{T}_d$ we find

$$\Gamma_t = F_2; \qquad \Gamma_\alpha = A_1 + E + F_2.$$

Methane, by (8.51), has fundamentals of species A_1, E and F_2. The selection rules show that these are all Raman active but that only the two fundamentals of species F_2 are infra-red active.

(iii) *Linear molecules*

We saw in Section 8.10 that a linear molecule without a centre of symmetry (point group $\mathscr{C}_{\infty v}$) has longitudinal and transverse fundamentals of species Σ^+ and Π respectively. The character table of $\mathscr{C}_{\infty v}$ shows that Γ_t contains the IRs

Σ^+ and Π while Γ_α contains the IRs Σ^+, Π and Δ. We conclude that all the fundamentals of an unsymmetrical linear molecule are both infra-red and Raman active.

If a linear molecule has a centre of symmetry (point group $\mathscr{D}_{\infty h}$) the longitudinal fundamentals have species Σ_g^+ or Σ_u^+ and the transverse fundamentals have species Π_g or Π_u. The character table of $\mathscr{D}_{\infty h}$ shows that Γ_t contains the IRs Σ_u^+ and Π_u while Γ_α contains Σ_g^+, Π_g and Δ_g. It follows that the infra-red active fundamentals of a $\mathscr{D}_{\infty h}$ molecule are those of species Σ_u^+ and Π_u while the Raman active fundamentals are those of species Σ_g^+ and Π_g. No fundamental in a molecule of this type can be both infra-red and Raman active.

The selection rules for $\mathscr{D}_{\infty h}$ illustrate an important general rule. In any point group with a centre of symmetry, that is in any point group of the type $\mathscr{G} \times i$, the base vectors of a coordinate system with origin at the centre of symmetry, which are the base vectors of Γ_t, have their signs reversed by the inversion; they are of type u and all the IRs that are contained in Γ_t must be of this type. Thus only a fundamental with species of type u can be infra-red active. On the other hand, all of the base functions, of the form $x_i x_j$, of Γ_α are left unchanged by the inversion and the IRs that are contained in Γ_α must all be of type g. Thus any Raman active fundamental must be of type g.

Since the species of a fundamental of a molecule with a point group of this kind must be either of type u or of type g, we are led to the *rule of mutual exclusion: in any molecule with a centre of symmetry, no fundamental can be both infra-red and Raman active.* Generally, for molecules without a centre of symmetry it is found that some fundamentals are both infra-red and Raman active. Thus we have the important practical result that the occurrence of the same fundamental frequency in both the infra-red and the Raman spectrum of a molecule is evidence that it does not have a centre of symmetry; conversely, if the infra-red and Raman fundamentals are different one is justified in postulating a centre of symmetry.

8.14 Overtone and Combination Levels

Our treatment of molecular vibrations has been based on the 'harmonic approximation' in which the displacements of the nuclei from their equilibrium positions are assumed to be small enough to allow us to approximate the potential energy by the quadratic form (8.4). This assumption allows us to write down a wave function for a vibrating molecule in the form of a product of the harmonic oscillator wave functions (8.20). For wave functions of this specific kind one can show that the probability of a transition from the ground state to an overtone or combination level is very small. The fact that such transitions are observed to give rise to fairly strong bands in the spectra of many molecules is due to the inadequacy of the harmonic approximation. The displacements of the nuclei from their equilibrium positions are not always small and for an accurate treatment one must take account of the higher order terms in the potential energy which are neglected in the harmonic approximation.

The additional *anharmonic* terms may be treated as a perturbation (see Section 7.4). The perturbation does not alter the fact that the wave functions of the various vibrational energy levels must generate IRs of the molecular point group, neither does it alter the selection rules which govern transitions from the ground state to states of higher energy, since these rules are based on symmetry arguments which make no assumptions about the nature of the wave functions except that they must generate IRs of the point group.

Consider for example, a combination level that is associated with two different fundamentals $v^{(\rho)}$ and $v^{(\sigma)}$. On the assumption of a harmonic potential energy, this level will lie at an energy $h(v^{(\rho)} + v^{(\sigma)})$ above the ground state and its wave functions will consist of products of the form

$$Q_{\rho i} Q_{\sigma j} \Psi_0; \quad i = 1, \ldots, n_\rho; \; j = 1, \ldots, n_\sigma. \tag{8.68}$$

These $n_\rho n_\sigma$ products, taken together, form a basis for the direct product representation $\Gamma_\rho \times \Gamma_\sigma$. Quite often, this product representation is reducible and then it will be possible to find appropriate combinations of the functions (8.68) which generate the different IRs that are contained in $\Gamma_\rho \times \Gamma_\sigma$. In the harmonic approximation the functions belonging to the different IRs in $\Gamma_\rho \times \Gamma_\sigma$ are all degenerate, a kind of accidental degeneracy, but as soon as one takes the anharmonic perturbation into account this accidental degeneracy will disappear and instead of a single combination level of species $\Gamma_\rho \times \Gamma_\sigma$ one will find, in practice, a group of levels which lie fairly close together at an energy above the ground state of approximately $h(v^{(\rho)} + v^{(\sigma)})$; there is one such level for each IR that is contained in $\Gamma_\rho \times \Gamma_\sigma$. If some of these IRs coincide with those contained in Γ_t or Γ_α, transitions from the ground state to the corresponding levels at a frequency approximately equal to $v^{(\rho)} + v^{(\sigma)}$ may occur in the infra-red or Raman spectrum. These transitions, although they are allowed by symmetry, will, in general, occur with rather weaker intensity than the fundamental transitions.

Similar considerations apply to overtone levels. The determination of the species contained in an overtone of a degenerate fundamental is difficult and we shall not discuss it. Suffice it to say that, in general, when the anharmonic perturbations are taken into account, an overtone level splits into a number of levels with definite symmetry species and that transitions from the ground state to some of these levels may be allowed by the selection rules.

Thus the infra-red and Raman spectra of a molecule generally show a number of strong bands arising from the active fundamentals and a rather larger number of weaker bands which correspond to the overtone and combination frequencies of the molecule.

Fermi Resonance

There is a not infrequently occurring exception to the general statement made above. It may happen that an active fundamental level lies fairly close to an overtone or combination level with the same symmetry species. We then have the situation described at the end of Section 7.4; the effect of the anharmonic perturbation is to produce two levels whose wave functions consist of a mixture in roughly equal proportions of the unperturbed wave functions belonging to the fundamental level and the overtone or combination level. In this case the transitions from the ground state to the two levels will have approximately equal probabilities and the spectrum will show two strong bands close together instead of one strong and one weak band. This phenomenon is known as *Fermi resonance*.

8.15 Example: Ethylene

Planar C_2H_4, illustrated in Fig. 8.6, has point group $\mathscr{D}_{2h}$. We choose xyz

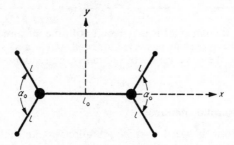

8.6 Ethylene.

axes at the centre of symmetry with the molecular plane as the xy plane and the $C{=}C$ bond as the x-axis.

Enumeration of the fundamentals

We use the method of Section 8.8, summarized in equation (8.49) and Table 8.2, to obtain the characters of Γ_{vib}. The results for the various classes of $\mathscr{D}_{2h}$ are:

	E	$C_2(z)$	$C_2(y)$	$C_2(x)$	i	$\sigma(xy)$	$\sigma(xz)$	$\sigma(yz)$
n_R	6	0	0	2	0	6	2	0
χ_R	3	−1	−1	−1	−3	1	1	1
χ_{vib}	12	2	2	0	0	6	2	0

The reduction of this representation, using (6.5) and the character table of $\mathscr{D}_{2h}$, gives

$$\Gamma_{vib} = 3A_g + 2B_{1g} + B_{2g} + A_u + B_{1u} + 2B_{2u} + 2B_{3u}.$$

The molecule therefore has twelve different fundamentals.

Activities of the fundamentals

The character table shows that for a $\mathscr{D}_{2h}$ molecule $\Gamma_t = B_{1u} + B_{2u} + B_{3u}$ and that the IRs contained in Γ_α are A_g, B_{1g}, B_{2g} and B_{3g}. The selection rules therefore give the following activities for the fundamentals of C_2H_4. (An active fundamental is indicated by $+$, an inactive fundamental by $-$.)

Fundamentals	$3A_g$	$2B_{1g}$	B_{2g}	A_u	B_{1u}	$2B_{2u}$	$2B_{3u}$
Infra-red activity	$-$	$-$	$-$	$-$	$+$	$+$	$+$
Raman activity	$+$	$+$	$+$	$-$	$-$	$-$	$-$

We see that the A_u fundamental is inactive in both the infra-red and the Raman spectra and that the molecule has five infra-red active and six Raman active fundamentals. Since there is a centre of symmetry, no fundamental is both infra-red and Raman active.

Nature of the fundamental vibrations

We first distinguish between *in-plane* vibrations where the displacements of the nuclei take place in the molecular xy plane and *out-of-plane* vibrations in which the nuclear displacements are perpendicular to this plane. Any in-plane configuration is left unchanged by $\sigma(xy)$; consequently, the in-plane vibrations must give rise to fundamentals whose symmetry species are such that $\sigma(xy)$ and E have the same, positive character. On the other hand, the signs of all the nuclear displacements in any out-of-plane configuration are reversed by $\sigma(xy)$; consequently, the out-of-plane vibrations give rise to fundamentals whose symmetry species are such that the character of $\sigma(xy)$ is negative. Examination of the character table of $\mathscr{D}_{2h}$ shows that the fundamentals of ethylene divide into:

     In-plane fundamentals: $3A_g$, $2B_{1g}$, $2B_{2u}$, $2B_{3u}$

     Out-of-plane fundamentals: A_u, B_{2g}, B_{1u}.

Since all the IRs are one-dimensional, this shows that the $3 \times 6 - 6 = 12$ vibrational coordinates divide into a set of nine coordinates describing the in-plane vibrations and a set of three coordinates describing the out-of-plane vibrations.

The coordinates may be chosen as shown in Fig. 8.7. The in-plane coordinates are the increments s_0 and $s_1, \ldots, s_4$ in the $C{=}C$ and the four $C{-}H$ bond lengths, the increments α_1, α_2 in the two HCH angles, and two angles β_1, β_2 which describe in-plane bending of the CH_2 triangles relative to the $C{=}C$ bond. These sets of coordinates give rise to representations of $\mathscr{D}_{2h}$ which we denote, respectively, by Γ_{CC}, Γ_{CH}, Γ_{HCH}, Γ_{HCC}.

The three out-of-plane coordinates are two angles γ_1, γ_2 which describe out-of-plane bending of the CH_2 triangles relative to the $C{=}C$ bond and a third angle, the angle between the planes of the two CH_2 triangles, which describes twisting of the molecule about the $C{=}C$ axis. These coordinates give rise to representations which we denote by Γ'_{HCC} and Γ_T respectively.

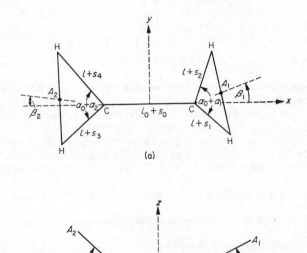

8.7 Internal coordinates for ethylene: (a) in-plane, (b) out-of-plane. (A_1 and A_2 are the midpoints of the lines joining the proton pairs.)

The characters of these representations are easily written down by considering the effects of a symmetry operation R on a configuration in which only the coordinates of the representation under consideration are different from zero. Thus, as in the methane example of Section 8.9, the character of R in one of the bond stretching representations Γ_{CC} or Γ_{CH} is equal to the number of bonds left in position by R. The character of R in Γ_{HCH} is zero if R interchanges the two CH_2 triangles and hence interchanges α_1 and α_2, while $\chi = 2$ if R leaves the CH_2 triangles in position or reflects or rotates each triangle into itself since such operations do not affect α_1 or α_2. The character of R in Γ_{HCC} is zero if R interchanges β_1 and β_2, while $\chi = 2$ if R does not alter β_1 and β_2 and $\chi = -2$ if R reverses the signs of these angles. Similar results hold for the out-of-plane bending representation Γ'_{HCC}. Finally, for Γ_T it can be seen that the proper rotations of $\mathscr{D}_{2h}$ do not affect the angle of twist while all the other operations of $\mathscr{D}_{2h}$ reverse the sign of this angle; thus Γ_T has $\chi = 1$ for the proper rotations and $\chi = -1$ for the improper rotations. These results are summarized in the following table which gives the characters of the various representations and their reduction into IRs of $\mathscr{D}_{2h}$.

	E	$C_2(z)$	$C_2(y)$	$C_2(x)$	i	$\sigma(xy)$	$\sigma(xz)$	$\sigma(yz)$	
Γ_{CC}	1	1	1	1	1	1	1	1	A_g
Γ_{CH}	4	0	0	0	0	4	0	0	$A_g + B_{1g} + B_{2u} + B_{3u}$
Γ_{HCH}	2	0	0	2	0	2	2	0	$A_g + B_{3u}$
Γ_{HCC}	2	0	0	-2	0	2	-2	0	$B_{1g} + B_{2u}$
Γ'_{HCC}	2	0	0	-2	0	-2	2	0	$B_{2g} + B_{1u}$
Γ_T	1	1	1	1	-1	-1	-1	-1	A_u

If we note the ways in which the various IRs of Γ_{vib} occur in $\Gamma_{CC}, \ldots, \Gamma_T$ we may conclude that:

(i) The three A_g fundamentals are associated with in-plane vibrations which contain varying proportions of C=C and C—H stretches and HCH angle changes.

(ii) The two B_{1g} and the two B_{2u} fundamentals are associated with vibrations in which the C=C bond length and the HCH angles remain fixed and which contain different proportions of C—H stretching and in-plane bending vibrations.

(iii) The two B_{3u} fundamentals depend on C—H stretches and HCH angle changes only.

(iv) The B_{2g} and B_{1u} fundamentals arise from out-of-plane bending of the molecule.

(v) The totally inactive A_u fundamental is associated with a torsional oscillation of the molecule.

PROBLEMS

(In the following problems, infra-red is abbreviated to i.r. and Raman to R.; active fundamentals are indicated by +, inactive fundamentals by −.)

8.1. Two of the possible structures for a Y—X—X—Y molecule are the *cis*-planar ($\mathscr{C}_{2v}$) and *trans*-planar ($\mathscr{C}_{2h}$) forms. Show that the fundamentals for these two structures have the following symmetry species and activities. (In the $\mathscr{C}_{2v}$ case take the x axis along the X—X bond and the y axis perpendicular to the molecular plane.)

	$\mathscr{C}_{2v}$			$\mathscr{C}_{2h}$		
Fundamentals	$3A_1$	$2B_1$	A_2	$3A_g$	$2B_u$	A_u
i.r. activity	+	+	−	−	+	+
R. activity	+	+	+	+	−	−

Both forms have five in-plane fundamentals ($3A_1 + 2B_1$ or $3A_g + 2B_u$) and one out-of-plane fundamental (A_2 or A_u), but their i.r. and R. spectra are completely different.

8.2. The ion CO_3^{2-} has a planar structure with the carbon nucleus at the centre of an equilateral triangle formed by the oxygen nuclei. Show that the ion has four fundamentals with the following symmetry species and activities.

Fundamentals	A_1'	$2E'$	A_2'
i.r. activity	−	+	+
R. activity	+	+	−

8.3. Show that the A_1' and E' fundamentals of CO_3^{2-} arise from in-plane vibrations. Taking internal coordinates for the in-plane configurations to be the changes in the three CO bond lengths and two of the OCO bond angles, show that the bond stretching coordinates generate the IRs A_1' and E' and hence that the two angular coordinates generate E'. The two E' fundamentals thus correspond to in-plane vibrations in which there are simultaneous changes in bond lengths and bond angles.

8.4. If a deuteron is substituted for one of the protons in methane, one obtains the $\mathscr{C}_{3v}$ molecule CH_3D. Show that this molecule has six fundamentals, three of species A_1 and three of species E, and that all these fundamentals are both i.r. and R. active.

8.5. Deduce the result of Problem 8.4 from the result (8.51) for methane by treating the change from CH_4 to CH_3D as a perturbation which reduces the symmetry from $\mathscr{T}_d$ to $\mathscr{C}_{3v}$. (Compare Problem 7.2.)

8.6. Show that benzene ($\mathscr{D}_{6h}$) has altogether twenty different fundamentals which are associated in the following way with in-plane and out-of-plane vibrations.

In-plane fundamentals	$2A_{1g}$	A_{2g}	$4E_{2g}$	$2B_{1u}$	$2B_{2u}$	$3E_{1u}$
i.r. activity	−	−	−	−	−	+
R. activity	+	−	+	−	−	−

Out-of-plane fundamentals	$2B_{2g}$	E_{1g}	A_{2u}	$2E_{2u}$
i.r. activity	−	−	+	−
R. activity	−	+	−	−

(The characters of Γ_{vib} are those given in Problem 6.8.)

8.7. Show that an octahedrally coordinated MX_6 molecule (point group $\mathcal{O}_h$) has six fundamentals with the following species and activities.

Fundamentals	A_{1g}	E_g	F_{2g}	$2F_{1u}$	F_{2u}
i.r. activity	−	−	−	+	−
R. activity	+	+	+	−	−

Show that the A_{1g} and E_g fundamentals are associated with pure M—X stretching vibrations and that bond stretching vibrations also contribute to the two F_{1u} fundamentals. (The characters of Γ_{vib} are those given in Problem 6.7.)

Chapter 9

MOLECULAR ORBITALS

9.1 The Orbital Approximation

In discussing the electronic structure of a molecule in the Born–Oppenheimer approximation, one treats the molecule as a system of n electrons moving, under their mutual interactions, in the field of the nuclei of the molecule. The motions of the nuclei about their equilibrium positions are disregarded and they are treated as fixed particles which define the molecular framework or skeleton in which the electrons move.

The forces which act on the electrons and govern their motions are of several different kinds. First and foremost, there are the electrostatic attractions of the electrons towards the nuclei and the electrostatic repulsions between the electrons. Next, there are various magnetic interactions which arise because the electrons and nuclei are not simple charged particles but also have intrinsic magnetic moments associated with their spins. Finally, a nucleus is not just a point particle but has its own structure and charge distribution which means that the electrostatic interaction between an electron and a nucleus is not a pure central force and that it contains quadrupole and higher order terms as well.

Of all these interactions, the electrostatic attractions of the electrons towards the nuclei, regarded as point particles, and the electrostatic repulsions between the electrons are by far the most important and for most purposes it is sufficient to consider only these. The other interactions may, if necessary, be taken into account as perturbations after one has solved the problem of the electronic motions on the assumption of pure electrostatic forces. A consideration of these effects, however, lies beyond the scope of this book. We shall consider only the dominant electrostatic interactions.

On the assumption of pure electrostatic forces, the Hamiltonian for the electron system has the form

$$H = \sum_{p=1}^{n} T(p) + \sum_{p=1}^{n} V_N(p) + \sum_{p,q} V_e(p, q). \qquad (9.1)$$

In this expression, $T(p)$ is the differential operator $-(h^2/8\pi^2 m)\nabla_p^2$ which represents the kinetic energy of electron p, $V_N(p)$ is the potential energy of p due to its attractions towards the various nuclei of the molecule, and $V_e(p, q)$ is the energy of the electrostatic repulsion between the pair of electrons p and q. The summation in the last term of (9.1) is a summation over all the $\frac{1}{2}n(n-1)$ pairs of electrons.

Because of the repulsions, the motion of an individual electron is affected by, and itself affects, the motions of the other $n-1$ electrons and it is this mutual interaction between the electrons which makes an exact solution of the Schrödinger equation with Hamiltonian (9.1) so difficult. The system of n electrons forms a whole which cannot be regarded simply as a collection of n independently moving particles.

The usual method of dealing with this difficulty is that of the *self-consistent field*. Particularly when n is large, one may argue that a steady state of motion of the electrons can be effectively represented by a static smoothed out distribution of charge within the molecule and that the interactions between an individual electron and the other electrons may, to a good approximation, be replaced by the interaction between the electron and the electric field produced by the smoothed out charge distribution. The potential energy of electron p in this field will be given by some function $U(p)$ of the coordinates of p and we may, approximately, replace the Hamiltonian of (9.1) by

$$H_{scf} = \sum_{p=1}^{n} H_0(p), \quad \text{where} \quad H_0(p) = T(p)+V_N(p)+U(p). \quad (9.2)$$

With a Hamiltonian of this form, the arguments of Section 7.5 become applicable. The wave function for the system of n electrons may be expressed as a product of single particle wave functions, or *orbitals*, which describe the motions of the individual electrons in the field of the nuclei and the smoothed out field produced by all the electrons taken together. The orbital for electron p is a solution of the single particle Schrödinger equation

$$H_0(p)\psi(p) = \epsilon_p\psi(p), \quad (9.3)$$

where ϵ_p is the *orbital energy*. There is one such equation for each electron and, in these equations, H_0 is an *effective Hamiltonian* for an electron which takes the interaction between it and the other electrons into account by means of the function U.

This function, of course, depends on the actual motions of all the electrons and it can ultimately be expressed in terms of the orbitals which are the solutions of (9.3). It is here that the idea of self-consistency comes in. If we begin by assuming a definite form, say U_1, for U, this will give rise to a definite set of orbitals satisfying the equations (9.3). These orbitals, in turn, will define a definite form, say U_2, for U. The correct solution of the problem will have been found when $U_1 = U_2$ and the smoothed out charge distribution reproduces itself.

We are not concerned here with the methods by which this self-consistent solution may be found, still less with the complications that arise when one extends the argument to take account of the spins of the electrons and the Pauli exclusion principle. What is important for our purposes is the qualitative conclusion that, at least to a fairly good approximation, it is reasonable to think of a system of interacting electrons in terms of orbitals which describe the motions of the individual electrons and which are solutions of equations like (9.3) with some effective Hamiltonian H_0.

As we saw in Sections 7.1 and 7.2, the correct Hamiltonian (9.1) is invariant under the symmetry operations of the point group of a molecule and the same must be true of the approximate Hamiltonian (9.2). This means that, whatever its detailed form may be, the effective single particle Hamiltonian H_0 will possess the complete symmetry of the molecular point group and that the conclusions of Section 7.3 will apply to the orbitals which are the solutions of (9.3). This equation has allowable solutions for certain values of the orbital energy ϵ and for each such value the solutions define a function space which generates an IR of the molecular point group. The consequences of this fact will be developed in the rest of this chapter. We begin the discussion by considering the relatively simple case of an atom.

9.2 Atomic Orbitals

The effective Hamiltonian for an electron in an atom has the form

$$H_0 = -(h^2/8\pi^2 m)\nabla^2 + V(r),$$

where the effective potential energy $V(r)$, which includes the smoothed out interaction between the electron under consideration and the other electrons as well as its attraction towards the nucleus, is a function of the distance r between the electron and the nucleus. With this form of H_0, (9.3) becomes

$$\nabla^2 \psi + (8\pi^2 m/h^2)[\epsilon - V(r)]\psi = 0, \tag{9.4}$$

and the allowable values of the orbital energy ϵ are determined by the condition that $\psi \to 0$ as $r \to \infty$. This equation is most easily dealt with if one describes the position of the electron by means of the spherical polar coordinates (r, θ, ϕ) that are defined in Fig. 3.8. Standard methods are then available for finding the solutions of (9.4). These are described in most books on quantum mechanics (see, for example, [1], Section 18) and we shall here merely quote the results that are obtained, expressing them in a form that is relevant to our group-theoretical considerations.

The values of ϵ that are allowed in (9.4) by the boundary conditions will depend on the form of $V(r)$, but, whatever these values may be, the solutions of (9.4) which belong to the same value of ϵ form a function space whose basis generates an IR of the three-dimensional rotation group $\mathscr{R}_3$, the point group of an atom. These IRs were described briefly in Section 6.3(c); we stated there that they are characterized by a number j which is either an integer or half an odd integer. It turns out, for reasons that we shall not discuss, that the only IRs of $\mathscr{R}_3$ that can arise from solutions of (9.4) are those characterized by integral values of j. We denote the integer which characterizes an IR by l; l may have any of the values $0, 1, 2, \ldots$ and the IR which corresponds to a given value of l has dimension $2l+1$. Instead of using the values $l=0, 1, 2, 3, 4, \ldots$ it is usual to refer to these IRs by the spectroscopic symbols $s, p, d, f, g, \ldots$ in the manner explained in Section 6.3.

There will be many different values of ϵ that give rise to the same IR of $\mathscr{R}_3$. We arrange these in order of increasing ϵ and distinguish them from each other by a number n, with the *convention* that, for given l, we begin the sequence with $n=l+1$. (Thus for $l=0$, $n=1, 2, 3, \ldots$; for $l=1$, $n=2, 3, \ldots$; etc.) In this way we obtain the sequences of orbital energy levels that are summarized in Table 9.1. The first column of the table gives the letter symbol for an IR of $\mathscr{R}_3$, the next two columns give the corresponding l value and dimension of the IR, and the labelling of the various orbital energy levels is shown in the remainder of the table.

TABLE 9.1. *Characterization of atomic orbital energy levels*

IR	l	$2l+1$	Levels				
s	0	1	$1s$	$2s$	$3s$	$4s$	$\ldots$
p	1	3		$2p$	$3p$	$4p$	$\ldots$
d	2	5			$3d$	$4d$	$\ldots$
f	3	7				$4f$	$\ldots$
$\ldots$	$\ldots$	$\ldots$					$\ldots$

Information about the actual numerical values of the orbital energies can be obtained empirically from an analysis of atomic spectra and theoretically by detailed self-consistent field calculations. For large atomic number the order of the levels is

$$1s \ll 2s < 2p \ll 3s < 3p < 3d < 4s \cdots.$$

This order is maintained as the atomic number decreases, except that the $3d$ level rises in energy relative to the others and for lighter atoms it has a higher energy than the $4s$ level. The levels with $n \geqslant 4$ lie relatively close together and their order depends very much on atomic number.

The $2l+1$ linearly independent atomic orbitals which serve as base functions for the function space formed by the solutions of (9.4) that belong to a given nl orbital energy level may be chosen in many different ways. In discussions of atomic spectra, the most convenient choice is to label the different base functions with a number m which can have any of the $2l+1$ integral values $m = l, l-1, \ldots, -l$. The corresponding atomic orbitals may be written in the form

$$\psi_{nlm}(r, \theta, \phi) = F_{nl}(r) Y_l^m(\theta, \phi) \tag{9.5}$$

where the radial function $F_{nl}(r)$, which depends on the form of $V(r)$ in (9.4), is the same for all orbitals belonging to the nl level and the angular functions $Y_l^m(\theta, \phi)$ are certain definite functions of θ and ϕ, known as spherical harmonics, of the form

$$Y_l^m(\theta, \phi) = P_l^m(\theta) e^{im\phi},$$

where P_l^m is a certain function of θ which depends on the values of l and of $|m|$. In particular, the s orbitals ($l = 0$) are spherically symmetric functions of r, independent of θ and ϕ, while the p and d orbitals ($l = 1$ and 2 respectively) are the functions of r, θ, ϕ defined in (3.34a, b) and (3.35).

This way of choosing the basis functions is well suited to atomic problems since there is a direct connection between the quantum numbers l and m and the angular momentum of an electron in the atomic orbitals which they specify. When one uses atomic orbitals in molecular problems, however, it is usually more convenient to choose basis functions which are real and which are simply expressed in terms of the x, y, z coordinates of the electron. Suitable p and d orbitals of this kind are defined in (3.25) and (3.26) and we shall use these functions in the rest of this chapter.

It is useful to have an idea of the strong directional properties of these forms for the p and d orbitals. If one uses spherical polar coordinates, the orbitals have the form

$$\psi(r, \theta, \phi) = F(r) A(\theta, \phi)$$

where $A(\theta, \phi)$ is some combination of the variables $x/r = \sin\theta \cos\phi$, $y/r = \sin\theta \sin\phi$, and $z/r = \cos\theta$. We can illustrate the angular variation of the orbitals, i.e. the variation of $A(\theta, \phi)$ with θ and ϕ, by constructing polar diagrams as follows: given a point P with coordinates (r_P, θ_P, ϕ_P), take the line OP, where O is the origin, and mark off a point P' on it such that $OP' = A(\theta_P, \phi_P)$; do this for all values of θ and ϕ and draw the surface that is formed by the points P'. The points on this surface which are furthest away from O show the directions in which the orbital has its maximum values. Since the sign, as well as the magnitude, of an orbital is important one also indicates on a polar diagram the regions where the orbital is positive and those where it is negative.

The polar diagram for p_z is shown in Fig. 9.1(a) and p_x and p_y have similar diagrams which point along the x and y axes respectively. The polar diagrams for d_{z^2}, d_{xy} and $d_{x^2-y^2}$ are also shown in the figure. The diagrams for d_{xy} and $d_{x^2-y^2}$ have exactly the same shape and one can be obtained from the other by rotation through $45°$ about the z axis. The orbitals d_{yz} and d_{xz} have diagrams similar to that for d_{xy}. Although the diagram for d_{z^2} looks very different from the diagrams for the other d orbitals, it is in fact a superposition of the diagrams that would be obtained for $d_{z^2-x^2}$ and $d_{z^2-y^2}$ orbitals.

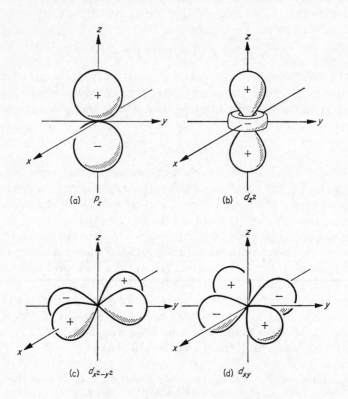

9.1 Polar diagrams for p and d orbitals.

9.3 Electron Spin and the Pauli Principle

In describing atomic orbitals in the preceding section, we introduced the quantum numbers l and m by reference to the IRs of the rotation group. This is a somewhat abstract way of describing them; they are usually introduced into the theory as physically significant quantities related to the angular momentum of an electron in the orbital ψ_{nlm}. In such an orbital, the electron possesses an angular momentum of magnitude $[l(l+1)]^{1/2}h/2\pi$ and the orbitals ψ_{nlm} with varying m describe the $2l+1$ possible states of the electron with this angular momentum; they are states in which the component of the angular momentum along the z axis has the quantized values $mh/2\pi$ where $m=l$, $l-1, \ldots, -l$.

In order to explain various facts about atomic spectra it is necessary to suppose that an electron possesses an intrinsic angular momentum, due to a spin about its axis, in addition to the orbital angular momentum mentioned above. This spin angular momentum must be analogous to the orbital angular momentum in that its magnitude will be $[s(s+1)]^{1/2}h/2\pi$ where s is a spin quantum number representing the spin of the electron; for given s the electron will be able to exist in $2s+1$ different spin states, specified by a quantum number m_s such that the component of its spin angular momentum along the z axis has the values $m_s(h/2\pi)$ with $m_s = s, s-1, \ldots, -s$. The analysis of atomic spectra, reinforced by Dirac's relativistic theory of an electron, shows that an electron has spin $s = \frac{1}{2}$ and that it has just two spin states specified by $m_s = \frac{1}{2}$ and $-\frac{1}{2}$.

We can express this result in terms of wave functions by saying that an electron has an internal spin coordinate ω which can have the values $\omega = 1$ or $\omega = -1$ only. The two spin states specified by $m_s = \frac{1}{2}$ and $m_s = -\frac{1}{2}$ are represented by twc spin wave functions, $\alpha(\omega)$ and $\beta(\omega)$ respectively, such that $\alpha = 1$ and $\beta = 0$ when $\omega = 1$ while $\alpha = 0$ and $\beta = 1$ when $\omega = -1$. A complete wave function for an electron is a function of the four variables x, y, z and ω and if the electron is in the orbital state $\psi(x, y, z)$ its total wave function will be a combination of the *spin-orbitals* $\psi(x, y, z)\alpha(\omega)$ and $\psi(x, y, z)\beta(\omega)$. Thus the electron spin introduces an additional degeneracy: each of the $2l+1$ degenerate orbitals which belong to the nl orbital energy level has a double spin degeneracy and the orbital level has $2(2l+1)$ spin-orbitals associated with it.

Let us now consider an atom with n electrons. In the orbital approximation that we have been discussing, a wave function for the n-electron system will be a product of n spin-orbitals, one for each electron. All the spin-orbitals in the product that belong to the same nl orbital energy level will give the same contribution to the energy of the n-electron wave function, and the energy level to which this wave function belongs can be specified by giving the numbers of electrons that occupy spin-orbitals belonging to the different orbital levels.

These occupation numbers are restricted by the *Pauli exclusion principle* which states that two electrons cannot occupy the same spin-orbital. This principle has the consequence that an nl level, with $2(2l+1)$ spin-orbitals, can hold at most $2(2l+1)$ electrons. Thus, an s level ($l=0$) can hold at most two electrons, a p level ($l=1$) cannot be occupied by more than six electrons, a d level ($l=2$) by more than ten electrons, and so on.

A set of occupation numbers for the various orbital levels defines an *electron configuration* for the atom. The ground state configuration is obtained by filling the lower lying orbital levels, in the order $1s$, $2s$, $2p$, $\ldots$, with as many electrons as are allowed by the Pauli principle. For example, the ground state configuration for carbon with six electrons is obtained by filling the $1s$ and $2s$

orbitals with two electrons each and placing the remaining two electrons in the $2p$ orbital; this placing of the electrons into orbitals is indicated by the notation $(1s)^2(2s)^2(2p)^2$. Similarly, neon, with ten electrons, has the ground state configuration $(1s)^2(2s)^2(2p)^6$. In this configuration the $1s$, $2s$ and $2p$ levels each hold the maximum possible number of electrons and we say that neon has a *closed shell* ground state. As one goes beyond neon in the periodic table, the $3s$ and $3p$ and then the $4s$ and $3d$ orbitals begin to be filled. In this way, as is well known, the simple orbital picture, coupled with the Pauli principle, gives a remarkably consistent explanation of the periodic system of the elements and the variation of their chemical properties with atomic number.

We shall not discuss the refinements that have to be introduced into the orbital approximation in order to explain the details of atomic structure but proceed instead to show how the approximation may be applied to the problem of the electronic structure of molecules.

9.4 Molecular Orbitals

In the orbital approximation, the effective Hamiltonian for an electron in a molecule will have the form

$$H_0 = -(h^2/8\pi^2 m)\nabla^2 + V,$$

where V is the effective potential energy which includes the smoothed out interaction of the electron under consideration with the other electrons as well as its attractions towards the nuclei. The equation which determines the various possible molecular orbitals ψ and their energies ϵ is

$$\nabla^2\psi + (8\pi^2 m/h^2)(\epsilon - V)\psi = 0, \tag{9.6}$$

and one requires solutions of this equation which satisfy the boundary condition $\psi \to 0$ as x, y or $z \to \infty$, where x, y, z are the coordinates of the electron.

Despite the apparent similarity of this equation to (9.4), it is in fact very different. Since the potential energy depends upon the attractions of the electron towards several different points, V is not simply a function of the distance of the electron from a single point; it is a complicated function of the three coordinates of the electron. For this reason, the methods that can be used to find solutions of the atomic orbital equation (9.4) are no longer applicable and there is no general expression, analogous to the expression (9.5) for an atomic orbital, for a molecular orbital. Even the simple case of the H_2^+ ion, in which there are only two attracting centres and no problem of self-consistency, requires fairly elaborate mathematical techniques for its solution, and the determination of accurate self-consistent field orbitals for molecules containing more nuclei and electrons presents a very difficult problem.

This means that for practical purposes one generally has resort to rather crude approximations for the actual molecular orbitals. These cannot be expected to give good quantitative results in the calculation of molecular properties. They are, nevertheless, of great qualitative value for the understanding of the electronic structures of many different types of molecules.

Whatever its complexity, (9.6) is soluble in principle. For a given potential energy V, the boundary condition on ψ determines the allowable molecular orbital energies ϵ, and the solutions of (9.6) that belong to any particular orbital level will form a function space whose basis generates an IR of the point group of the molecule. We may, accordingly, label the various molecular orbital levels by the symbols for the IRs that are associated with them; this labelling is precisely analogous to the characterization of atomic orbitals as $s, p, d, \ldots$ orbitals. The dimension of the IR that is associated with a particular orbital energy level gives the orbital degeneracy of the level. Thus, levels with A or B type IRs are non-degenerate; a level of type E is doubly degenerate and it will be possible to express the wave function for an electron in an E level in terms of two linearly independent molecular orbitals; a level of type T is triply-degenerate and has three independent molecular orbitals associated with it.

For example, the point group $\mathscr{T}_d$ of methane has five different IRs, A_1, A_2, E, T_1 and T_2. Consequently, any molecular orbital for a methane electron will be associated with one of these IRs and one would speak, for instance, of a non-degenerate a_1 orbital or a triply-degenerate t_2 orbital. Note here the *convention* that lower-case letters are used to label individual molecular orbitals.

An electron in a molecule retains its spin properties which are described in exactly the same way as in the preceding section. Thus each molecular orbital function $\psi(x, y, z)$ gives rise to two molecular spin-orbitals $\psi(x, y, z)\alpha(\omega)$ and $\psi(x, y, z)\beta(\omega)$. When one comes to consider placing a number of electrons into the molecular orbital levels, the Pauli principle still applies: no two electrons can have the same molecular spin-orbital. This means that the maximum number of electrons that can be placed in a level of type γ is $2n_\gamma$ where n_γ is the dimension of the corresponding IR Γ. Thus an a or b level can hold at most two electrons, an e level can hold up to four electrons, and a t level can hold up to six electrons.

Just as we did with atoms, we can imagine that the various molecular orbital levels for a given molecule have been arranged in order of increasing energy. Then an energy level for the n electrons of the molecule may be specified by giving the number of electrons that occupy each molecular orbital level. This set of occupation numbers defines an electron configuration for the molecule; the ground state configuration is found by filling the lowest lying molecular orbital levels to the maximum extent consistent with the Pauli principle.

EXAMPLE: *Methane*

Because of the symmetrical arrangement of the protons in methane a conceivable approximation for the potential energy in (9.6) would be obtained by replacing the four protons by an equivalent spherical shell of charge of radius equal to the CH bond length. This would put (9.6) into a form resembling (9.4) and, in this spherically symmetric approximation, the molecular orbitals would resemble the $1s$, $2s$ and $2p$ atomic orbitals of carbon or neon in that the lowest two orbital levels would be of s type and the next orbital would be triply degenerate of type p. One would, therefore, expect that, in a correct treatment of methane, the three lowest lying molecular orbitals would belong to IRs of $\mathscr{T}_d$ that resembled the s and p IRs of $\mathscr{R}_3$ as far as possible.

Since an s orbital is non-degenerate and is unchanged by any symmetry operation, the corresponding molecular orbital in $\mathscr{T}_d$ symmetry will generate the identical representation, i.e. it will be an a_1 molecular orbital. We conclude that the two lowest lying orbital levels in methane are both of this type and we designate them the $1a_1$ and $2a_1$ levels.

As we saw in Example 1 of Section 4.7, the effect of a symmetry operation R on a set of p_x, p_y, p_z orbitals is described by the same matrix that gives the effect of R on the base vectors of a coordinate system. Matrices of this kind are described in Section 4.2; from them we see that p_x, p_y, p_z form the basis for a representation whose character for a rotation is $\chi[C(\alpha)] = 1 + 2 \cos \alpha$ [cf. (4.10)], for an improper rotation is $\chi[S(\alpha)] = -1 + 2 \cos \alpha$ [cf. (4.15)], and for a reflection is $\chi(\sigma) = 1$ [cf. (4.13) or (4.14)]. If one considers the symmetry operations of $\mathscr{T}_d$, these formulae show that p_x, p_y, p_z form a basis for a representation of $\mathscr{T}_d$ in which

$$\chi(E) = 3, \quad \chi(C_3) = 0, \quad \chi(C_2) = -1, \quad \chi(S_4) = -1, \quad \chi(\sigma) = 1.$$

From the character table of $\mathscr{T}_d$ we see that this is just the IR T_2 of $\mathscr{T}_d$. We conclude that the correct molecular orbital in methane, which corresponds to a $2p$ orbital in the spherical approximation, is a triply degenerate t_2 orbital.

Thus we argue that the order of the molecular orbital energy levels in methane is $1a_1$, $2a_1$, t_2, ... The three lowest lying molecular orbital levels can hold 2, 2 and 6 electrons respectively and our conclusion is that the ten electrons of methane have a *closed shell* ground state configuration of the form $(1a_1)^2(2a_1)^2(t_2)^6$.

Detailed self-consistent field calculations for methane have been made on this basis with considerable success [28].

9.5 The LCAO Approximation

When a number of atoms unite to form a molecule, it is reasonable to suppose that the inner shell electrons (i.e. those electrons which, in the ground state of an atom, form closed shells with a rare gas configuration) remain in their atomic orbitals and are hardly affected by the formation of the molecule. The bonding in the molecule, on this view, is due to the valence electrons of the atoms; these electrons go into molecular orbitals spread out over the whole molecule instead of remaining in individual atomic orbitals. When such an electron is close to a particular atom, its motion will be determined almost entirely by its interactions with the nucleus and inner shell electrons of that atom, and its interactions with the other more distant atoms of the molecule will be relatively unimportant. One would, therefore, expect a molecular orbital, in the neighbourhood of an atom, to resemble one of the atomic orbitals that would be occupied by a valence electron in the ground state or a low lying excited state of that atom.

These considerations lead one to the idea that it should be possible, at least approximately, to express a molecular orbital as a *linear combination of atomic orbitals* of the form

$$\psi = \sum_i a_i \phi_i, \tag{9.7}$$

where ϕ_i is an atomic orbital centred on atom i and the a_i are numerical coefficients that describe the relative importance of the different atomic orbitals in (9.7). A molecular orbital of this form is generally referred to as an LCAO–MO and we shall use this abbreviation from now on, together with the corresponding abbreviations of 'molecular orbital' to MO and 'atomic orbital' to AO.

EXAMPLE

As an example of the kind of considerations that are involved in LCAO theory, consider the octahedral ion $MoCl_6^{3-}$. The 42 electrons of molybdenum have the ground state configuration

$$(1s)^2(2s)^2(2p)^6(3s)^2(3p)^6(3d)^{10}(4s)^2(4p)^6(4d)^5(5s).$$

The valence electrons which contribute to the bonding are the six electrons in the $4d$ and $5s$ orbitals; the remaining electrons are inner shell electrons with the closed shell configuration of krypton and we need not consider them. Molybdenum also has a $5p$ orbital with an energy fairly close to the $4d$ and $5s$ orbital energies and one might, therefore, assume that the $4d$, $5s$ and $5p$ AOs of molybdenum should be used in the formation of LCAO–MOs.

The ground state configuration of chlorine is $(1s)^2(2s)^2(2p)^6(3s)^2(3p)^5$ and, if the electrons in closed shells are ignored, one may argue that each chlorine atom provides five $3p$ electrons to fill the MO levels.

On these assumptions, if we number the chlorine atoms from 1 to 6, the LCAO–MOs of $MoCl_6^{3-}$ will have the general form

$$\psi = a_0\phi_0 + \sum_{i=1}^{6} a_i\phi_i, \tag{9.8}$$

where ϕ_0 is one of the five $4d$, or the $5s$, or one of the three $5p$ AOs of molybdenum and ϕ_i is one of the three $3p$ AOs centred on the chlorine atom i.

There are altogether 27 different AOs that may appear in (9.8) and this general expression covers a very large number of possibilities. To carry the LCAO treatment to its conclusion we must somehow select, out of all the possible linear combinations, those which can correspond to actual MOs and then we must decide on the order in which the different MO energy levels should be ranked and find out what their degeneracies are. Only when this has been done will it be possible to see how the 39 valence electrons of $MoCl_6^{3-}$ should be placed in the different MO levels to form the ground and excited states of the ion.

This example illustrates, in an extreme form, the problem that must be solved if the LCAO method is to be of practical use. It is essential to have some fairly simple way of picking out, from amongst many possibilities, just those linear combinations which can correspond to actual MOs and to have some general criteria for deciding what their relative energies will be.

Group theory plays an essential part in finding suitable linear combinations of a given set of AOs. The way in which it is used will be made clear in the various specific examples that are discussed in the rest of this chapter, but, in general terms, the application of group theory is based upon the argument that, since the correct MOs associated with a particular orbital energy level generate a definite IR of the molecular point group, the approximate LCAO–MOs must, similarly, generate IRs of the point group. Now, as we shall see in more detail in the examples that follow, any given set of AOs that are to be used in the construction of LCAO–MOs for a particular molecule will form a basis for a reducible representation, say Γ_{AO}, of the molecular point group. If this representation can be reduced into the form

$$\Gamma_{AO} = \Gamma_1 + \Gamma_2 + \cdots$$

where $\Gamma_1, \Gamma_2, \ldots$ are IRs of the point group with dimensions $n_1, n_2, \ldots$, it follows that we shall be able to find n_1 linear combinations of the given AOs which form a basis for Γ_1, n_2 linear combinations which form a basis for Γ_2, etc. It is these linear combinations, which generate definite IRs of the molecular point group, that must be used to form the LCAO–MOs, and the problem of finding LCAO–MOs is materially simplified, and sometimes even completely solved, by the process of reducing Γ_{AO}.

Once the form to be taken for an LCAO–MO has been decided upon, there remains the problem of estimating the corresponding orbital energy. Here, because of the difficulties and uncertainties in quantitative calculations, qualitative arguments based upon the concepts of bonding and anti-bonding orbitals are of great value. These matters are discussed in Section 9.7. We mention here only the general result that, if ψ is an approximate solution of (9.6), its orbital energy is given by

$$\epsilon = \int \psi H_0 \psi \, d\tau / \int \psi^2 \, d\tau, \qquad (9.9)$$

on the assumption, which we can always make, that ψ is a real function. If, as sometimes happens, ψ is not an absolutely definite function but contains some variable parameters, the best values to choose for these parameters are those which make the corresponding ϵ, defined by (9.9), a minimum.

9.6 Diatomic Molecules

The ideas that are involved in the construction of LCAO–MOs are well illustrated by a consideration of diatomic molecules and we shall take the nitrogen molecule as a typical example. Each nitrogen atom has the ground state configuration $(1s)^2(2s)^2(2p)^3$ and so, if we ignore the inner shell $1s$ electrons, the molecule has ten valence electrons to be placed in MOs formed from the $2s$ and $2p$ AOs on each atom. We denote the $2s$ AOs on the two atoms by s_1 and s_2 respectively, and the $2p$ AOs by p_{1x}, p_{1y}, p_{1z} and p_{2x}, p_{2y}, p_{2z} respectively; we choose the z axis to be the axis of the molecule so that the p_x and p_y orbitals are perpendicular to the molecular axis and the p_z orbitals point along the axis.

Our first task is to discuss the representation of the point group $\mathscr{D}_{\infty h}$ of the molecule that is generated by this set of AOs, and we begin by considering the p orbitals.

The polar diagrams of p_{1z} and p_{2z} are shown in Fig. 9.2. Note here the

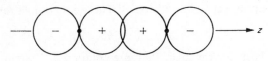

9.2 Nitrogen p_z orbitals.

way in which we have defined these functions: on atom 1 we take the z axis to point towards atom 2 so that the positive lobe of p_{1z} also points towards atom 2, while on atom 2 we take the z axis in the opposite direction so that the positive lobe of p_{2z} points towards atom 1. Notice also that the orbitals overlap each other to some extent. This is a pictorial representation of the fact that, although the magnitude of the functions p_{1z} and p_{2z} falls off rapidly as one goes away from their respective centres, nevertheless there is a region between the atoms where both p_{1z} and p_{2z} have appreciable values.

The pictorial representation of AOs by means of their polar diagrams has the advantage that we can see how a symmetry operation affects an AO by looking at its effect on the corresponding polar diagram. Thus, since p_{1z} and p_{2z} are symmetrical about the molecular axis, a rotation $C(\alpha)$ about this axis, or a reflection σ_v in a plane containing the axis, leaves them unaltered:

i.e. $C(\alpha)p_{kz} = p_{kz}$ and $\sigma_v p_{kz} = p_{kz}, \quad k = 1 \text{ or } 2.$ (9.10a)

The effect of inversion in the centre of symmetry of the molecule is simply to interchange the polar diagrams of p_{1z} and p_{2z}: the positive lobe of p_{1z} turns into the positive lobe of p_{2z} and the negative lobe of p_{1z} turns into the negative lobe of p_{2z}, and vice versa. Hence

$$ip_{1z} = p_{2z}, \qquad ip_{2z} = p_{1z}.$$ (9.10b)

Equations (9.10a,b) show that p_{1z} and p_{2z} form a basis for a representation in which $C(\alpha)$ and σ_v are both represented by the unit matrix $\begin{bmatrix} 1 & 0 \\ 0 & 1 \end{bmatrix}$ with character $\chi=2$ and in which i is represented by the matrix $\begin{bmatrix} 0 & 1 \\ 1 & 0 \end{bmatrix}$ with character $\chi=0$. These results are sufficient to establish, with the help of the character table of $\mathscr{D}_{\infty h}$, that p_{1z} and p_{2z} form the basis of a two-dimensional representation of $\mathscr{D}_{\infty h}$ which can be reduced into two component one-dimensional representations $\Sigma_g{}^+$ and $\Sigma_u{}^+$. The combinations of p_{1z} and p_{2z} that effect the reduction are

$$p_{\sigma g} = N_{\sigma g}(p_{1z}+p_{2z}) \quad \text{and} \quad p_{\sigma u} = N_{\sigma u}(p_{1z}-p_{2z}), \qquad (9.11)$$

where $N_{\sigma g}$ and $N_{\sigma u}$ are constants whose values are irrelevant for the purpose of reducing the representation but which are inserted so that we may later on normalize the functions $p_{\sigma g}$ and $p_{\sigma u}$. That these are, indeed, the correct combinations may be seen from (9.10a,b). These equations show that

$$C(\alpha)p_{\sigma g} = \sigma_v p_{\sigma g} = ip_{\sigma g} = p_{\sigma g}$$

so that $p_{\sigma g}$ is a basis for the identical representation $\Sigma_g{}^+$. Similarly,

$$C(\alpha)p_{\sigma u} = \sigma_v p_{\sigma u} = -ip_{\sigma u} = p_{\sigma u}$$

and $p_{\sigma u}$ is a basis for $\Sigma_u{}^+$.

The next AOs to be considered are the p_x and p_y orbitals. If we choose parallel x and y axes on the two atoms, the polar diagrams of p_{1x} and p_{2x} are as illustrated in Fig. 9.3. These functions vanish at all points on the yz

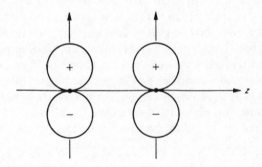

9.3 Nitrogen p_x (or p_y) orbitals.

plane but they overlap each other at points off this plane. The overlap is, however, rather smaller than it is for the p_z orbitals which point directly towards each other. The polar diagrams for p_{1y} and p_{2y} are obtained from Fig. 9.3 by rotating it through 90° about the molecular axis. We now consider the effect of a symmetry operation on these four functions.

The effect of a rotation $C(\alpha)$ about the molecular axis on the pair of functions p_{1x} and p_{1y}, and also on the pair p_{2x} and p_{2y}, is exactly the same as the effect of a rotation $C(\alpha)$ about the e_3 axis of a coordinate system on the base vectors e_1 and e_2. This was discussed in Section 4.2 and from (4.9) we see that

$$C(\alpha)p_{1x} = \cos \alpha \cdot p_{1x} + \sin \alpha \cdot p_{1y}, \qquad C(\alpha)p_{1y} = -\sin \alpha \cdot p_{1x} + \cos \alpha \cdot p_{1y},$$

$$C(\alpha)p_{2x} = \cos \alpha \cdot p_{2x} + \sin \alpha \cdot p_{2y}, \qquad C(\alpha)p_{2y} = -\sin \alpha \cdot p_{2x} + \cos \alpha \cdot p_{2y}.$$

These equations show that, with respect to $p_{1x}, p_{1y}, p_{2x}, p_{2y}$ taken in this order as base functions, $C(\alpha)$ is represented by the matrix

$$\begin{bmatrix} \cos \alpha & -\sin \alpha & 0 & 0 \\ \sin \alpha & \cos \alpha & 0 & 0 \\ 0 & 0 & \cos \alpha & -\sin \alpha \\ 0 & 0 & \sin \alpha & \cos \alpha \end{bmatrix}$$

with character $\chi = 4 \cos \alpha$.

In exactly the same way we see, on using (4.12), that a reflection σ_v in a plane which passes through the molecular axis and which makes an angle β with the xz plane is represented, with respect to $p_{1x}, \ldots, p_{2y}$ as basis, by the matrix

$$\begin{bmatrix} \cos 2\beta & \sin 2\beta & 0 & 0 \\ \sin 2\beta & -\cos 2\beta & 0 & 0 \\ 0 & 0 & \cos 2\beta & \sin 2\beta \\ 0 & 0 & \sin 2\beta & -\cos 2\beta \end{bmatrix}$$

with character $\chi = 0$.

Finally, we note that under inversion in the centre of symmetry the positive lobe of p_{1x} is brought into the position of the negative lobe of p_{2x} and the negative lobe of p_{1x} is brought into the position of the positive lobe of p_{2x}. Thus p_{1x} is changed into the negative of p_{2x} by the inversion. Similar arguments apply to the other functions, and

$$ip_{1x} = -p_{2x}, \quad ip_{1y} = -p_{2y}, \quad ip_{2x} = -p_{1x}, \quad ip_{2y} = -p_{1y}.$$

The inversion operation is, therefore, represented in this basis by the matrix

$$\begin{bmatrix} 0 & 0 & -1 & 0 \\ 0 & 0 & 0 & -1 \\ -1 & 0 & 0 & 0 \\ 0 & -1 & 0 & 0 \end{bmatrix}$$

with character $\chi = 0$.

These results are sufficient to show, from inspection of the character table, that the four functions $p_{1x}, \ldots, p_{2y}$ generate a four-dimensional representation of $\mathcal{D}_{\infty h}$ which can be reduced into two component two-dimensional

IRs, Π_g and Π_u. It is readily seen that the linear combinations of $p_{1x}, \ldots, p_{2y}$ which reduce the four-dimensional representation may be taken to be the pairs of functions

$$p_{\pi ux} = N_{\pi u}(p_{1x}+p_{2x}), \qquad p_{\pi uy} = N_{\pi u}(p_{1y}+p_{2y}), \qquad (9.12)$$

which form a basis for Π_u, and

$$p_{\pi gx} = N_{\pi g}(p_{1x}-p_{2x}), \qquad p_{\pi gy} = N_{\pi g}(p_{1y}-p_{2y}), \qquad (9.13)$$

which form a basis for Π_g. Here $N_{\pi u}$ and $N_{\pi g}$ are normalizing constants put in for later convenience.

We have still to consider the pair of 2s AOs, s_1 and s_2. These functions have spherical symmetry about their respective centres and their polar diagrams are shown in Fig. 9.4. It is clear from this figure that s_1 and s_2 behave in all

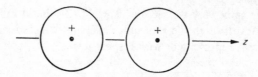

9.4 Nitrogen s orbitals.

respects like p_{1z} and p_{2z} under the symmetry operations of $\mathscr{D}_{\infty h}$. Consequently, s_1 and s_2, like p_{1z} and p_{2z}, form a basis for a reducible two-dimensional representation of $\mathscr{D}_{\infty h}$ that can be reduced into its component one-dimensional representations Σ_g^+ and Σ_u^+ by taking the linear combinations

$$s_{\sigma g} = N'_{\sigma g}(s_1+s_2) \quad \text{and} \quad s_{\sigma u} = N'_{\sigma u}(s_1-s_2) \qquad (9.14)$$

as basis functions.

The results that we have obtained are summarized by saying that the eight AOs $s_1, p_{1x}, p_{1y}, p_{1z}, s_2, p_{2x}, p_{2y}, p_{2z}$ generate a reducible representation Γ_{AO} of $\mathscr{D}_{\infty h}$ which can be reduced into the form

$$\Gamma_{AO} = 2\Sigma_g^+ + 2\Sigma_u^+ + \Pi_g + \Pi_u \qquad (9.15)$$

by taking as a basis the linear combinations of AOs that are given in equations (9.11, 12, 13, 14). As we saw at the end of the previous section, this means that, from the eight AOs, we can form LCAO–MOs that correspond to six different MO energy levels, one level for each IR contained in Γ_{AO}. These six levels are classified according to the IRs with which they are associated: there will be two different non-degenerate σ_g^+ levels, two different non-degenerate σ_u^+ levels, one doubly-degenerate π_u level, and one doubly-degenerate π_g level. Suitable pairs of LCAO–MOs for the π_u and π_g levels are given by (9.12) and (9.13) respectively. The most general forms for the MOs belonging to the two σ_g levels are linear combinations of the functions $p_{\sigma g}$ and $s_{\sigma g}$ defined in (9.11) and (9.14) and, similarly, the most general forms for the MOs belonging to the two σ_u levels are linear combinations of the functions $p_{\sigma u}$ and $s_{\sigma u}$.

This is as far as a group-theoretical analysis based on general symmetry arguments can take us; further conclusions about the relative energies of the levels and the particular combinations of s_σ and p_σ functions that will actually be found in the σ levels must be based upon other, more physical arguments.

9.7 Bonding and Anti-bonding Orbitals

In attempting to find the correct order of energy in which to place the LCAO–MOs that were found in the preceding section, we begin by remarking that the $2s$ level in a nitrogen atom has a lower energy than the $2p$ level and that we would, correspondingly, expect the $2s$ AOs to form MOs of rather lower energy than the MOs formed from the $2p$ AOs. Since our theory is primarily a qualitative one, it is, therefore, reasonable to ignore the theoretically possible mixing of $2s$ and $2p$ AOs that may occur in the LCAO–MOs of the σ levels. We assume that the σ_g^+ and σ_u^+ levels of lower energy, which we designate the $1\sigma_g^+$ and $1\sigma_u^+$ levels, have energies comparable with that of the $2s$ level in a nitrogen atom and that their LCAO–MOs are given by (9.14); similarly, we assume that the σ_g^+ and σ_u^+ levels of higher energy, designated the $2\sigma_g^+$ and $2\sigma_u^+$ levels, have energies comparable with that of the $2p$ level in a nitrogen atom and that their LCAO–MOs are given by (9.11).

The individual LCAO expressions that appear in (9.11, 12, 13, 14) arise from combinations of two identical AOs, say ϕ_1 and ϕ_2, on the two atoms; these combinations have the forms

$$\psi_+ = N_+(\phi_1 + \phi_2), \qquad \psi_- = N_-(\phi_1 - \phi_2). \qquad (9.16)$$

Thus, if $\phi_1 = s_1$ and $\phi_2 = s_2$, ψ_+ and ψ_- are MOs for the $1\sigma_g^+$ and $1\sigma_u^+$ levels respectively; if $\phi_1 = p_{1z}$ and $\phi_2 = p_{2z}$, ψ_+ and ψ_- are MOs for the $2\sigma_g^+$ and $2\sigma_u^+$ levels respectively; if $\phi_1 = p_{1x}$ and $\phi_2 = p_{2x}$, or if $\phi_1 = p_{1y}$ and $\phi_2 = p_{2y}$, ψ_+ and ψ_- are MOs for the π_u and π_g levels respectively.

The results that we need may be established by considering the characteristic differences between orbitals of the two types, ψ_+ and ψ_-. Before proceeding to discuss their energies, however, we shall *normalize* the LCAO–MOs. When an electron moves in a (real) MO ψ, the probability of finding the electron inside a small volume $d\tau$ surrounding a point P is $[\psi(P)]^2 \, d\tau$, where $\psi(P)$ is the value of ψ at P. Since the electron must certainly be somewhere, the probability interpretation of ψ demands that it should be such that

$$\int \psi^2 \, d\tau = 1,$$

and we should, therefore, always deal with MOs that satisfy this normalization condition. If we consider ψ_+, for example, the condition means that we must choose the constant N_+ in such a way that

$$\int \psi_+{}^2 \, d\tau = N_+{}^2 \left\{ \int \phi_1{}^2 \, d\tau + \int \phi_2{}^2 \, d\tau + 2 \int \phi_1 \phi_2 \, d\tau \right\} = 1. \qquad (9.17)$$

We shall suppose that the AOs that are used in the construction of LCAO–MOs have already been individually normalized. Thus ϕ_1 and ϕ_2 will satisfy

$$\int \phi_1{}^2 \, d\tau = \int \phi_2{}^2 \, d\tau = 1,$$

and it remains to consider the *overlap integral*

$$S = \int \phi_1 \phi_2 \, d\tau.$$

If the two atoms were actually coincident, ϕ_1 would coincide exactly with ϕ_2 and one would have $S = 1$. If, on the other hand, the atoms were so far apart that ϕ_1 was effectively zero in regions where ϕ_2 was appreciable, and conversely, S would vanish. In general, ϕ_1 and ϕ_2 will overlap to some extent and S has a value intermediate between 0 and 1. The actual value of S will depend on the detailed form of ϕ_1 and ϕ_2. The more they overlap, the greater will be the value of S. Thus, for the $2p$ AOs, one would expect the integral $S(p_\sigma)$, which describes the overlap of the p_z orbitals, to be greater than the integral $S(p_\pi)$ which describes the overlap of the p_x or the p_y orbitals.

In terms of the overlap integral, (9.17) is

$$\int \psi_+{}^2 \, d\tau = N_+{}^2 (2 + 2S) = 1,$$

and ψ_+ is, therefore, normalized by putting

$$N_+ = 1/[2(1+S)]^{1/2}. \qquad (9.18a)$$

In just the same way, we find that ψ_- is normalized by putting

$$N_- = 1/[2(1-S)]^{1/2}. \qquad (9.18b)$$

The energies of the MOs ψ_+ and ψ_- are given by the general formula (9.9). The formula requires us to evaluate the integral $\int \psi H_0 \psi \, d\tau$, where H_0 is the effective Hamiltonian. When ψ is expressed in terms of ϕ_1 and ϕ_2, this integral involves separate integrals of the form

$$H_{ij} = \int \phi_i H_0 \phi_j \, d\tau; \qquad i, j = 1, 2.$$

Since ϕ_1 and ϕ_2 are identical functions, $H_{11} = H_{22}$; we may assume that the value of H_{11} (or H_{22}) will be fairly close to the energy of ϕ_1 (or ϕ_2) considered as an atomic orbital. We denote this energy by ϵ'.

For the integrals H_{12} and H_{21} we note that H_0 will be what is called an Hermitian operator with the property that

$$\int \phi_1 H_0 \phi_2 \, d\tau = \int \phi_2 H_0 \phi_1 \, d\tau$$

for any two real functions ϕ_1 and ϕ_2. Thus $H_{12} = H_{21} = \beta$, say. The integral β that is defined in this way is called the *resonance integral*; it is given this name because of a mechanical analogy which has caused much confusion in the past and which we shall not discuss. One cannot say much about the value of β without a detailed calculation based upon the assumption of specific forms for H_0 and the functions ϕ_1 and ϕ_2. For our present purposes, it suffices to say that β is negative and that one may assume that it bears a rough proportionality to the overlap integral S.

If we choose the values for N_+ and N_- that are given in (9.18a,b), ψ_+ and ψ_- are normalized functions and (9.9) gives their energies as

$$\epsilon_+ = \int \psi_+ H_0 \psi_+ \, d\tau = (\epsilon' + \beta)/(1 + S) \tag{9.19a}$$

and

$$\epsilon_- = \int \psi_- H_0 \psi_- \, d\tau = (\epsilon' - \beta)/(1 - S). \tag{9.19b}$$

When the overlap integral is fairly small, one can neglect it in the denominators of (9.19a,b); this gives the *approximate* values

$$\epsilon_+ = \epsilon' + \beta, \qquad \epsilon_- = \epsilon' - \beta. \tag{9.20}$$

Since β is negative, these results show that when MOs are formed from two identical AOs of energy ϵ', the ψ_+ orbital has an energy which is lower than ϵ' by approximately the amount of the resonance integral while the energy of the ψ_- orbital lies above ϵ' by approximately the same amount. We say that ψ_+ is a *bonding* orbital and that ψ_- is an *anti-bonding* orbital.

The energy difference between the bonding and anti-bonding orbitals formed from a given pair of AOs on the two atoms is associated with a marked qualitative difference between the forms of ψ_+ and ψ_-. Since ϕ_1 and ϕ_2 are identical functions with a positive overlap, ϕ_1 is equal to ϕ_2 at all points on the symmetry plane that is perpendicular to the molecular axis and ψ_- must vanish at all points on this plane. Thus ψ_- describes a state in which the electron is confined to two distinct regions centred approximately on the two atoms. In picturesque language, we may say that an electron in the anti-bonding ψ_- orbital spends half its time on each atom but is never found in the region between the atoms. The bonding ψ_+ orbital, on the other hand, describes a state in which the electron has a fair probability of being found in the space between the atoms at points where it is simultaneously attracted towards both atoms. The nature of these orbitals is shown diagrammatically in Fig. 9.5. The figure shows a characteristic difference between the MOs formed from s or p_z AOs which overlap along the molecular axis and which give rise to the $\sigma_g{}^+$ bonding and $\sigma_u{}^+$ anti-bonding orbitals and the MOs formed from the p_x or p_y AOs which overlap at points off the molecular axis and which give rise to the π_u bonding and π_g anti-bonding orbitals.

We may assume that the energy difference between the 2s and 2p levels of a nitrogen atom is large enough to ensure that the energy of the $1\sigma_u^+$ anti-bonding level arising from the $2s$ AOs lies below the lowest bonding level arising from the $2p$ AOs. The only question that remains to be decided is that of the ordering of the bonding and anti-bonding combinations of the $2p$ AOs. Now (9.20) shows that, as long as the overlap integral S is not too large, a bonding orbital is lowered in energy, and an anti-bonding orbital is raised in energy, relative to the corresponding atomic energy level by an amount equal approximately to the magnitude of the resonance integral.

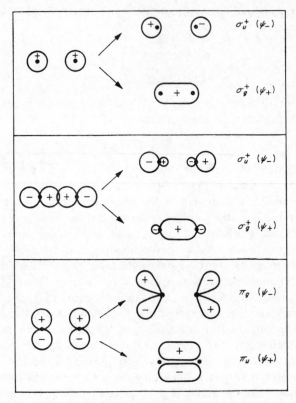

9.5 Schematic representations of bonding and anti-bonding orbitals.

This integral is roughly proportional to S so that we would expect the bonding (and, equally, the anti-bonding) effect in the σ orbitals formed from p_z AOs with a strong overlap along the molecular axis to be more important than it is in the π orbitals formed from p_x or p_y AOs with a weaker overlap at points off the molecular axis. If this is correct, the order of MO levels arising from the $2p$ AOs will be $2\sigma_g^+$, π_u, π_g, $2\sigma_u^+$. In this way we obtain the *energy level diagram* shown in Fig. 9.6; the MO levels are shown in the centre of the diagram while the atomic energy levels from which the MO levels are derived are shown on either side.

Once we know the order of the energy levels we can proceed to fill them with the valence electrons of the molecule and to write down the electron configurations of the ground and excited states. In accordance with the Pauli principle, a σ level, being non-degenerate, can hold up to two electrons and a π level, being doubly-degenerate, can hold up to four electrons. If we place the ten valence electrons of N_2 in the lowest lying levels of Fig. 9.6, ignoring

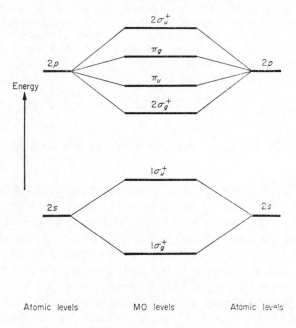

9.6 The energy level diagram for N_2.

the inner K shell electrons, we obtain the ground state configuration $(1\sigma_g{}^+)^2(1\sigma_u{}^+)^2(2\sigma_g{}^+)^2(\pi_u)^4$. This is a closed shell configuration since every MO level is occupied to its fullest extent. The bonding and anti-bonding effects of the electrons in the $1\sigma_g{}^+$ and $1\sigma_u{}^+$ levels effectively cancel each other and the bonding in the molecule arises from the two electrons in the $2\sigma_g{}^+$ level (a σ bond) and the four electrons in the π_u level (a double π bond).

Molecules similar to N_2, like O_2 and F_2, may be treated in the same way. Their energy level diagrams will be similar to that shown in Fig. 9.6. Thus the twelve valence electrons of O_2 will have the ground state configuration $(1\sigma_g{}^+)^2(1\sigma_u{}^+)^2(2\sigma_g{}^+)^2(\pi_u)^4(\pi_g)^2$ with two electrons in the anti-bonding π_g level. The anti-bonding effect of these two electrons effectively cancels half the π bonding given by the four π_u electrons: O_2 is a double-bonded molecule with one σ bond and one π bond. The ground state configuration of O_2 is interesting because it is not a closed shell; it has only two electrons in a π_g orbital which could hold four electrons.

The fluorine molecule has fourteen valence electrons and a closed shell ground state configuration $(1\sigma_g{}^+)^2(1\sigma_u{}^+)^2(2\sigma_g{}^+)^2(\pi_u)^4(\pi_g)^4$. Here the four electrons in the anti-bonding π_g level cancel the bonding due to the four electrons in the bonding π_u level and the bonding in F_2 is effectively a σ bond due to the two electrons in the $2\sigma_g{}^+$ level.

Notation: We have labelled the MO levels by the symbols for their associated IRs, since this is the convention that is adopted for polyatomic molecules. There are, however, two other systems of labelling the levels of diatomic molecules that are more commonly to be found in the literature. The symbols used in the different systems are set out below.

$1\sigma_g{}^+$	$1\sigma_u{}^+$	$2\sigma_g{}^+$	π_u	π_g	$2\sigma_u{}^+$
$\sigma 2s$	$\sigma^* 2s$	$\sigma 2p$	$\pi 2p$	$\pi^* 2p$	$\sigma^* 2p$
$z\sigma$	$y\sigma$	$x\sigma$	$w\pi$	$v\pi$	$u\sigma$

In general, it is fairly common usage to denote an anti-bonding level by an asterisk.

It is of some interest to review the essentially qualitative nature of the argument that led to the energy level diagram of Fig. 9.6. The argument made use of two quite different aspects of the LCAO approximation. Firstly, we were able to apply general considerations of symmetry to obtain the symmetry classifications of the lower lying MO levels and the forms of the corresponding LCAO–MOs. Secondly, because in the LCAO approximation the energy of a level depends upon overlap and resonance integrals involving the AOs, we were able to use quite general qualitative arguments about σ and π bonding and anti-bonding orbitals to decide upon a particular order for the MO levels. No specific assumptions about the actual form of the effective Hamiltonian or the detailed radial dependence of the AOs were required.

Now the energy level diagram of Fig. 9.6 can be exhaustively tested by a detailed analysis of the electronic spectra of molecules like N_2, O_2 and F_2; this analysis shows that the diagram is, in fact, correct. Precisely because we were able to construct the diagram on the basis of very general qualitative arguments, we may take this agreement between theory and experiment as strong evidence that the LCAO approximation provides a valid qualitative description of the bonding in diatomic molecules and we are encouraged in the hope that the method may profitably be applied to polyatomic molecules also. The qualitative and tentative nature of the LCAO method must, however, be remembered in every application and any energy level diagram that it suggests must be treated with reserve until it has been tested by comparison with experiment.

9.8 Benzene

An important application of the LCAO method is the description it enables us to give of π bonding in certain types of organic molecules. We shall consider benzene as a typical example. In this molecule the electrons that participate in the bonding are the four electrons in $2s$ and $2p$ AOs on each carbon atom and the $1s$ electron of each hydrogen atom, a total of 30 electrons. These electrons will go into MOs which, in the LCAO approximation, are linear combinations of the six hydrogen $1s$ AOs and the sets of $2s$, $2p_x$, $2p_y$ and $2p_z$ AOs on each carbon atom.

In order to define the $2p$ AOs we suppose that a set of xyz axes has been chosen for each carbon atom and that all the z axes are parallel and point in the same direction perpendicular to the plane of the molecule. With this choice of axes, the polar diagrams of the $2p_z$ AOs are as indicated in Fig. 9.7. The $2p_z$ orbitals are capable of π type overlaps with each other and they

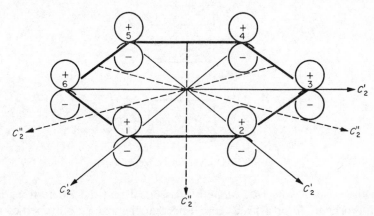

9.7 Benzene p_z orbitals.

are distinguished from the other AOs by the effect on them of a reflection σ_h in the molecular plane. This reflection reverses the directions (i.e. it interchanges the positive and negative lobes) of all the $2p_z$ AOs; the $2s$ carbon and $1s$ hydrogen AOs and the $2p_x$ and $2p_y$ carbon AOs, on the other hand, are left unaltered by σ_h. Because of this difference, the $2p_z$ AOs can never be mixed with the other orbitals in any LCAO–MO.

Now the $2s$, $2p_x$ and $2p_y$ AOs on a carbon atom can have substantial σ type overlaps with the similar AOs on the adjacent carbon atoms and with the $1s$ AO on the adjacent hydrogen atom. The hydrogen $1s$ AOs and the carbon $2s$, $2p_x$ and $2p_y$ AOs, therefore, form a set of 24 AOs from which one will be able to produce strongly bonding and strongly anti-bonding LCAO–MOs. Since a bonding orbital will always have its anti-bonding counterpart, there will be 12 σ bonding MOs and 12 σ anti-bonding MOs and, in the ground state of the molecule, the 12 bonding levels will be filled with 24 electrons. The remaining six electrons must go into MOs formed from the $2p_z$ carbon AOs; because of their π type overlaps, the bonding and anti-bonding combinations of these AOs will have energies which lie between those of the σ bonding and the σ anti-bonding levels. A general indication of the energy level diagram that would be expected is given in Fig. 9.8.

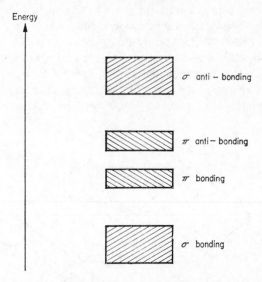

9.8 MO levels in benzene.

In the *π-electron approximation* it is assumed that the 24 electrons in σ bonding orbitals form a fixed 'core' and that the aromatic properties and electronic spectrum of the molecule are determined by the six π electrons which move in the field of the nuclei and the average field of the core electrons. In this approximation, we simply ignore the σ electrons and consider only the π electrons, assuming that their motion is governed by an effective Hamiltonian that somehow incorporates the average effect of the σ electrons. Our problem then is to determine the symmetries of the LCAO–MOs that can be formed from the $2p_z$ AOs and to estimate their energies.

The six $2p_z$ AOs form a basis for a reducible representation Γ_{AO} of the point group $\mathscr{D}_{6h}$ of benzene. Since $\mathscr{D}_{6h} = \mathscr{D}_6 \times i$, we can obtain most of the information we require from a consideration of the simpler group $\mathscr{D}_6$. The symmetry operations of $\mathscr{D}_6$ divide into the classes E; $2C_6$; $2C_3$; C_2; $3C_2'$; $3C_2''$. Here C_2' and C_2'' are rotations about the two different sets of twofold axes lying in the molecular plane, as indicated in Fig. 9.7, and the other operations are rotations about the main symmetry axis of the molecule.

The characters of Γ_{AO} are easily written down. The effect of the operator O_R, corresponding to the symmetry operation R, on the p_z orbitals can be discovered by examining the effect of R on the polar diagrams shown in Fig. 9.7. We denote the p_z AOs on the various atoms by $p_1, p_2, \ldots, p_6$. Then the 6×6 matrices $D(R)$ of Γ_{AO} are defined by the relations

$$O_R p_k = \sum_{j=1}^{6} [D(R)]_{jk} p_j,$$

and the character of R in Γ_{AO} is the sum of the diagonal elements:

$$\chi(R) = \sum_{k=1}^{6} [D(R)]_{kk}.$$

Now if R is a symmetry operation of $\mathscr{D}_6$, it can have one of three effects on an orbital p_k. Either it leaves p_k unaltered, or it reverses the direction of p_k, or it moves p_k into the position of some other orbital p_l with or without a reversal of direction. Thus

$$\text{either} \quad O_R p_k = p_k \quad \text{and} \quad [D(R)]_{kk} = 1,$$

$$\text{or} \quad O_R p_k = -p_k \quad \text{and} \quad [D(R)]_{kk} = -1,$$

$$\text{or} \quad O_R p_k = \pm p_l \quad \text{and} \quad [D(R)]_{kk} = 0.$$

Hence an orbital that is left alone by R gives a contribution $+1$ to the character, an orbital that has its direction reversed by R gives a contribution -1 to the character, and an orbital that is moved onto another atom by R gives a zero contribution to the character. For the operations of $\mathscr{D}_6$ we see that E leaves all the orbitals alone and has character $\chi = 6$, that each operation of the type C_6, C_3, C_2, or C_2'' moves all the orbitals onto different atoms and has character $\chi = 0$, and that an operation of the type C_2' reverses the directions of two of the orbitals and moves the other orbitals onto different atoms so that it has character $\chi = -2$. Thus Γ_{AO} has the set of characters set out below.

$\mathscr{D}_6$	E	$2C_6$	$2C_3$	C_2	$3C_2'$	$3C_2''$
Γ_{AO}	6	0	0	0	-2	0

We now use (6.5) and the character table of $\mathscr{D}_6$ to find the IRs that are contained in Γ_{AO}. Since the characters of these IRs are all real, the number of times that the IR Γ_v occurs in Γ_{AO} is, from (6.5), given by

$$a_v = \frac{1}{12} \{\chi^{(v)}(E) \cdot 6 + 0 + 0 + 0 + 3\chi^{(v)}(C_2') \cdot (-2) + 0\} = \tfrac{1}{2}\{\chi^{(v)}(E) - \chi^{(v)}(C_2')\}.$$

On looking at the values of the characters $\chi^{(\nu)}(E)$ and $\chi^{(\nu)}(C_2')$ that are given in the character table of $\mathcal{D}_6$, we see that the IRs A_2, B_2, E_1 and E_2 each occur once in Γ_{AO} and that A_1 and B_1 do not appear at all.

It will, therefore, be possible to find linear combinations of $p_1, \ldots, p_6$ which serve as bases for the IRs A_2, B_2, E_1 and E_2 of $\mathcal{D}_6$, and these linear combinations will, necessarily, generate IRs of the complete point group $\mathcal{D}_{6h}$ of benzene. The IRs of $\mathcal{D}_{6h}$ that will be concerned are easily identified by noting that each orbital p_k, and so any linear combination of the p_k, changes sign under the reflection σ_h in the molecular plane. Thus any IR of $\mathcal{D}_{6h}$ whose basis consists of linear combinations of the p_k must be such that $\chi(\sigma_h)$ is negative. Each IR of $\mathcal{D}_6$ gives rise to just one such IR of $\mathcal{D}_{6h}$ which can be identified from the character table of $\mathcal{D}_{6h}$. Examination of the character table shows that, when the complete group $\mathcal{D}_{6h}$ is considered, the reduction of Γ_{AO} is

$$\Gamma_{AO}^{\bullet} = A_{2u} + B_{2g} + E_{1g} + E_{2u}. \tag{9.21}$$

The linear combinations of $p_1, \ldots, p_6$ that form bases for these IRs may be found by using the projection operator method described in Section 6.6. For the purpose of finding the appropriate linear combinations it is sufficient to consider the projection operators for the IRs A_2, B_2, E_1 and E_2 of $\mathcal{D}_6$. The general form of the projection operator $P^{(\mu)}$ for an IR Γ_μ of a point group is given by (6.13). If the characters of the IRs of $\mathcal{D}_6$ are inserted into (6.13), the required projection operators are found to be:

$$P^{(A_2)} = E + (C_6 + C_6^{-1}) + (C_3 + C_3^{-1}) + C_2 - \left(\sum C_2'\right) - \left(\sum C_2''\right),$$

$$P^{(B_2)} = E - (C_6 + C_6^{-1}) + (C_3 + C_3^{-1}) - C_2 - \left(\sum C_2'\right) + \left(\sum C_2''\right),$$

$$P^{(E_1)} = 2E + (C_6 + C_6^{-1}) - (C_3 + C_3^{-1}) - 2C_2,$$

$$P^{(E_2)} = 2E - (C_6 + C_6^{-1}) - (C_3 + C_3^{-1}) + 2C_2.$$

In these expressions, $\sum C_2'$ and $\sum C_2''$ refer to the sum over the three operations C_2' and the three operations C_2'' respectively.

The argument leading to (6.17) shows that when one of these operators is applied to a base function p_k of Γ_{AO} it will generate a linear combination of $p_1, \ldots, p_6$ which belongs to the corresponding IR of $\mathcal{D}_6$. Figure 9.7 can be used to see what the effects of the symmetry operations of $\mathcal{D}_6$ on the base functions p_k are. On applying $P^{(A_2)}$ to p_1 in particular, one finds

$$P^{(A_2)}p_1 = p_1 + (p_2 + p_6) + (p_3 + p_5) + p_4 - (-p_1 - p_3 - p_5) - (-p_2 - p_4 - p_6)$$

$$= 2(p_1 + p_2 + p_3 + p_4 + p_5 + p_6).$$

Thus, as is fairly obvious from inspection, the LCAO–MO which acts as a basis for the one-dimensional IR A_{2u} of $\mathcal{D}_{6h}$ is

$$\psi(a_2) = N_a(p_1 + p_2 + p_3 + p_4 + p_5 + p_6) \tag{9.22}$$

where N_a is a normalizing factor. This combination has a positive overlap between the AOs on adjacent atoms and so it will be a bonding orbital.

In the same way, one finds that

$$P^{(B_2)}p_1 = p_1 - (p_2 + p_6) + (p_3 + p_5) - p_4 - (-p_1 - p_3 - p_5) + (-p_2 - p_4 - p_6)$$

$$= 2(p_1 - p_2 + p_3 - p_4 + p_5 - p_6).$$

Thus the LCAO–MO for the IR B_{2g} of $\mathscr{D}_{6h}$ is

$$\psi(b_2) = N_b(p_1 - p_2 + p_3 - p_4 + p_5 - p_6) \tag{9.23}$$

where N_b is a normalizing factor. This combination involves a negative overlap between the AOs on adjacent atoms and it must be an anti-bonding orbital.

We come now to the two-dimensional IR E_{1g}. If we apply the operator $P^{(E_1)}$ to one of the p_k base functions, we shall obtain a linear combination of $p_1, \ldots, p_6$ which, when normalized, will be a suitable LCAO–MO $\psi(e_1)$ for the e_{1g} level. It will be possible, since E_{1g} is two-dimensional, to find another linear combination of $p_1, \ldots, p_6$ which is orthogonal to $\psi(e_1)$ and which will serve as the second LCAO–MO belonging to the e_{1g} level. But, since both these MOs must have the same energy, we can calculate the energy of the e_{1g} level from a knowledge of just one of them. A suitable form for $\psi(e_1)$ will be obtained by applying $P^{(E_1)}$ to p_1. This gives

$$P^{(E_1)}p_1 = 2p_1 + (p_2 + p_6) - (p_3 + p_5) - 2p_4$$

so that we can take

$$\psi(e_1) = N_e\{(p_6 + 2p_1 + p_2) - (p_3 + 2p_4 + p_5)\} \tag{9.24}$$

as a suitable normalized LCAO–MO belonging to the e_{1g} level. This orbital has bonding character between the three adjacent AOs p_6, p_1, p_2 and also between the three adjacent AOs p_3, p_4, p_5 but it has an anti-bonding character between p_2 and p_3 and between p_5 and p_6. We would, therefore, expect the e_{1g} level to be bonding but not so strongly bonding as the a_{2u} level.

Exactly similar arguments apply to the E_{2u} IR. We apply the operator $P^{(E_2)}$ to p_1 to obtain

$$P^{(E_2)}p_1 = 2p_1 - (p_2 + p_6) - (p_3 + p_5) + 2p_4.$$

A suitable form for a normalized LCAO–MO belonging to the e_{2u} level is, therefore,

$$\psi(e_2) = N_e'\{(2p_1 - p_2 - p_6) + (2p_4 - p_3 - p_5)\}. \tag{9.25}$$

This orbital has anti-bonding character between p_6, p_1, p_2 and between p_3, p_4, p_5 but it has bonding character between p_2 and p_3 and between p_5 and p_6. We would, therefore, expect the e_{2u} level to be anti-bonding on the whole, but not so strongly anti-bonding as the b_{2g} level.

The qualitative conclusions that we have drawn from this analysis of the symmetry properties of the $2p_z$ AOs in benzene may be stated thus: from the reduction of Γ_{AO} given in (9.21) it follows that the $2p_z$ AOs on the carbon atoms give rise to four distinct MO levels; suitable LCAO–MOs for these levels are given by (9.22, 23, 24, 25) and, from a consideration of the bonding and anti-bonding combinations of the $2p_z$ AOs that are contained in these MOs, we expect the order of increasing energy of MO levels to be a_{2u}, e_{1g}, e_{2u}, b_{2g}. Since an a level can hold two electrons and an e level can hold four electrons, the ground state configuration of the six π electrons in benzene should be $(a_{2u})^2(e_{1g})^4$, a closed shell ground state in which the bonding orbitals are fully occupied and the anti-bonding orbitals are empty.

To make the theory more precise and to obtain an estimate for the energies of these levels, one needs, first of all, to know the values of the overlap integrals

$$S_{ij} = \int p_i p_j \, d\tau$$

in order to calculate the normalizing factors for the various LCAO–MOs. Once the MOs have been normalized, their energies can be calculated from (9.9); this requires a knowledge of the integrals

$$H_{ij} = \int p_i H_0 p_j \, d\tau = \int p_j H_0 p_i \, d\tau$$

where H_0 is the effective Hamiltonian. In order to simplify the calculation as much as possible one generally makes use of the *Hückel approximation*. In this approximation it is assumed that the only integrals H_{ij} that are of any importance are ones that involve the same AO ($i=j$) or AOs on two adjacent atoms ($i=j+1$). Since $p_1, \ldots, p_6$ are identical functions, the approximation means that we put $H_{ij}=0$ except for

$$H_{11} = H_{22} = \cdots = H_{66} = \alpha, \qquad H_{21} = H_{32} = \cdots = H_{16} = \beta. \quad (9.26)$$

Here α is the energy that a π electron would have if it was forced to remain in a $2p_z$ AO localized on one of the carbon atoms, and β is the resonance integral between a pair of $2p_z$ AOs on adjacent atoms. In principle, α and β should be calculated from a knowledge of H_0 and of the form of the $2p_z$ AOs, but in practice they are treated as parameters whose values are to be estimated from experimentally measured quantities.

Since H_{ij} may be presumed to be roughly proportional to the corresponding overlap integral S_{ij}, the above approximation means that we must also neglect the overlap integrals between non-adjacent atoms and this seems reasonable enough. The Hückel approximation goes further, however, and also neglects the overlap integrals between adjacent atoms. These assumptions of the Hückel method, namely that we assume

$$S_{12} = \int p_1 p_2 \, d\tau = 0 \quad \text{but} \quad H_{12} = \int p_1 H_0 p_2 \, d\tau \neq 0,$$

appear to be inconsistent. In spite of this inconsistency, however, the Hückel approximation has been extraordinarily successful in explaining and predicting the properties of those organic molecules for which the π-electron approximation is valid. The theoretical bases of the π-electron approximation and of Hückel's additional approximations have been the subject of much study; the reasons for the rather surprising success of the method and also for its limitations are now fairly well understood. We shall not attempt to go into the matter but will merely illustrate the way in which the Hückel approximations are applied to benzene.

We suppose that $p_1, \ldots, p_6$ have been individually normalized and we consider a general linear combination of $p_1, \ldots, p_6$ of the form

$$\psi = N(c_1 p_1 + c_2 p_2 + c_3 p_3 + c_4 p_4 + c_5 p_5 + c_6 p_6) \tag{9.27}$$

where $c_1, \ldots, c_6$ are real coefficients and N is a normalizing factor. In the Hückel approximation we ignore every overlap integral, i.e. since the p_k are already normalized, we replace $S_{ij} = \int p_i p_j \, d\tau$ by 1 if $i=j$ and by 0 if $i \neq j$. Then the normalization of ψ is given by

$$\int \psi^2 \, d\tau = N^2 \int (c_1 p_1 + \cdots + c_6 p_6)^2 \, d\tau = N^2(c_1{}^2 + c_2{}^2 + \cdots + c_6{}^2).$$

This is equal to unity and ψ is normalized if

$$N^2 = 1/(c_1{}^2 + c_2{}^2 + \cdots + c_6{}^2). \tag{9.28}$$

The energy of the MO level to which the LCAO–MO (9.27) belongs is given by (9.9):

$$\epsilon = N^2 \int (c_1 p_1 + \cdots + c_6 p_6) H_0 (c_1 p_1 + \cdots + c_6 p_6) \, d\tau.$$

If we neglect all the H_{ij} integrals except those mentioned in (9.26), this gives

$$\epsilon = N^2 \{\alpha(c_1{}^2 + \cdots + c_6{}^2) + 2\beta(c_1 c_2 + c_2 c_3 + c_3 c_4 + c_4 c_5 + c_5 c_6 + c_6 c_1)\}.$$

If we define

$$C = c_1 c_2 + c_2 c_3 + \cdots + c_6 c_1$$

and use the value of N given by (9.28) we obtain the Hückel approximation to the energy of the LCAO–MO ψ given in (9.27):

$$\epsilon = \alpha + 2N^2 C\beta. \tag{9.29}$$

The values of $c_1, \ldots, c_6$ that correspond to LCAO–MOs belonging to the different MO levels in benzene are given by equations (9.22, 23, 24, 25). They are set out in Table 9.2 together with the corresponding values of N^2, C and ϵ.

TABLE 9.2. *Orbital energies in benzene*

Level	c_1	c_2	c_3	c_4	c_5	c_6	N^2	C	ϵ
a_{2u}	1	1	1	1	1	1	$1/6$	6	$\alpha+2\beta$
e_{1g}	2	1	-1	-2	-1	1	$1/12$	6	$\alpha+\beta$
e_{2u}	2	-1	-1	2	-1	-1	$1/12$	-6	$\alpha-\beta$
b_{2g}	1	-1	1	-1	1	-1	$1/6$	-6	$\alpha-2\beta$

Since the resonance integral β is negative, this calculation confirms the relative order of the levels that we predicted above on general considerations of the bonding or anti-bonding nature of the LCAO–MOs. The results of the calculation are displayed in the energy level diagram shown in Fig. 9.9.

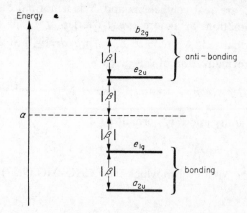

9.9 The π-electron MO levels in benzene.

The ground state configuration of the six π electrons in benzene is $(a_{2u})^2(e_{1g})^4$ and the total energy of these electrons in the Hückel approximation is

$$2(\alpha+2\beta)+4(\alpha+\beta) = 6\alpha+8\beta.$$

We may compare this with the energy of a hypothetical Kekulé structure for benzene in which the six π electrons are localized in three π bonds each containing two electrons (see Fig. 9.10). The wave functions for these electrons will be the diatomic bonding π orbitals that were discussed in the preceding section. When we neglect the overlap integral, the energy of an electron in such a bonding orbital is given by (9.20) as $\alpha+\beta$, on replacing ϵ' in (9.20) by the equivalent quantity α that was defined in (9.26). Thus if the six π electrons were localized in the π bonds of a Kekulé structure their total energy would be $6\alpha+6\beta$. A comparison of this energy with the energy of the electrons in the Hückel approximation shows that a change from a description of the molecule as a Kekulé structure to a description in terms of the MOs of the a_{2u} and e_{1g} levels gives an additional stability or 'delocalization energy' of amount $2|\beta|$. (In the valence bond treatment this additional stability comes from 'resonance' between the two Kekulé structures.) This comparison gives us a means of estimating β. On the one hand, we can measure the heat of formation of an actual benzene molecule and, on the other hand, we can calculate the energy of a Kekulé structure for benzene from a knowledge of the energies of C—C, C=C and C—H bonds in other molecules. The difference between these two energies gives an 'experimental' value for the resonance or delocalization energy $2|\beta|$.

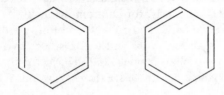

9.10 Kekulé structures for benzene.

Another way in which one can attempt to estimate β is by looking at the electronic spectrum of benzene. From the energy level diagram of Fig. 9.9 we see that the lowest lying excited state of benzene comes from promoting an electron from the e_{1g} bonding level to the e_{2u} anti-bonding level. On the simple Hückel view this would require an energy of amount $2|\beta|$ and would give an excited state with a configuration $(a_{2u})^2(e_{1g})^3(e_{2u})$. The electronic spectrum that is associated with a transition like this is rather complicated, as we shall see in the next chapter, but one can obtain an estimate of the basic energy difference $2|\beta|$ between the ground state and the first excited state from an analysis of the spectrum. This gives us a 'spectroscopic' value for β. Not surprisingly, in view of the numerous approximations and assumptions on which the Hückel theory is based, the spectroscopic value for β does not agree very well with the value calculated from the delocalization energy. It would, indeed, be extraordinary if all the properties of benzene could be described in terms of just one parameter; the surprising thing is that the Hückel theory is as successful as it is. For a further discussion of the Hückel method and its applications to other molecules the reader is referred to [20] and [21].

9.9 Transition-metal Complexes

There is a large class of transition-metal complexes which can usefully be discussed by the LCAO method. We shall consider, in particular, octahedrally coordinated MX_6 complexes with point group $\mathcal{O}_h$, where M is a 3d, 4d or 5d transition-metal and the X ligands are halogens. Very similar considerations apply to other kinds of ligands, e.g. H_2O, NH_3, and to complexes of other symmetries, e.g. $\mathcal{T}_d$ or $\mathcal{D}_{4h}$.

We begin by choosing the AOs that we shall use to form LCAO–MOs. In the ground state configuration of an atom from the first group of transition elements the inner shell electrons have the closed shell configuration of argon and they are presumed to form an inert core which plays no part in the formation of a molecule. The valence electrons of the atom in its ground state partially occupy the $3d$ and $4s$ levels. The lowest lying excited level available to the valence electrons is the $4p$ level which has an energy fairly close to the energies of the $3d$ and $4s$ levels. Accordingly, we assume that the transition-metal AOs that contribute to MO formation are the five $3d$ AOs, the $4s$ AO and the three $4p$ AOs. Similarly, for an atom belonging to the second transition group we take the $4d$, $5s$ and $5p$ AOs and for an atom from the third transition group we take the $5d$, $6s$ and $6p$ AOs. The five valence electrons of a halogen occupy p orbitals, namely $2p$ for F, $3p$ for Cl, $4p$ for Br and $5p$ for I, and we shall assume that these are the only ligand AOs that need to be considered.

This set of AOs includes all those that certainly must be considered in any LCAO description but one might wonder whether there are not other AOs that should also be included. Is it reasonable, for example, to ignore the $2s$ electrons of fluorine when it is known that the $2s$ electrons of carbon and nitrogen play a vital part in the bonding of molecules containing these elements? The theory that we are about to describe, however, does not claim to give anything more than a qualitative explanation of the energy level diagram of a molecule. It turns out that the restricted choice of AOs made above enables us to give an adequate description of the MO levels of the hexahalides and that the inclusion of other AOs, while it would, no doubt, allow us to write down LCAO–MOs which are better approximations to the actual MOs, does not change the important features of the energy level diagram in any essential way.

The discussion of an MX_6 molecule starts from the set of 27 AOs mentioned above; nine of these are contributed by the metal atom and the remainder by the six ligand atoms. We can use these AOs to form 27 linearly independent LCAO–MOs and our task is to classify the MOs according to the IRs of the point group $\mathcal{O}_h$ of the molecule and to produce an energy level diagram.

We begin by considering the 27-dimensional representation Γ_{AO} of $\mathcal{O}_h$ whose basis is the given set of AOs. A symmetry operation R of $\mathcal{O}_h$ interchanges some of the ligand atoms amongst themselves but it leaves the central metal atom in position. Consequently, the corresponding operator O_R, operating in the 27-dimensional function space of the AOs, turns a ligand AO into some other ligand AO or a combination of ligand AOs, and it turns a central atom AO into another central atom AO or a combination of central atom AOs. Ligand and central atom AOs can never be mixed by O_R; we can, therefore, immediately divide the function space of the AOs into a 9-dimensional invariant sub-space, whose base functions are the nine d, s and p AOs on the central atom, and an 18-dimensional invariant sub-space whose base functions are the p AOs on the six ligands. Thus we can immediately reduce Γ_{AO} into the form

$$\Gamma_{AO} = \Gamma_M + \Gamma_X \qquad (9.30)$$

where Γ_M is the representation of $\mathcal{O}_h$ that is provided by the central atom AOs and Γ_X is the representation that is provided by the ligand AOs. Our problem now is to reduce Γ_M and Γ_X and we consider these in turn.

The reduction of Γ_M

We choose the fourfold symmetry axes of the MX_6 octahedron, shown in Fig. 9.11, as the xyz axes at the central atom. If r denotes the distance of the point (x, y, z) from the centre, the nine normalized AOs which form the basis for Γ_M are:

$$s = F_s(r); \qquad (9.31)$$

$$p_x = F_p(r)x/r, \quad p_y = F_p(r)y/r, \quad p_z = F_p(r)z/r; \qquad (9.32)$$

$$d_{xy} = F_d(r)xy/r^2, \quad d_{xz} = F_d(r)xz/r^2, \quad d_{yz} = F_d(r)yz/r^2, \qquad (9.33)$$

$$d_{z^2} = (1/2\sqrt{3})F_d(r)(3z^2 - r^2)/r^2, \quad d_{x^2-y^2} = (1/2)F_d(r)(x^2 - y^2)/r^2. \qquad (9.34)$$

In these expressions $F_s(r)$, $F_p(r)$ and $F_d(r)$ are radial functions which include the appropriate normalization factors. (Compare (3.25) and (3.26).)

The effect of a symmetry operation on s and on p_x, p_y and p_z was discussed in the example at the end of Section 9.4. The function s remains unaltered by any symmetry operation and so, in this case, it generates the identical representation A_{1g} of $\mathcal{O}_h$.

The three functions p_x, p_y and p_z are transformed amongst themselves by a symmetry operation and generate a representation whose characters for a rotation $C(\alpha)$ and an improper rotation $S(\alpha)$ are

$$\chi[C(\alpha)] = 1 + 2 \cos \alpha, \qquad \chi[S(\alpha)] = -1 + 2 \cos \alpha. \qquad (9.35)$$

The latter expression includes the cases of a reflection $\sigma = S(2\pi)$ for which the character is $\chi(\sigma) = 1$ and the inversion $i = S(\pi)$ for which the character is $\chi(i) = -3$. The rotations that occur in $\mathcal{O}_h$ are C_3, C_2 and C_4 with angles of rotation $\alpha = 2\pi/3$, π and $\pi/2$ respectively; the corresponding values of $\cos \alpha$ are $-\frac{1}{2}$, -1 and 0. Apart from σ and i, the improper rotations that occur in $\mathcal{O}_h$ are S_6 and S_4 with angles of rotation $\pi/3$ and $\pi/2$ respectively; the corresponding values of $\cos \alpha$ are $\frac{1}{2}$ and 0. Substitution of these values for $\cos \alpha$

into (9.35) gives the characters of the representation of $\mathcal{O}_h$ that is generated by the three functions p_x, p_y and p_z; these are set out below for the various classes of $\mathcal{O}_h$.

E	$8C_3$	$3C_2$	$6C_4$	$6C_2'$	i	$8S_6$	$3\sigma_h$	$6S_4$	$6\sigma_d$
3	0	-1	1	-1	-3	0	1	-1	1

Reference to the character table of $\mathcal{O}_h$ shows that these are precisely the characters of T_{1u}; thus the three p functions form a basis for T_{1u}.

The effect of a symmetry operation on the d AOs was discussed in Example 2 of Section 4.7. The matrix representing a rotation $C(\alpha)$ about the z axis, i.e. the $\mathbf{e}_3$ axis, is given in (4.42a). The character of this matrix is

$$\chi[C(\alpha)] = 2\cos 2\alpha + 2\cos \alpha + 1 = 4\cos^2 \alpha + 2\cos \alpha - 1. \qquad (9.36)$$

This must be the character of any rotation $C(\alpha)$ in the space of the five d functions since we can always make our z axis coincide with the axis of rotation by a change of basis.

The derivation of (4.42a) may easily be modified to give the matrix which represents an improper rotation $S(\alpha) = \sigma_h C(\alpha)$. With the notation used in deriving (4.42a), we note that a reflection σ_h in the plane perpendicular to $\mathbf{e}_3$ reverses the signs of d_3 and d_4 but leaves d_1, d_2 and d_5 unchanged. The inclusion of these effects in the equations that led to (4.42a) shows that the character of an improper rotation in the space of the d AOs is

$$\chi[S(\alpha)] = 2\cos 2\alpha - 2\cos \alpha + 1 = 4\cos^2 \alpha - 2\cos \alpha - 1. \qquad (9.37)$$

Substitution of the appropriate values of $\cos \alpha$, including the special cases of $\sigma = S(2\pi)$ and $i = S(\pi)$, into (9.36) and (9.37) gives the characters of the five-dimensional representation of $\mathcal{O}_h$ that is generated by the d AOs; the characters are set out below for the various classes of $\mathcal{O}_h$.

E	$8C_3$	$3C_2$	$6C_4$	$6C_2'$	i	$8S_6$	$3\sigma_h$	$6S_4$	$6\sigma_d$
5	-1	1	-1	1	5	-1	1	-1	1

Since no IR of $\mathcal{O}_h$ can have a dimension greater than three, this five-dimensional representation must be reducible; inspection of the character table of $\mathcal{O}_h$ shows that the characters given above can be obtained by adding the characters of the IRs E_g and T_{2g}. This shows that we will be able to find a basis for the five-dimensional space of the d AOs which can be divided into a set of three base functions which generate the three-dimensional IR T_{2g} and a set of two base functions which generate the two-dimensional IR E_g.

Now under any symmetry operation of the octahedron the x, y, z axes that are defined in Fig. 9.11 are interchanged amongst themselves and so also are the three functions d_{xy}, d_{xz} and d_{yz}. These three functions, therefore, form by themselves a basis for a three-dimensional representation of $\mathcal{O}_h$, and this must be the T_{2g} representation. This leaves the pair of functions $d_{x^2-y^2}$ and d_{z^2}; these must form a basis for E_g.

We have now considered all the AOs belonging to the central atom. Our results show that they form a basis for a representation Γ_M of $\mathcal{O}_h$ which can be reduced into the form

$$\Gamma_M = A_{1g} + T_{1u} + T_{2g} + E_g. \tag{9.38}$$

The basis of A_{1g} is the s orbital; the three functions p_x, p_y, p_z are base functions for T_{1u}; three of the d AOs, often referred to as the d_ϵ orbitals, are base functions for T_{2g}; the remaining pair of d AOs, often called the d_γ orbitals, are base functions for E_g. When the x, y and z axes are chosen as in Fig. 9.11, the three T_{2g} or d_ϵ orbitals are d_{xy}, d_{xz} and d_{yz} and the two E_g or d_γ orbitals are $d_{x^2-y^2}$ and d_{z^2}.

EXAMPLES

We illustrate these results by considering a rotation C_2' through 180° about an axis which is perpendicular to the x axis and which bisects the angle between the y and z axes. The effect of C_2' is to reverse the direction of the x axis and to interchange the y and z axes. Thus C_2' moves the point (x, y, z) to a point with coordinates (x', y', z') where $x' = -x$, $y' = z$, $z' = y$. The effect of the corresponding operator O_C on a function $f(x, y, z)$ of position is given by (4.33):

$$(O_C f)(x', y', z') = f(x, y, z) = f(-x', z', y').$$

Since this holds for any point (x', y', z'), we may omit the primes and write

$$(O_C f)(x, y, z) = f(-x, z, y).$$

If we apply this result to the functions p_x, p_y, p_z we have, since the radial part $F_p(r)$ is not changed by the rotation,

$$O_C p_x = -p_x, \quad O_C p_y = p_z, \quad O_C p_z = p_y. \tag{9.39}$$

The matrix which represents C_2' with respect to p_x, p_y, p_z as basis is, therefore,

$$\begin{bmatrix} -1 & 0 & 0 \\ 0 & 0 & 1 \\ 0 & 1 & 0 \end{bmatrix}.$$

The character of this matrix is $\chi = -1$, the character of C_2' in T_{1u}.

Consider next the functions d_{xy}, d_{xz}, d_{yz}. We have

$$O_C d_{xy} = -d_{xz}, \quad O_C d_{xz} = -d_{xy}, \quad O_C d_{yz} = d_{zy} = d_{yz}. \tag{9.40}$$

The matrix which represents C_2' with respect to d_{xy}, d_{xz}, d_{yz} as basis is, therefore,

$$\begin{bmatrix} 0 & -1 & 0 \\ -1 & 0 & 0 \\ 0 & 0 & 1 \end{bmatrix}.$$

The character of this matrix is $\chi = 1$, the character of C_2' in T_{2g}.

Finally, consider the pair of functions $d_{x^2-y^2}$ and d_{z^2}. If we omit the factors which are common to both these functions and which are not changed by O_C, we are left with the functions

$$(x^2 - y^2) \quad \text{and} \quad \frac{1}{\sqrt{3}} (3z^2 - r^2) = \frac{1}{\sqrt{3}} (2z^2 - x^2 - y^2).$$

Application of O_C to these combinations of x, y and z gives after a little manipulation,

$$O_C(x^2 - y^2) = (x^2 - z^2) = \frac{1}{2} (x^2 - y^2) - \frac{\sqrt{3}}{2} \cdot \frac{1}{\sqrt{3}} (3z^2 - r^2),$$

$$O_C \frac{1}{\sqrt{3}} (3z^2 - r^2) = \frac{1}{\sqrt{3}} (3y^2 - r^2) = -\frac{\sqrt{3}}{2} (x^2 - y^2) - \frac{1}{2} \cdot \frac{1}{\sqrt{3}} (3z^2 - r^2).$$

These results show that

$$O_C d_{x^2-y^2} = \frac{1}{2} d_{x^2-y^2} - \frac{\sqrt{3}}{2} d_{z^2},$$

$$O_C d_{z^2} = -\frac{\sqrt{3}}{2} d_{x^2-y^2} - \frac{1}{2} d_{z^2}.$$

$$(9.41)$$

The matrix which represents C_2' with respect to $d_{x^2-y^2}$ and d_{z^2} as basis is, therefore,

$$\begin{bmatrix} \dfrac{1}{2} & -\dfrac{\sqrt{3}}{2} \\[2ex] -\dfrac{\sqrt{3}}{2} & -\dfrac{1}{2} \end{bmatrix}.$$

The character of this matrix is $\chi = 0$, which is the character of C_2' in E_g.

The reduction of Γ_X

We turn now to consider the p AOs on the ligands. Instead of drawing a full polar diagram for a p orbital, we can represent the orbital by an arrow which points from its negative lobe to its positive lobe. Arrows representing the three p AOs on each ligand are shown in Fig. 9.11. The orbitals are chosen as follows: on each ligand atom X take the p AO which points directly towards M along the M—X bond, and then choose two other p AOs at right-angles to this orbital and to each other. As far as the M—X bond is concerned, the p AO on X which points towards M is like a p_σ orbital in a diatomic molecule; we denote these AOs on the various ligands by $\sigma_1, \sigma_2, \ldots,$ σ_6. The other two p AOs on X are, as far as the M—X bond is concerned, like p_π orbitals in a diatomic molecule; we denote these pairs of AOs on the various ligands by $\pi_1, \pi_1'; \pi_2, \pi_2'; \ldots; \pi_6, \pi_6'$.

This particular way of choosing the p AOs has the advantage that it immediately divides them into two distinct sets; a symmetry operation of $\mathscr{O}_h$

will interchange the σ orbitals amongst themselves and it will interchange
the π orbitals amongst themselves, but it will never change a σ orbital into a
π orbital or a π orbital into a σ orbital. This means that we can straightaway
write

$$\Gamma_X = \Gamma_\sigma + \Gamma_\pi, \tag{9.42}$$

where Γ_σ is a representation whose basis consists of the six σ orbitals $\sigma_1, \ldots, \sigma_6$
and Γ_π is a representation which has the twelve π orbitals $\pi_1, \pi_1', \ldots, \pi_6, \pi_6'$ as
its basis.

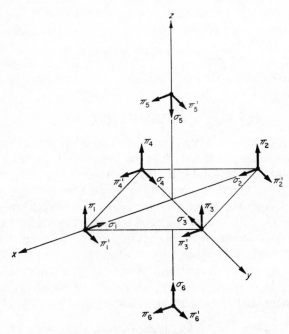

9.11 Ligand orbitals for an MX_6 octahedral complex.

Apart from their different behaviour under symmetry operations, there is
also a physical difference between the σ and π orbitals. Since the σ orbitals
point directly towards the central atom they may be expected to have strong
overlaps with the central atom AOs and to form strongly bonding and anti-
bonding combinations with them. The π orbitals on the other hand, being at
right-angles to the M—X bonds, will have rather weaker overlaps with the
central atom AOs and may be expected to combine with them to form less
strongly bonding and anti-bonding LCAO–MOs. In a general way, then,
the octahedral symmetry allows us to make the same sort of distinction
between σ and π bonding that we were able to make in the consideration of
diatomic molecules.

We begin the reduction of Γ_x by considering Γ_σ. If $D(R)$ is the matrix that represents the symmetry operation R in Γ_σ, we shall have

$$O_R\sigma_k = \sum_{j=1}^{6} [D(R)]_{jk}\sigma_j,$$

and we wish to find the character

$$\chi(R) = \sum_{k=1}^{6} [D(R)]_{kk}$$

of R in Γ_σ. Now for all the symmetry operations R of $\mathcal{O}_h$, either R leaves the ligand atom k in position in which case O_R does not affect σ_k so that

$$O_R\sigma_k = \sigma_k \quad \text{and} \quad [D(R)]_{kk} = 1,$$

or R moves the ligand atom k into the position of some other atom l in which case O_R changes σ_k into σ_l so that

$$O_R\sigma_k = \sigma_l \quad \text{and} \quad [D(R)]_{kk} = 0.$$

It follows that each ligand atom that is left unmoved by R gives a contribution $+1$ to the character and that each ligand atom that is moved by R gives a zero contribution to the character: the character of R in Γ_σ is equal to the number of ligand atoms that are left in position by R. Now many of the symmetry operations of $\mathcal{O}_h$ move all the ligand atoms; such operations have character $\chi=0$ in Γ_σ. The only symmetry operations with non-zero characters in Γ_σ are: E which leaves all six ligands in position; the rotations C_2 and C_4 about the x, y and z axes which leave two ligands in position; the reflections σ_h in the xy, yz and xz planes which leave four ligands in position; and the reflections σ_d in diagonal planes which leave two ligands in position. We therefore obtain the following set of characters for Γ_σ:

E	$8C_3$	$3C_2$	$6C_4$	$6C_2'$	i	$8S_6$	$3\sigma_h$	$6S_4$	$6\sigma_d$
6	0	2	2	0	0	0	4	0	2

When it is applied to this set of characters, the rule (6.5) for finding the irreducible components of a reducible representation, used in conjunction with the character table of $\mathcal{O}_h$, shows that

$$\Gamma_\sigma = A_{1g} + E_g + T_{1u}. \tag{9.43}$$

This shows that it is possible to find a new basis for Γ_σ, in which the base functions are linear combinations of $\sigma_1, \ldots, \sigma_6$, such that the matrices of Γ_σ have the completely reduced form indicated by (9.43). There will be one linear combination of $\sigma_1, \ldots, \sigma_6$ which is left unchanged by all the symmetry operations of $\mathcal{O}_h$ and which is a basis for A_{1g}, there will be two linear combinations of $\sigma_1, \ldots, \sigma_6$ which form a basis for E_g and there will be three linear combinations which form a basis for T_{1u}. For many purposes, this is all we need to know, but it is of some interest to find the correct linear combinations for the various IRs.

These linear combinations can be found by the projection operator method described in Section 6.6 but, because of the rather large number of symmetry operations contained in $\mathcal{O}_h$ or even in the simpler group $\mathcal{O}$, the method is clumsy. Fortunately, it is fairly easy to find the correct combinations by inspection. We shall make the simplifying assumption that the ligand atoms are sufficiently far apart for the overlap integrals between AOs on different ligands to be negligible. It is not necessary to make this assumption, but it is a reasonable approximation which makes it very easy to write down normalizing factors and to see whether two linear combinations of $\sigma_1, \ldots, \sigma_6$ are orthogonal. Since we may suppose that $\sigma_1, \ldots, \sigma_6$ are normalized AOs, the neglect of their overlap integrals means that we assume that they form an orthonormal basis for Γ_σ satisfying

$$(\sigma_i, \sigma_j) = \int \sigma_i \sigma_j \, d\tau = \delta_{ij}.$$

Then a linear combination $\sigma_a = \sum_{i=1}^{6} a_i \sigma_i$, with real coefficients a_i, is normalized if

$$(\sigma_a, \sigma_a) = \int \sigma_a{}^2 \, d\tau = \sum_{i=1}^{6} a_i{}^2 = 1,$$

and σ_a is orthogonal to another linear combination $\sigma_b = \sum_{i=1}^{6} b_i \sigma_i$ with real coefficients b_i if

$$(\sigma_a, \sigma_b) = \int \sigma_a \sigma_b \, d\tau = \sum_{i=1}^{6} a_i b_i = 0.$$

(Compare equations (3.23) and (3.24) of Section 3.5.)

A symmetry operation of $\mathcal{O}_h$ permutes the AOs $\sigma_1, \ldots, \sigma_6$ amongst themselves; if the symmetry operation is applied to the algebraic sum of the σ AOs, we shall obtain the same sum of functions with the terms arranged in a different order. This means that the normalized function

$$\sigma_s = \frac{1}{\sqrt{6}} (\sigma_1 + \sigma_2 + \sigma_3 + \sigma_4 + \sigma_5 + \sigma_6) \tag{9.44}$$

has the property that

$$O_R \sigma_s = \sigma_s$$

for every symmetry operation of $\mathcal{O}_h$ and that it is a base function for the identical representation A_{1g}.

The linear combinations of $\sigma_1, \ldots, \sigma_6$ that form bases for the degenerate representations T_{1u} and E_g may be chosen in many different ways. Since our eventual purpose is to form LCAO–MOs which involve mixtures of ligand and central atom AOs, we shall try to find combinations of the ligand orbitals that resemble those on the central atom as far as possible; we consider the T_{1u} representation first.

The central atom AOs that form a basis for T_{1u} are p_x, p_y and p_z; these behave, under the symmetry operations of $\mathcal{O}_h$, like vectors directed along the positive x, y and z axes. The positive lobe of p_x points towards ligand atom 1 and the negative lobe of p_x points towards ligand atom 2; a normalized combination of ligand AOs which has a similar directional property is

$$\sigma_x = \frac{1}{\sqrt{2}}\,(\sigma_1 - \sigma_2) \qquad\qquad (9.45a)$$

and two other combinations that are related in similar fashion to the y and z axes are

$$\sigma_y = \frac{1}{\sqrt{2}}\,(\sigma_3 - \sigma_4), \qquad \sigma_z = \frac{1}{\sqrt{2}}\,(\sigma_5 - \sigma_6). \qquad (9.45b)$$

These three combinations are orthogonal to each other and to the function σ_s defined by (9.44); they form an orthonormal basis for T_{1u} and the effects of a symmetry operation R on σ_x, σ_y, σ_z are exactly the same as the effects of R on p_x, p_y, p_z.

We verify this statement for the operation C_2', a rotation through 180° about an axis, perpendicular to the x axis, which bisects the angle between the y and z axes. If O_C denotes the corresponding operator, reference to Fig. 9.11 shows that, under O_C, the AOs σ_1, σ_2, σ_3, σ_4, σ_5, σ_6 change respectively into σ_2, σ_1, σ_5, σ_6, σ_3, σ_4. Thus

$$O_C\sigma_x = \frac{1}{\sqrt{2}}\,(\sigma_2 - \sigma_1) = -\sigma_x, \quad O_C\sigma_y = \frac{1}{\sqrt{2}}\,(\sigma_5 - \sigma_6) = \sigma_z,$$

$$O_C\sigma_z = \frac{1}{\sqrt{2}}\,(\sigma_3 - \sigma_4) = \sigma_y.$$

A comparison of these equations with (9.39) shows that the combinations σ_x, σ_y, σ_z behave, under C_2', exactly like the central atom p_x, p_y and p_z orbitals.

We are left with the problem of finding two combinations of $\sigma_1, \ldots, \sigma_6$ which belong to E_g. The central atom AOs that form a basis for E_g are $d_{x^2-y^2}$ and d_{z^2}. The polar diagram for $d_{x^2-y^2}$, shown in Fig. 9.1, has positive lobes directed along the positive and negative x axes and negative lobes directed along the positive and negative y axes. A similar, normalized combination of ligand AOs is

$$\sigma_{x^2-y^2} = \tfrac{1}{2}(\sigma_1 + \sigma_2 - \sigma_3 - \sigma_4). \qquad (9.46a)$$

This is orthogonal to the combinations σ_s, σ_x, σ_y, σ_z which form bases for A_{1g} and T_{1u}; and so it must be a suitable basis function for E_g. The central atom d AO which joins with $d_{x^2-y^2}$ to form a basis for E_g is d_{z^2} which is proportional to

$$3z^2 - r^2 = 2z^2 - x^2 - y^2;$$

the corresponding combination of ligand AOs is

$$\sigma_{z^2} = \frac{1}{2\sqrt{3}}(2\sigma_5 + 2\sigma_6 - \sigma_1 - \sigma_2 - \sigma_3 - \sigma_4). \tag{9.46b}$$

This combination of the ligand AOs is orthogonal to σ_s, σ_x, σ_y, σ_z so that it must belong to the E_g representation. It is also orthogonal to $\sigma_{x^2-y^2}$ so that $\sigma_{x^2-y^2}$ and σ_{z^2} together form an orthonormal basis for E_g. From the way in which they were constructed it is evident that $\sigma_{x^2-y^2}$ and σ_{z^2} behave, under a symmetry operation of $\mathcal{O}_h$, in exactly the same way as the corresponding pair of orbitals $d_{x^2-y^2}$ and d_{z^2} on the central atom.

We verify this statement for the operation C_2' that was described above. The effects of the corresponding operator O_C on $\sigma_{x^2-y^2}$ and σ_{z^2} are given by

$$O_C \sigma_{x^2-y^2} = \frac{1}{2}(\sigma_2 + \sigma_1 - \sigma_5 - \sigma_6),$$

$$O_C \sigma_{z^2} = \frac{1}{2\sqrt{3}}(2\sigma_3 + 2\sigma_4 - \sigma_2 - \sigma_1 - \sigma_5 - \sigma_6).$$

A little manipulation then gives

$$O_C \sigma_{x^2-y^2} = \frac{1}{2}\sigma_{x^2-y^2} - \frac{\sqrt{3}}{2}\sigma_{z^2},$$

$$O_C \sigma_{z^2} = -\frac{\sqrt{3}}{2}\sigma_{x^2-y^2} - \frac{1}{2}\sigma_{z^2}.$$

These equations have exactly the same form as the equations (9.41) which describe the effects of O_C on $d_{x^2-y^2}$ and d_{z^2}.

The twelve-dimensional representation Γ_π, whose basis consists of the twelve ligand π AOs, may be dealt with in the same way as Γ_σ. The π orbitals on any ligand atom that is moved to another position by a symmetry operation give a zero contribution to the character. If a symmetry operation leaves ligand atom k in position, it may leave π_k unaltered, in which case π_k contributes $+1$ to the character, or it may reverse the direction of π_k, in which case π_k contributes -1 to the character, or it may turn π_k into $\pm \pi_k'$, in which case π_k gives a zero contribution to the character. The same remarks apply to the other AO π_k' on atom k.

Any symmetry operation belonging to the classes C_3, C_2', i, S_6 and S_4 of $\mathcal{O}_h$ will move all the ligand atoms; it will, therefore, have a zero character in Γ_π. The identical operation E leaves all the π orbitals alone and it has character $\chi(E) = 12$. The rotations C_4 and C_2 about the x, y and z axes leave two atoms in position. If we consider rotations about the x axis so that the two atoms concerned are numbered 1 and 2, we see from Fig. 9.11 that C_4 changes π_1 into π_1' and π_1' into $-\pi_1$ and that this pair of AOs gives a zero contribution to the character. The same is true of the pair of π AOs on atom 2; thus $\chi(C_4) = 0$. The rotation C_2 about the x axis reverses the signs of π_1 and π_1' and this pair of AOs, therefore, gives a contribution -2 to the character of C_2. So does the pair of π AOs on atom 2; thus $\chi(C_2) = -4$. The reflections σ_d in diagonal planes leave two atoms in position. If we take the symmetry plane which contains the z axis and which bisects the angle between the x and y axes so that atoms 5 and 6 are left in position by σ_d, Fig. 9.11 shows that σ_d interchanges π_5 and π_5' and also π_6 and π_6'; thus $\chi(\sigma_d) = 0$. The remaining operations of $\mathcal{O}_h$ to be considered are the reflections σ_h in the xy, yz and zx planes. The reflection in the xy plane, which leaves atoms 1, 2, 3 and 4 in position, does not alter the π' AOs on these atoms but it reverses the directions of their π AOs. Each atom, therefore, gives a contribution of $1-1=0$ to the character and $\chi(\sigma_h) = 0$.

The complete set of characters for Γ_π is given below

E	$8C_3$	$3C_2$	$6C_4$	$6C_2'$	i	$8S_6$	$3\sigma_h$	$6S_4$	$6\sigma_d$
12	0	-4	0	0	0	0	0	0	0

With this set of characters for Γ_π, application of the rule (6.5) shows that

$$\Gamma_\pi = T_{1g} + T_{2g} + T_{1u} + T_{2u}. \qquad (9.47)$$

It will, therefore, be possible to find linear combinations of the π and π' AOs which are bases for these three-dimensional IRs of $\mathcal{O}_h$. In writing down these combinations we shall ignore the overlap integrals between AOs on different ligands and we shall regard the π and π' AOs as twelve orthonormal basis functions for Γ_π.

The T_{1u} representation, as we have seen, is generated by vectors pointing along the x, y and z axes. If we consider the x axis, it appears from Fig. 9.11 that four of the π type AOs, namely π_3', π_4', π_5, π_6, are symmetrically disposed parallel to the x axis and point in the positive x direction. The sets π_1', π_2', π_5', π_6' and π_1, π_2, π_3, π_4 are similarly related to the y and z axes. Suitable normalized and orthogonal base functions for the T_{1u} representation are, therefore,

$$\pi_x = \tfrac{1}{2}(\pi_3' + \pi_4' + \pi_5 + \pi_6), \quad \pi_y = \tfrac{1}{2}(\pi_1' + \pi_2' + \pi_5' + \pi_6'),$$
$$\pi_z = \tfrac{1}{2}(\pi_1 + \pi_2 + \pi_3 + \pi_4). \qquad (9.48)$$

The central atom AOs that provide a basis for T_{2g} are d_{xy}, d_{xz} and d_{yz}. If we consider d_{xy}, for example, Fig. 9.12 shows that a set of ligand AOs with the same symmetry properties is π'_1, $-\pi'_2$, π'_3, $-\pi'_4$. Similar sets corresponding to d_{xz} and d_{yz} are π_1, $-\pi_2$, π_5, $-\pi_6$ and π_3, $-\pi_4$, π'_5, $-\pi'_6$. Thus three normalized and orthogonal base functions for the T_{2g} representation are

$$\pi_{xy} = \tfrac{1}{2}(\pi'_1 - \pi'_2 + \pi'_3 - \pi'_4), \quad \pi_{xz} = \tfrac{1}{2}(\pi_1 - \pi_2 + \pi_5 - \pi_6),$$

$$\pi_{yz} = \tfrac{1}{2}(\pi_3 - \pi_4 + \pi'_5 - \pi'_6). \tag{9.49}$$

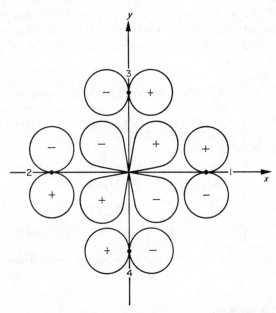

9.12 π-bonding with a d_{xy} orbital.

It remains to find combinations which form bases for T_{1g} and T_{2u}. There are no central atom AOs of these types and we must look for other arguments. In the character table of $\mathcal{O}_h$, the T_{1g} representation is associated with the symbols R_x, R_y and R_z. The meaning of these symbols is explained in Chapter 8; briefly, R_x, R_y and R_z stand for rotations about the x, y and z axes. If we bear the directional properties of the π type AOs in mind, we see from Fig. 9.11 that a rotation about the x axis corresponds to the set π_3, $-\pi_4$, $-\pi'_5$, π'_6 of ligand AOs, that a rotation about the y axis corresponds to the set π_1, $-\pi_2$, $-\pi_5$, π_6, and that a rotation about the z axis corresponds to the set π'_1, $-\pi'_2$, $-\pi'_3$, π'_4. Thus three normalized and orthogonal base functions for the T_{1g} representation are

$$\pi_a = \tfrac{1}{2}(\pi_3 - \pi_4 - \pi'_5 + \pi'_6), \quad \pi_b = \tfrac{1}{2}(\pi_1 - \pi_2 - \pi_5 + \pi_6),$$

$$\pi_c = \tfrac{1}{2}(\pi'_1 - \pi'_2 - \pi'_3 + \pi'_4). \tag{9.50}$$

The base functions for the T_{2u} representation must be orthogonal to the sets of functions defined in (9.48, 49, 50). A suitable set of normalized and orthogonal functions is

$$\pi_a' = \tfrac{1}{2}(\pi_3' + \pi_4' - \pi_5 - \pi_6), \quad \pi_b' = \tfrac{1}{2}(\pi_1' + \pi_2' - \pi_5' - \pi_6').$$
$$\pi_c' = \tfrac{1}{2}(\pi_1 + \pi_2 - \pi_3 - \pi_4). \tag{9.51}$$

We have now completed the investigation of the symmetry properties of the 27 AOs on the central and ligand atoms. The results are summarized in Table 9.3; this table lists the central atom AOs and the combinations of ligand σ and π AOs which serve as bases for the IRs of $\mathcal{O}_h$ that arise in the reduction of Γ_M and Γ_X.

TABLE 9.3. *IRs and orbitals for* MX_6 *complexes*

IR	Central Atom	Ligand σ	Ligand π
A_{1g}	s	σ_s	—
T_{1u}	p_x, p_y, p_z	$\sigma_x, \sigma_y, \sigma_z$	π_x, π_y, π_z
E_g	$d_{x^2-y^2}, d_{z^2}$	$\sigma_{x^2-y^2}, \sigma_{z^2}$	—
T_{2g}	d_{xy}, d_{xz}, d_{yz}	—	$\pi_{xy}, \pi_{xz}, \pi_{yz}$
T_{1g}	—	—	π_a, π_b, π_c
T_{2u}	—	—	π_a', π_b', π_c'

The σ combinations are defined in (9.44, 45, 46) and the π combinations are defined in (9.48, 49, 50, 51).

The energy level diagram

We are now in a position to understand the energy level diagram for a MX_6 complex. From the reduction of Γ_{AO} that is summarized in Table 9.3 one sees that it will be possible to form LCAO–MOs from central atom and ligand AOs which belong to MO energy levels of the following kinds:

a_{1g}: two non-degenerate levels with MOs formed from combinations of central atom s and ligand σ AOs.

t_{1u}: three triply-degenerate levels with MOs formed from combinations of central atom p and ligand σ and π AOs.

e_g: two doubly-degenerate levels with MOs formed from combinations of central atom d_γ and ligand σ AOs.

t_{2g}: two triply-degenerate levels with MOs formed from combinations of central atom d_ϵ and ligand π AOs.

t_{1g} and t_{2u}: one triply-degenerate level of each type with MOs that depend on the ligand π AOs only.

(When there are different levels of the same symmetry, we distinguish them by a 'principal quantum number' n, numbering them in sequence from the lowest level of a given symmetry. Thus we speak of the $1a_{1g}$ and $2a_{1g}$ levels, or the $1t_{1u}$, $2t_{1u}$ and $3t_{1u}$ levels.)

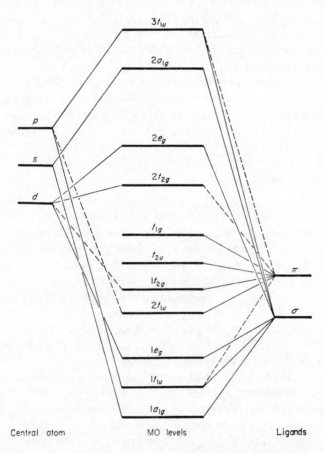

9.13 The energy level diagram for an MX_6 molecule. (The ligand σ and π orbitals have the same energy, on the assumptions made in the text; they are drawn with different energies for the sake of clarity.)

A combination of qualitative arguments with empirical investigations of the spectra of many different MX_6 complexes leads to the energy level diagram that is shown in Fig. 9.13. The qualitative arguments on which the diagram is based depend on our ideas about the formation of bonding and anti-bonding orbitals.

The a_{1g} levels will have MOs which are orthogonal combinations of central atom s and ligand σ AOs of the form

$$\psi(1a_{1g}) = a_1 s + b_1 \sigma_s, \qquad \psi(2a_{1g}) = a_2 s + b_2 \sigma_s$$

where a_1, b_1 and a_2, b_2 are numerical coefficients that determine the relative weights of s and σ_s in the MOs. Since all the σ orbitals have a positive overlap with the central atom s orbital, the $1a_{1g}$ level will be a bonding combination in which a_1 and b_1 have the same sign and the $2a_{1g}$ level will be an anti-bonding combination in which a_2 and b_2 have opposite signs. In order to determine the values of the a and b coefficients and the actual energies of these levels one would have to use the expression (9.9) for the energy of a MO level. The best values of a_1 and b_1 are those which make the calculated energy of the $1a_{1g}$ level a minimum and a_2 and b_2 are determined from these values by the condition that the $2a_{1g}$ orbital must be orthogonal to the $1a_{1g}$ orbital. To perform this calculation one would need to know the value of the overlap integral between the central atom s and the ligand σ_s orbitals and also the values of the integrals

$$\int s H_0 s \, d\tau, \quad \int \sigma_s H_0 \sigma_s \, d\tau, \quad \int s H_0 \sigma_s \, d\tau = \int \sigma_s H_0 s \, d\tau$$

which depend on the effective Hamiltonian. These integrals involve too many unknown quantities for any detailed calculations to be very convincing, but on general qualitative grounds one may argue that, because of their strong overlap, s and σ_s will appear with approximately equal weight in the LCAO–MOs and that the energy of their bonding combination will be considerably less than, and the energy of their anti-bonding combination will be considerably greater than, the energies of the s and σ AOs. This is indicated in Fig. 9.13 where the $1a_{1g}$ level is given the lowest energy of all the MO levels and the $2a_{1g}$ level nearly the highest.

Very much the same arguments apply to the two e_g levels whose MOs are mixtures of the central atom $d_{x^2-y^2}$ and d_{z^2} orbitals with the corresponding combinations of ligand σ orbitals; these mixtures produce the bonding $1e_g$ and the anti-bonding $2e_g$ levels shown in Fig. 9.13. Here the evidence suggests that the ligand σ orbitals probably predominate in the bonding $1e_g$ level and that the central atom d_γ orbitals predominate in the anti-bonding $2e_g$ level.

The t_{1u} levels are rather more complicated. The nt_{1u} level, where $n=1$, 2 or 3, has three MOs $\psi_x(nt_{1u})$, $\psi_y(nt_{1u})$, $\psi_z(nt_{1u})$ of the general form

$$\psi_j(nt_{1u}) = a_n p_j + b_n \sigma_j + c_n \pi_j, \quad j = x, y, z,$$

with coefficients a_n, b_n, c_n which determine the relative weights of the different types of AO that contribute to the MO. The lowest level, $1t_{1u}$, is a strongly bonding combination of central atom p and ligand σ orbitals with a small contribution from the ligand π orbitals which have only a small overlap with the central atom p orbitals. The intermediate level, $2t_{1u}$, corresponds to a π bonding combination of ligand π with central atom p orbitals in which the ligand orbitals predominate. The $3t_{1u}$ level is strongly anti-bonding.

The t_{2g} levels are π bonding and anti-bonding combinations of the central atom d_ϵ orbitals with ligand π orbitals of the general form

$$\psi_{xy}(t_{2g}) = ad_{xy} + b\pi_{xy}.$$

The ligand orbitals predominate in the bonding $1t_{2g}$ level and the central atom orbitals predominate in the anti-bonding $2t_{2g}$ level.

We are left with the t_{1g} and t_{2u} levels which are non-bonding as far as the central atom is concerned since there are no central atom orbitals with these symmetries. Experimental results suggest that the t_{1g} level has rather higher energy than the t_{2u} level.

These qualitative arguments give us some understanding of why the energy level diagram of Fig. 9.13 is drawn as it is, but it must be emphasized that these arguments by themselves can do no more than suggest a reasonable arrangement of the MO energy levels. The justification of the energy level diagram that we have drawn lies in the remarkable success it has had in explaining and correlating the optical and magnetic properties of an extra-ordinarily large number of MX_6 complexes constructed from many different transition metals and many different ligands.

The chief features of the diagram are:

(a) A set of low lying strongly σ-bonding levels $1a_{1g}$, $1t_{1u}$, $1e_g$ which can hold 12 electrons altogether.

(b) A set of levels whose MOs consist mainly or entirely of combinations of the ligand π orbitals; these are the bonding $2t_{1u}$ and $1t_{2g}$ and the non-bonding t_{2u} and t_{1g} levels which can accommodate altogether 24 electrons.

(c) The triply-degenerate $2t_{2g}$ level whose MOs are predominantly the central atom d_ϵ AOs with a small anti-bonding admixture of ligand π AOs.

(d) The doubly-degenerate $2e_g$ level whose MOs consist of anti-bonding combinations of the central atom d_γ and ligand σ AOs.

(e) The strongly anti-bonding $2a_{1g}$ and $3t_{1u}$ levels.

In the hexahalide and similar complexes one will have somewhat more than 36 electrons to accommodate in these levels. The lowest lying levels, mentioned in (a), can hold 12 electrons and the π type levels, mentioned in (b), can hold 24 electrons so that 36 electrons of the complex will go into these levels, filling them completely and forming a closed shell configuration which we designate schematically by $(\sigma)^{12}(\pi)^{24}$. The remaining electrons will go into the $2t_{2g}$ and $2e_g$ levels and it is these levels that are of prime importance in determining the properties of the complex.

EXAMPLE: $MoCl_6^{3-}$, IrF_6

The Mo valence electrons have the ground state configuration $(3d)^5(4s)$ and there are six of them to be considered. Each Cl atom contributes five electrons and the complex as a whole has an additional three electrons; the total number of electrons that must be placed into the MO energy levels is, therefore, 39. As we have seen, 36 of these will go into the σ bonding and the π levels; the three electrons left over must go into the $2t_{2g}$ level. The ground state configuration of $MoCl_6^{3-}$ would, therefore, be written as $(\sigma)^{12}(\pi)^{24}(t_{2g})^3$. (Since there is no possibility of confusion, it is customary to omit the '2' from the label of the $2t_{2g}$ level and to designate it simply by t_{2g}; the same remark applies to the $2e_g$ level which is usually denoted simply by e_g.)

The Ir valence electrons have the ground state configuration $(5d)^7(6s)^2$ and there are nine of them to be added to the 30 electrons contributed by the F ligands in IrF_6. This molecule will, therefore, have exactly the same kind of ground state configuration as $MoCl_6^{3-}$ and the absorption spectra of both complexes are determined by the facts that their ground states have three t_{2g} electrons lying outside closed shells and that the first unoccupied MO energy level in both complexes is an e_g level.

Complexes without π electrons

In the hexahalide MX_6 complexes, the π AOs on the ligands play an important part in the formation of LCAO–MOs, but there are many transition-metal complexes in which the ligands have no π electrons available for bonding to the central atom. If X is NH_3, for example, one can assume that the electrons forming the N—H bonds are firmly held in their appropriate MOs and that it is only the lone pair of electrons on the nitrogen atom that is available to form a bond with the central metal atom. Another common ligand of this type is H_2O and one may consider $[Cr(H_2O)_6]^{3+}$ as a typical example.

The ligands in these complexes provide a set of six σ orbitals like the ones we have been considering and these ligand orbitals can form σ bonding LCAO–MOs with the appropriate central atom orbitals giving rise to bonding a_{1g}, t_{1u} and e_g levels which are capable of holding altogether twelve electrons. There are no ligand π orbitals to be considered and the energy level diagram will, therefore, be obtained from Fig. 9.13 by simply striking out the levels marked $2t_{1u}$, $1t_{2g}$, t_{2u} and t_{1g}. This leaves a t_{2g} level which now is formed entirely from non-bonding central atom d_ϵ orbitals and an anti-bonding e_g level formed from central atom d_γ orbitals and the appropriate combinations of ligand σ orbitals.

A configuration for a complex of this type will therefore contain twelve electrons in the σ bonding levels and a number of electrons in the non-bonding t_{2g} and anti-bonding e_g levels. In $[Cr(H_2O)_6]^{3+}$, for example, there are twelve bonding electrons provided by the ligands and the three valence electrons of Cr^{3+} must go into the t_{2g} level, giving a ground state configuration $(\sigma)^{12}(t_{2g})^3$. This complex is, therefore, rather similar in many of its properties to $MoCl_6^{3-}$ or IrF_6.

The molecular orbital treatment of transition-metal complexes stems from two papers by Van Vleck [22]. This simple approach has been developed into an extensive theory, ligand-field theory, for a discussion of which the the reader is referred to [23]–[26].

<h2>PROBLEMS</h2>

9.1. Use the methods of Section 9.8 to prove the following results for C_5H_5 (cyclopentadienyl radical) assumed to have a ring structure with point group $\mathscr{D}_{5h} = \mathscr{D}_5 \times \sigma_h$. The five π electrons go into MOs consisting of linear combinations of p_z orbitals on the carbon atoms; these orbitals are denoted by $p_0, p_2, \ldots, p_4$ numbered consecutively round the ring.

(a) There are three MO levels associated respectively with the IRs A_2'', E_1'', E_2'' of $\mathscr{D}_{5h}$.

(b) Neglecting overlap between $p_0, \ldots, p_4$, suitable normalized MOs for these levels are:

$$\psi(a_2) = \sqrt{(1/5)}(p_0 + p_1 + p_2 + p_3 + p_4)$$

$$\psi(e_1) = \sqrt{(2/5)}(p_0 + \cos \gamma p_1 + \cos 2\gamma p_2 + \cos 2\gamma p_3 + \cos \gamma p_4)$$

$$\psi(e_2) = \sqrt{(2/5)}(p_0 + \cos 2\gamma p_1 + \cos \gamma p_2 + \cos \gamma p_3 + \cos 2\gamma p_4)$$

where $\gamma = 2\pi/5 = 72°$. (The e_1'' and e_2'' levels each have another MO orthogonal to the ones written down. The above expressions are found by applying the projection operators, defined by (6.13), for the A_2, E_1 and E_2 representations of $\mathscr{D}_5$ to p_0.)

(c) The energies of the MO levels in the Hückel approximation (9.29) are:

$$a_2'': \alpha + 2\beta; \quad e_1'': \alpha + (2 \cos \gamma)\beta; \quad e_2'': \alpha + (2 \cos 2\gamma)\beta.$$

The a_2'' and e_1'' levels are bonding, the e_2'' level is anti-bonding and the ground state configuration for the five π electrons is $(a_2'')^2(e_1'')^3$.
(*Note*: if $\gamma = 2\pi/5$, $\cos \gamma + \cos 2\gamma = -1/2$, $\cos \gamma \cos 2\gamma = -1/4$, $1 + 2 \cos^2 \gamma + 2 \cos^2 2\gamma = 5/2$. Approximate values of the cosines are $\cos \gamma \fallingdotseq 0.3$, $\cos 2\gamma \fallingdotseq -0.8$.)

9.2. In copper phthalocyanine, the copper atom is at the centre of a square whose corners are occupied by nitrogen atoms; the molecule has point group $\mathscr{D}_{4h}$. Bonding of the copper to the rest of the molecule can occur via σ orbitals on the nitrogens which point directly towards the copper along the diagonals of the square and π type orbitals on the nitrogens which are perpendicular to the molecular plane. Show that these orbitals form bases for the representations

$$\Gamma_\sigma = A_{1g} + B_{1g} + E_u; \qquad \Gamma_\pi = A_{2u} + B_{2u} + E_g$$

and that σ type bonding can occur with the copper $4s$, $3d_{x^2-y^2}$ and $3d_{z^2}$ orbitals. (The xy axes at the copper atom point along the diagonals of the square which are the C_2' axes for $\mathscr{D}_{4h}$.)

9.3. The permanganate ion MnO_4^- has a tetrahedral structure with point group $\mathscr{T}_d$. The oxygen atoms each provide three $2p$ AOs for the formation of LCAO–MOs. Choose these on each atom so that one, the σ orbital, points directly towards the central Mn atom and two, the π orbitals, are perpendicular to the Mn—O bond and to each other. Show that the four σ orbitals and the eight π orbitals give rise to representations Γ_σ and Γ_π of $\mathscr{T}_d$ with characters

	E	$8C_3$	$3C_2$	$6S_4$	$6\sigma_d$
Γ_σ	4	1	0	0	2
Γ_π	8	-1	0	0	0

and that $\Gamma_\sigma = A_1 + T_2$, $\Gamma_\pi = E + T_1 + T_2$.

(The linear combinations of the σ and π orbitals which form bases for these IRs are given by WOLFSBERG, M. and HELMHOLZ, L., *J. Chem. Phys.*, **20**, 837 (1952).)

9.4. On the assumption that the central Mn atom in permanganate provides $3d$ and $4s$ AOs which combine with the oxygen AOs discussed in Problem 9.3 to form LCAO–MOs, use the information given in the character table of $\mathscr{T}_d$ to show that there will be altogether eight MO levels with IRs as follows:

(a) a_1: two levels formed from bonding and anti-bonding combinations of Mn $4s$ with oxygen σ orbitals.

(b) e: two levels formed from bonding and anti-bonding combinations of Mn $d_{x^2-y^2}$ and d_{z^2} with oxygen π orbitals.

(c) t_2: three levels formed from various combinations of Mn d_{xy}, d_{xz}, d_{yz} with oxygen σ and π orbitals.

(d) t_1: one level whose MOs consist of non-bonding combinations of oxygen π orbitals.

(For possible energy level diagrams for ions of this type see [25], p. 242.)

Chapter 10

ELECTRONIC SPECTRA

10.1 Electron Configurations and Terms

Within the limits of the orbital approximation, a state of the electrons in a molecule is specified by an electron configuration which tells us how many electrons there are in the various MO energy levels. For example, as we saw in Section 9.8, the π electrons in benzene have a ground state with the closed shell configuration $(a_{2u})^2(e_{1g})^4$ and their first excited state is obtained by promoting one of the e_{1g} electrons into the e_{2u} MO level to give the configuration $(a_{2u})^2(e_{1g})^3(e_{2u})^1$. (See Fig. 9.9.)

The overall classification of electronic states by their electron configurations is, however, too crude to give an explanation of the details of the electronic spectrum of a molecule. A closed shell configuration, like the ground state configuration of benzene for example, does indeed give a unique specification of the state of the electrons since, in accordance with the Pauli principle, a closed shell corresponds to a state in which every MO is occupied by two electrons with opposite spins. The situation is quite different, however, when the configuration contains incompletely filled shells since there will then be considerable freedom in choosing orbital and spin wave functions for the various electrons. To each such choice there corresponds a definite wave function for all the electrons taken together; this function is the product of the various spin-orbital functions that were chosen for the individual electrons, suitably anti-symmetrized to take account of the Pauli principle. Although they all arise from the same underlying configuration, these wave functions describe states of the electrons which differ from each other in their orbital motions and their spins. Consequently, these wave functions may differ from each other in their energies when the inter-electronic repulsions are taken properly into account. Thus a given electron configuration may give rise to several quite distinct electronic states with different energies. These different states are called the *terms* of the configuration and our first problem is to see how the terms of a given configuration may be classified and characterized.

The way in which the terms are classified is best explained by means of a specific example. We choose the e_{1g} level of benzene for this purpose and devote the next section to an analysis of configurations of the type $(e_{1g})^n$ where $n = 1, 2, 3, 4$.

10.2 The Terms of $(e_{1g})^n$

We can always choose the MOs that belong to the e_{1g} level of benzene to be real functions, orthogonal to each other and normalized. We denote such a pair of MOs by ϕ_a and ϕ_b. The actual forms of ϕ_a and ϕ_b are irrelevant to our present purpose; all that we need to know about them is that they provide a real orthonormal basis for the representation E_{1g} of $\mathscr{D}_{6h}$.

These functions describe the orbital motion of an electron in the e_{1g} level. Its spin state is specified by the component of its spin vector along a definite chosen axis, say the z axis. We denote this z component of the spin by m_s. An electron, with total spin $s = \frac{1}{2}$, can have $m_s = \frac{1}{2}$ or $m_s = -\frac{1}{2}$ and we use α and β to denote the corresponding spin wave functions.

Thus the e_{1g} level provides altogether four spin-orbitals; two of these, $\phi_a\alpha$ and $\phi_b\alpha$, have $m_s = \frac{1}{2}$ and the other two, $\phi_a\beta$ and $\phi_b\beta$, have $m_s = -\frac{1}{2}$. We now proceed to discuss the wave functions for n electrons that arise from the configurations $(e_{1g})^n$ where $n = 1, 2, 3, 4$. In the discussion we shall need to talk about the effect of a symmetry operation on the spin-orbitals; we *define* this by saying that when the operator O_R representing the symmetry operation R is applied to a spin-orbital it changes the orbital part into a new function but it has no effect on the spin part: i.e.

$$O_R(\phi\alpha) = (O_R\phi)\alpha, \qquad O_R(\phi\beta) = (O_R\phi)\beta \qquad (10.1)$$

where $\phi = \phi_a$ or ϕ_b. This definition means that the pair of spin-orbitals $\phi_a\alpha$, $\phi_b\alpha$ forms a basis for E_{1g} and so also does the pair $\phi_a\beta$, $\phi_b\beta$.

The configuration $(e_{1g})^1$

The wave functions for the single electron in this configuration are the spin-orbitals described above; the electron has four possible wave functions, all with the same energy, and the configuration $(e_{1g})^1$ produces a single term with a total degeneracy of four. This degeneracy is described by saying that the electron, with spin $s = \frac{1}{2}$, has two spin states with $m_s = \frac{1}{2}$ and $-\frac{1}{2}$: in the spin state with $m_s = \frac{1}{2}$ the electron has two possible wave functions, $\phi_a\alpha$ and $\phi_b\alpha$, which form a basis for E_{1g}; similarly, when the electron is in the spin state with $m_s = -\frac{1}{2}$ it has two possible wave functions, $\phi_a\beta$ and $\phi_b\beta$, which also form a basis for E_{1g}.

All this is summarized in the statement that the configuration $(e_{1g})^1$ produces the term $^2E_{1g}$. The upper left-hand suffix in this *term symbol* indicates that there are two possible spin states for the electron and the IR symbol E_{1g} indicates that the wave functions which belong to either of these spin states form a basis for E_{1g}.

The configuration $(e_{1g})^2$

When there are two electrons in the e_{1g} level, the first electron may be in any one of the four spin-orbitals and, in accordance with the exclusion principle, the second electron must then be in one of the remaining three spin-orbitals. It is therefore possible to write down twelve distinct products of spin-orbitals for the two electrons; a typical product is $\phi_a(1)\alpha(1)\phi_b(2)\alpha(2)$ in which electron 1 has spin $m_s = \frac{1}{2}$ and is in the orbital ϕ_a and electron 2 also has spin $m_s = \frac{1}{2}$ and is in the orbital ϕ_b. Since the electrons are identical particles, indistinguishable from one another, the product $\phi_a(2)\alpha(2)\phi_b(1)\alpha(1)$, which is obtained from the above product by interchanging the two electrons, must correspond to the same physical state of the electrons and a general linear combination of these two products could be considered as a possible wave function for this state. In particular, one may consider the two independent combinations

$$\psi_{\pm} = \phi_a(1)\alpha(1)\phi_b(2)\alpha(2) \pm \phi_a(2)\alpha(2)\phi_b(1)\alpha(1)$$

$$= [\phi_a(1)\phi_b(2) \pm \phi_a(2)\phi_b(1)]\alpha(1)\alpha(2)$$

which are formed by adding and subtracting the two products. These combinations are distinguished from each other by the fact that ψ_+ is unchanged when the coordinates of the two electrons are interchanged while ψ_- changes sign when the two electrons are interchanged: ψ_+ is symmetrical and ψ_- is anti-symmetrical in the coordinates of the two electrons. The twelve different individual products of pairs of spin-orbitals may be combined in this way to produce six symmetrical combinations like ψ_+ and six anti-symmetrical combinations like ψ_-.

We now invoke the general form of the Pauli principle which says that a state of a system of electrons is described by a wave function which must be a totally anti-symmetric function of the coordinates of the electrons, i.e. the wave function must change sign if the coordinates, including the spin co-ordinates, of any two electrons are interchanged. When it is applied to the wave functions for the system of two electrons that we are considering, this principle means that we must ignore the six symmetrical ψ_+ combinations and that the wave functions for the two electrons will be formed from the six anti-symmetrical ψ_- combinations. The $(e_{1g})^2$ configuration, therefore, gives rise to just six independent wave functions and we must see how to classify these.

The ψ_- combination that we have written down is a product of a spin part and an orbital part and it is convenient to discuss these separately. We begin by considering the spin wave functions for the two electrons.

A product of spin wave functions like $\alpha(1)\alpha(2)$ describes a state in which both electrons have a spin component $m_s = \frac{1}{2}$ along the z axis, i.e. it describes a state in which the z component of the total spin of the two electrons taken together is $M_S = 1$. (We shall always use capital letters for quantities associated with the total spin of a number of electrons.) We can form three other products of spin wave functions, namely $\alpha(1)\beta(2)$, $\alpha(2)\beta(1)$, $\beta(1)\beta(2)$, and these have spin components $M_S = 0$, 0 and -1 respectively. The products with $M_S = 1$ and -1 are both symmetrical under an interchange of the two electrons and we can produce a symmetrical and an anti-symmetrical combination of the two products with $M_S = 0$ by forming their sum and their difference. In this way we can write down three spin wave functions, $\alpha(1)\alpha(2)$, $[\alpha(1)\beta(2) + \alpha(2)\beta(1)]/\sqrt{2}$ and $\beta(1)\beta(2)$, which have $M_S = 1$, 0 and -1 respectively and which are symmetrical in the coordinates of the two electrons, and one spin wave function, $[\alpha(1)\beta(2) - \alpha(2)\beta(1)]/\sqrt{2}$, which has $M_S = 0$ and which is anti-symmetrical in the electron coordinates.

We now recall the general property of spin angular momentum that was briefly mentioned in Section 9.3: a system of electrons with total spin S has a spin angular momentum of magnitude $[S(S+1)]^{\frac{1}{2}}h/2\pi$ and, for given S, the system can exist in $2S+1$ different spin states which are characterized by the values $M_S = S, S-1, \ldots, -S$ of the component of the total spin along a given axis. If we apply this statement to the spin wave functions for two electrons we see that the three symmetrical spin wave functions with $M_S = 1, 0, -1$ are the three wave functions for a state with total spin $S = 1$ and that the single anti-symmetrical spin wave function with $M_S = 0$ is the single wave function for a state with total spin $S = 0$; i.e. the individual spins $s_1 = \frac{1}{2}$ and $s_2 = \frac{1}{2}$ of the two electrons can be combined to give a total spin $S = 1$ (unpaired electrons) or a total spin $S = 0$ (paired electrons). The three states with $S = 1$ are called a spin triplet and the single state with $S = 0$ is a spin singlet. For our purposes below we note that the triplet spin states are all symmetrical in the electron coordinates while the singlet spin state is anti-symmetrical.

We turn now to consider the orbital functions for the two electrons. These will be formed from combinations of the four products $\phi_a(1)\phi_a(2)$, $\phi_a(1)\phi_b(2)$, $\phi_b(1)\phi_a(2)$ and $\phi_b(1)\phi_b(2)$. Since ϕ_a and ϕ_b are base functions for E_{1g}, these four products are a basis for the product representation $E_{1g} \times E_{1g}$. The rules for direct products that are given in Appendix I show that, for $\mathscr{D}_{6h}$,

$$E_{1g} \times E_{1g} = A_{1g} + A_{2g} + E_{2g}. \tag{10.2}$$

This reduction of the product representation means that it will be possible to find a linear combination of the four products listed above which is invariant under all the operations of $\mathscr{D}_{6h}$ and which forms a basis for the identical representation A_{1g}; there will be another linear combination which forms a basis for A_{2g}; and there will be a pair of combinations which together form a basis for the two-dimensional representation E_{2g}. It is shown in Appendix F that these combinations are

for A_{1g}: $\phi_a(1)\phi_a(2) + \phi_b(1)\phi_b(2)$;

for A_{2g}: $\phi_a(1)\phi_b(2) - \phi_b(1)\phi_a(2)$;

for E_{2g}: $\begin{cases} \phi_a(1)\phi_a(2) - \phi_b(1)\phi_b(2), \\ \phi_a(1)\phi_b(2) + \phi_b(1)\phi_a(2). \end{cases}$

(10.3)

These combinations arise directly from the reduction of $E_{1g} \times E_{1g}$. We notice, however, that as well as forming bases for IRs of $\mathscr{D}_{6h}$ they also have definite symmetry properties in respect of their dependence on the electron coordinates; the A_{1g} combination and both the E_{2g} combinations are symmetrical functions of the coordinates of the two electrons while the A_{2g} combination is an anti-symmetrical function of these coordinates.

This completes the separate discussion of the spin and orbital wave functions for the two electrons. It only remains to multiply them together so as to obtain the complete wave functions for the two electrons. The requirement of anti-symmetry for the complete wave functions means that an orbital function which is symmetrical in the coordinates of the two electrons must be combined with an anti-symmetrical spin function and that an anti-symmetrical orbital function must be combined with a symmetrical spin function.

Thus the symmetrical A_{1g} orbital function must be multiplied by the anti-symmetrical spin singlet function. This gives a single wave function for the two electrons which forms a basis for A_{1g} and which has $S=0$ and $M_S=0$. This state of the electrons is characterized by the term symbol $^1A_{1g}$, where the upper left-hand suffix indicates that the electrons in this state have a unique spin with only one M_S value so that there is no spin degeneracy.

The pair of symmetrical E_{2g} orbital functions, likewise, can only be multiplied by the anti-symmetrical spin singlet function. This produces two wave functions both of which have $S=0$ and $M_S=0$ and which form a basis for E_{2g}. Because they form a basis for a single IR of the molecular point group, these two wave functions must be degenerate; they describe a state of the two electrons which can be characterized by the term symbol $^1E_{2g}$.

We come, finally, to the A_{2g} orbital function. This is an anti-symmetrical function and so it produces an acceptable wave function for the two electrons when it is multiplied by any one of the three symmetrical spin triplet functions. In this way we obtain three different wave functions each of which forms a basis for A_{2g}. These three wave functions correspond to the three states with $M_S = 1, 0, -1$ of a system with total spin $S = 1$. Since the Hamiltonian (9.1) contains no reference to the spins of the electrons, a set of wave functions which differ only in their M_S values must be degenerate. Thus the A_{2g} orbital function gives rise to a single term with a triple spin degeneracy and we indicate this by the term symbol $^3A_{2g}$.

This discussion of the $(e_{1g})^2$ configuration is summarized in the statement that $(e_{1g})^2$ produces six wave functions which can be classified by their spin degeneracies and their behaviour under the symmetry operations of the molecular point group into the three terms $^1A_{1g}$, $^1E_{2g}$, $^3A_{2g}$.

The configuration $(e_{1g})^3$

When three electrons are placed into the e_{1g} level, three of the available spin-orbitals will be occupied and one will be left empty; there will be four different possible wave functions for the three electrons and these can be characterized by the *empty* spin-orbital. We say that $(e_{1g})^3$ has one hole in the e_{1g} shell. Since the e_{1g} spin-orbitals are equivalent to each other, we conclude that the four wave functions of $(e_{1g})^3$ are degenerate and that they form a single term.

The spin wave functions for the three electrons must be combinations of products like $\alpha(1)\beta(2)\alpha(3)$ for which $M_S = \frac{1}{2}$ or like $\alpha(1)\beta(2)\beta(3)$ for which $M_S = -\frac{1}{2}$ since, because there are only two different MOs available, the exclusion principle forbids the occurrence of the products $\alpha(1)\alpha(2)\alpha(3)$ and $\beta(1)\beta(2)\beta(3)$. Thus all the possible spin states for three electrons in an e_{1g} level have $S = \frac{1}{2}$ and $M_S = \frac{1}{2}$ or $-\frac{1}{2}$ and any term produced by $(e_{1g})^3$ must have a double spin degeneracy.

It follows that any wave function of $(e_{1g})^3$ which has $M_S = \frac{1}{2}$ will be matched by a corresponding wave function with $M_S = -\frac{1}{2}$. Since all the four possible wave functions are degenerate, this means that they can be divided into a pair with $M_S = \frac{1}{2}$ which generates a certain IR of the molecular point group and a pair with $M_S = -\frac{1}{2}$ which generates the same IR. Thus the term produced by $(e_{1g})^3$ must be of the type characterized by the symbol ^2E, where E is a two-dimensional IR. We shall see below that the IR involved must be E_{1g} and that $(e_{1g})^3$, with one hole in the e_{1g} shell, has the same term symbol as $(e_{1g})^1$.

The configuration $(e_{1g})^4$

When there are four electrons in the e_{1g} level we have a closed shell configuration in which each of the available spin-orbitals is occupied. There is, therefore, just one non-degenerate state for the four electrons. This must be a spin singlet state with $M_S = 0$ and $S = 0$ and it will be characterized by a term symbol of the form $^1\Gamma$ where Γ is a one-dimensional IR of $\mathcal{D}_{6h}$. We shall see in the next section that a closed shell configuration always gives rise to the identical representation of a point group, so that, in this case, $(e_{1g})^4$ produces the term $^1A_{1g}$.

10.3 Term Classifications in General

The results of the preceding section have illustrated the way in which the terms of a configuration are classified. The essential points are

(i) that in a given term the total electron spin has a definite value S and that there are $2S + 1$ different spin states with $M_S = S, S-1, \ldots, -S$;

(ii) that for each of these M_S values there is a definite set of wave functions which forms the basis of an IR Γ_μ of the molecular point group, the same IR occurring for all the different M_S values of the term.

The term is characterized by the value of S and by Γ_μ and one signifies this by the term symbol $^{2S+1}\Gamma_\mu$ where the upper left-hand suffix $2S + 1$ gives the spin degeneracy of the term. The total degeneracy of the term, i.e. the number of independent wave functions that it describes, is $(2S + 1)n_\mu$ where n_μ is the dimension of Γ_μ.

Terms involving a single MO level

We discussed the $(e_{1g})^n$ configurations of benzene with point group $\mathcal{D}_{6h}$ in some detail in the last Section. The only really complicated configuration was $(e_{1g})^2$ and our analysis of its terms was based on the fact that for $\mathcal{D}_{6h}$

$$E_{1g} \times E_{1g} = A_{1g} + A_{2g} + E_{2g}.$$

A similar rule holds for the product $E \times E$ of a two-dimensional IR with itself in most of the other point groups and the arguments of Appendix F show that the terms of $(e)^2$ for any e level of this type are always $^1A_1$, $^3A_2$ and ^1E. In some point groups, however, the direct product gives

$$E \times E = A_1 + A_2 + B_1 + B_2,$$

and for these groups, as shown in Appendix F, the terms of $(e)^2$ are $^1A_1$, $^3A_2$, $^1B_1$, $^1B_2$.

It remains to discuss the configurations $(a)^1$, $(a)^2$, $(b)^1$, $(b)^2$ where a and b are non-degenerate MO levels and also the $(t)^n$ configurations that can arise in molecules with $\mathcal{O}_h$ or $\mathcal{T}_d$ symmetry.

For a non-degenerate level of type a or b there is just one MO, say ϕ and this produces two spin-orbitals, $\phi\alpha$ and $\phi\beta$. Thus $(a)^1$ and $(b)^1$ each give a single term with $S=\frac{1}{2}$, $2S+1=2$, which are described by the respective term symbols ^2A and ^2B. When two electrons are placed in an a or b level to give the closed shell configurations $(a)^2$ or $(b)^2$ the only possible anti-symmetrical wave function is

$$\phi(1)\phi(2)\cdot\frac{1}{\sqrt{2}}\left[\alpha(1)\beta(2)-\alpha(2)\beta(1)\right]$$

which is a spin singlet with $S=0$. This function is a basis for the representation $A \times A$ or $B \times B$ and this is always the identical representation, variously denoted by A, A_g, A', A_1, A_{1g} or A'_1 according to the point group involved. If we let Γ_1 stand for the identical representation of any point group, the term of $(a)^2$ or $(b)^2$ is always $^1\Gamma_1$.

This argument can be extended to deal with any closed shell configuration; it is shown in Appendix G that all the possible closed shell configurations, namely $(a)^2$, $(b)^2$, $(e)^4$ and $(t)^6$, produce a single $^1\Gamma_1$ term.

The terms of $(t)^n$ are derived in Appendix G. (This Appendix uses some of the results for configurations involving different MO levels that are discussed below.) Apart from $(t)^1$ with a single ^2T term and $(t)^6$ with the term $^1\Gamma_1$, one has to consider $(t)^2$, $(t)^3$, $(t)^4$ and $(t)^5$. The configuration $(t)^5$ has one hole in the t shell and its six wave functions can be characterized by the unused spin-orbital; they, therefore, resemble the wave functions of the single electron in $(t)^1$ in respect of their spin and orbital properties. Similarly, $(t)^4$ can be regarded as two holes in the t shell and its wave functions have the same spin and orbital properties as those of the two electrons in $(t)^2$. There is, for any kind of level, a general equivalence between holes and electrons: the rule, proved in Appendix G, is that $(\gamma)^n$ and $(\gamma)^{N-n}$ produce an identical set of terms, where N is the total number of electrons that can be accommodated in the γ level. Applied to a t level, this means that the term symbols for $(t)^5$ are the same as those for $(t)^1$ and that the term symbols for $(t)^4$ are the same as those for $(t)^2$. We discussed a similar equivalence between the terms of $(e_{1g})^3$ and $(e_{1g})^1$ in the last section.

The results we have obtained for $(e)^n$ and the results that are given in Appendix G for $(t)^n$ are summarized in Table 10.1 which lists the terms that arise from $(\gamma)^n$ configurations for all the point groups.

For groups of the form $\mathscr{G} \times i$ the MO levels and the terms of a configuration are classified by the IRs of $\mathscr{G}$ with the addition of g or u suffixes. The entries in the table refer to the configurations and terms of $\mathscr{G}$. In all cases, when the larger group is involved, a $(\gamma)^n$ configuration in the table can be read as either $(\gamma_g)^n$ or $(\gamma_u)^n$ and the remarks in the table show how the terms written down for $(\gamma)^n$ are turned into the terms appropriate to $\mathscr{G} \times i$ by the addition of g or u suffixes. Similar considerations apply to groups of the form $\mathscr{G} \times \sigma_h$.

The only configurations that are not listed in the table are the closed shells $(\gamma)^N$, which always give the term $^1\Gamma_1$, and the configurations $(\gamma)^1$ and $(\gamma)^{N-1}$ which contain one electron or one hole and which always give the term $^2\Gamma$ where Γ is the IR that is associated with the γ level.

TABLE 10.1. *Terms of* $(\gamma)^n$.

Groups	Configurations	Terms	Remarks
$\mathscr{D}_{6h}, \mathscr{C}_{6v}, \mathscr{D}_6,$ $\mathscr{C}_{6h}, \mathscr{C}_6$	$(e_1)^2, (e_2)^2$	$^3A_2, {}^1A_1, {}^1E_2$	All terms g in $\mathscr{D}_{6h}, \mathscr{C}_{6h}$ $A_1 = A_2 = A$ in $\mathscr{C}_{6h}, \mathscr{C}_6$
$\mathscr{D}_{6d}$	$(e_1)^2, (e_5)^2$ $(e_2)^2, (e_4)^2$ $(e_3)^2$	$^3A_2, {}^1A_1, {}^1E_2$ $^3A_2, {}^1A_1, {}^1E_4$ $^3A_2, {}^1A_1, {}^1B_1, {}^1B_2$	
$\mathscr{D}_{5h}, \mathscr{D}_{5d}, \mathscr{D}_5,$ $\mathscr{C}_{5v}, \mathscr{C}_{5h}, \mathscr{C}_5$	$(e_1)^2$ $(e_2)^2$	$^3A_2, {}^1A_1, {}^1E_2$ $^3A_2, {}^1A_1, {}^1E_1$	All terms g in $\mathscr{D}_{5d}$ All terms $'$ in $\mathscr{D}_{5h}, \mathscr{C}_{5h}$ $A_1 = A_2 = A$ in $\mathscr{C}_{5h}, \mathscr{C}_5$
$\mathscr{D}_{4h}, \mathscr{D}_4, \mathscr{C}_{4v},$ $\mathscr{C}_{4h}, \mathscr{C}_4, \mathscr{S}_4,$ $\mathscr{D}_{2d}$	$(e)^2$	$^3A_2, {}^1A_1, {}^1B_1, {}^1B_2$	All terms g in $\mathscr{D}_{4h}, \mathscr{C}_{4h}$ $A_1 = A_2 = A, B_1 = B_2 = B$ in $\mathscr{C}_{4h}, \mathscr{C}_4, \mathscr{S}_4$
$\mathscr{D}_{4d}$	$(e_1)^2, (e_3)^2$ $(e_2)^2$	$^3A_2, {}^1A_1, {}^1E_2$ $^3A_2, {}^1A_1, {}^1B_1, {}^1B_2$	
$\mathscr{D}_{3h}, \mathscr{D}_{3d}, \mathscr{D}_3,$ $\mathscr{C}_{3v}, \mathscr{C}_{3h}, \mathscr{C}_3$ $\mathscr{S}_6$	$(e)^2$	$^3A_2, {}^1A_1, {}^1E$	All terms g in $\mathscr{D}_{3d}, \mathscr{S}_6.$ All terms $'$ in $\mathscr{D}_{3h}, \mathscr{C}_{3h}$ $A_1 = A_2 = A$ in $\mathscr{C}_{3h}, \mathscr{S}_6, \mathscr{C}_3$
$\mathscr{O}_h, \mathscr{T}_d$	$(t_1)^2, (t_1)^4$ $(t_2)^2, (t_2)^4$ $(t_1)^3$ $(t_2)^3$	$^3T_1, {}^1A_1, {}^1E, {}^1T_2$ $^4A_1, {}^2E, {}^2T_1, {}^2T_2$ $^4A_2, {}^2E, {}^2T_1, {}^2T_2$	All terms g in $\mathscr{O}_h$ Terms in $\mathscr{O}_h \begin{cases} g \text{ for } t_{1g}, t_{2g} \\ u \text{ for } t_{1u}, t_{2u} \end{cases}$
	$(e)^2$	$^3A_2, {}^1A_1, {}^1E$	All terms g in $\mathscr{O}_h$

Terms involving different MO levels

We have so far considered only $(\gamma)^n$ configurations in which all the electrons are placed in a single MO level. We now discuss the more general case of configurations like $(\gamma)^p(\gamma')^q$ where γ and γ' are two different levels. The results we shall obtain are easily generalized to deal with configurations involving any number of different levels.

Suppose that $\psi(1, \ldots, p)$ is a properly anti-symmetrized wave function for p electrons, numbered from 1 to p, in $(\gamma)^p$ and that $\psi'(p+1, \ldots, p+q)$ is a properly anti-symmetrized wave function for q electrons, numbered from $p+1$ to $p+q$, in $(\gamma')^q$. Then a wave function for the $p+q$ electrons together can be constructed from the product of these two functions; this product is not, by itself, a suitable wave function because it is not totally anti-symmetrical in the coordinates of all the electrons, but it can be used to generate a properly anti-symmetrical wave function, For example, if $p=2$ and $q=1$, we would start from a product $\psi(1, 2)\psi'(3)$ where ψ is an anti-symmetrical function of the coordinates of two electrons, i.e. $\psi(i, j) = -\psi(j, i)$ where i and j could refer to any two electrons. Then the combination

$$\psi(1, 2)\psi'(3) + \psi(2, 3)\psi'(1) + \psi(3, 1)\psi'(2)$$

changes sign if electrons 1 and 2 or 2 and 3 or 1 and 3 are interchanged; it satisfies the Pauli principle and it is a possible wave function for the three electrons.

In general, whatever the values of p and q, one will always be able to anti-symmetrize the product $\psi\psi'$; this will give a possible wave function for the $p+q$ electrons which is characterized in its spin and orbital properties by the properties of ψ and ψ'. Any pair of wave functions ψ and ψ', one from $(\gamma)^p$ and the other from $(\gamma')^q$, may be used to form a wave function for $(\gamma)^p(\gamma')^q$ and all the wave functions of this configuration may be constructed in this way from the separate wave functions for $(\gamma)^p$ and $(\gamma')^q$.

Suppose that one of the terms of $(\gamma)^p$ is $^{2S_\alpha+1}\Gamma_\alpha$ with total degeneracy $(2S_\alpha+1)n_\alpha$ and that one of the terms of $(\gamma')^q$ is $^{2S_\beta+1}\Gamma_\beta$ with total degeneracy $(2S_\beta+1)n_\beta$. Then if we multiply every wave function contained in $^{2S_\alpha+1}\Gamma_\alpha$ by every wave function contained in $^{2S_\beta+1}\Gamma_\beta$ and anti-symmetrize the resulting products, we shall obtain $(2S_\alpha+1)(2S_\beta+1)n_\alpha n_\beta$ wave functions for $(\gamma)^p(\gamma')^q$ and we must now see how to divide this set of wave functions into its various terms.

A particular wave function of $^{2S_\alpha+1}\Gamma_\alpha$ describes a state of p electrons in which the z component of their total spin has a definite value M_α, and to each value of $M_\alpha = S_\alpha, S_\alpha-1, \ldots, -S_\alpha$ there correspond n_α different wave functions which form a basis for Γ_α. Similarly, in $^{2S_\beta+1}\Gamma_\beta$ there are n_β wave functions, which form a basis for Γ_β, for each value of the spin component $M_\beta = S_\beta, S_\beta-1, \ldots, -S_\beta$. If we pick out two definite values of M_α and M_β and multiply the corresponding wave functions together we shall obtain $n_\alpha n_\beta$ wave functions for the whole configuration which form a basis for the product representation $\Gamma_\alpha \times \Gamma_\beta$ and which describe a state of all the electrons in which the z component of their total spin is $M = M_\alpha + M_\beta$.

Thus if we take $M_\alpha = S_\alpha$ and $M_\beta = S_\beta$ we obtain a set of $n_\alpha n_\beta$ wave functions with $M = S_\alpha + S_\beta$. This is the maximum value of M that can possibly occur and so these wave functions must describe a spin state with total spin $S_0 = S_\alpha + S_\beta$ and $M = S_0$. It follows that the two terms of $(\gamma)^p$ and $(\gamma')^q$ with which we began must give rise to a term $^{2S_0+1}(\Gamma_\alpha \times \Gamma_\beta)$ of $(\gamma)^p(\gamma')^q$. Next, consider the values $M_\alpha = S_\alpha - 1$, $M_\beta = S_\beta$ and also $M_\alpha = S_\alpha$, $M_\beta = S_\beta - 1$. Multiplying the corresponding wave functions gives two different sets of wave functions for the whole configuration both of which form a basis for $\Gamma_\alpha \times \Gamma_\beta$ and both of which have $M = S_\alpha + S_\beta - 1 = S_0 - 1$. From these two sets of wave functions we must be able to construct a set which corresponds to the $M = S_0 - 1$ state of the term $^{2S_0+1}(\Gamma_\alpha \times \Gamma_\beta)$ which we have already seen must exist. We are left with $n_\alpha n_\beta$ wave functions which clearly define the states with $M = S_1$ of a term $^{2S_1+1}(\Gamma_\alpha \times \Gamma_\beta)$ with total spin $S_1 = S_0 - 1$. We can continue in this way, obtaining a sequence of terms

$$^{2S_0+1}(\Gamma_\alpha \times \Gamma_\beta), \ ^{2S_1+1}(\Gamma_\alpha \times \Gamma_\beta), \ ^{2S_2+1}(\Gamma_\alpha \times \Gamma_\beta), \ldots$$

where $S_0 = S_\alpha + S_\beta$, $S_1 = S_0 - 1$, $S_2 = S_0 - 2, \ldots$, until all the possible products of wave functions from the two terms with which we began have been exhausted.

Suppose that the sequence stops at the term with total spin $S_k = S_0 - k$. Then the whole set of terms contains altogether

$$(2S_0 + 1 + 2S_1 + 1 + \cdots + 2S_k + 1)n_\alpha n_\beta$$

wave functions. This number must be equal to $(2S_\alpha + 1)(2S_\beta + 1)n_\alpha n_\beta$ and a little arithmetic shows that this will be the case if $S_k = |S_\alpha - S_\beta|$.

This argument shows how it is possible to group the wave functions for $(\gamma)^p(\gamma')^q$ that arise when a term of $(\gamma)^p$ is combined with a term of $(\gamma')^q$ into terms corresponding to a number of distinct spin states. The result we have obtained can be summarized by a 'multiplication rule' for term symbols:

$$[(\gamma)^p: \ ^{2S_\alpha+1}\Gamma_\alpha] \times [(\gamma')^q: \ ^{2S_\beta+1}\Gamma_\beta] = (\gamma)^p(\gamma')^q: \sum_{S'} \ ^{2S'+1}(\Gamma_\alpha \times \Gamma_\beta) \qquad (10.4)$$

where the summation runs over the values

$$S' = S_\alpha + S_\beta, \ S_\alpha + S_\beta - 1, \ldots, |S_\alpha - S_\beta|.$$

The complete set of terms for $(\gamma)^p(\gamma')^q$ is obtained by combining every term of $(\gamma)^p$ with every term of $(\gamma')^q$ in this way. It may happen that $\Gamma_\alpha \times \Gamma_\beta$ is a reducible representation, i.e.

$$\Gamma_\alpha \times \Gamma_\beta = \Gamma_\mu + \Gamma_\nu + \cdots + \Gamma_\sigma$$

where $\Gamma_\mu, \Gamma_\nu, \ldots, \Gamma_\sigma$ are IRs of the molecular point group. In this case the symbol $^{2S'+1}(\Gamma_\alpha \times \Gamma_\beta)$ in (10.4) will stand for the set of terms

$$^{2S'+1}(\Gamma_\alpha \times \Gamma_\beta) = \ ^{2S'+1}\Gamma_\mu, \ ^{2S'+1}\Gamma_\nu, \ldots, \ ^{2S'+1}\Gamma_\sigma.$$

A very important special case occurs when one of the MO levels has a closed shell configuration. Suppose, for example, that $q = N'$ where N' is the total number of electrons that can be accommodated in the γ' level. Then the only term that $(\gamma')^{N'}$ produces is $^1\Gamma_1$, where Γ_1 is the identical representation. This term has $S = 0$ and so when it is combined with a term $^{2S_\alpha+1}\Gamma_\alpha$ from $(\gamma)^p$ there is only one spin value $S' = S_\alpha + 0 = S_\alpha$ for the resultant term. This term belongs to the representation $\Gamma_\alpha \times \Gamma_1 = \Gamma_\alpha$; thus (10.4) shows that

$$[(\gamma)^p : {}^{2S_\alpha+1}\Gamma_\alpha] \times [(\gamma')^{N'} : {}^1\Gamma_1] = (\gamma)^p(\gamma')^{N'} : {}^{2S_\alpha+1}\Gamma_\alpha.$$

It follows that the term classification for $(\gamma)^p(\gamma')^{N'}$ is identical with that for $(\gamma)^p$: *closed shells may be ignored for the purpose of classifying the terms of a general configuration.*

EXAMPLE: *Benzene configurations*

We apply (10.4) to the configurations of the π electrons in benzene that were mentioned at the beginning of Section 10.1. The ground state configuration is $(a_{2u})^2(e_{1g})^4$. Each closed shell gives a $^1A_{1g}$ term and the resultant term for the whole configuration, classifying the ground state wave function, is also $^1A_{1g}$.

When one of the electrons is promoted into the e_{2u} level we obtain the excited configuration $(a_{2u})^2(e_{1g})^3(e_{2u})^1$. The two electrons in $(a_{2u})^2$ form a closed shell and can be ignored. The configurations $(e_{1g})^3$ and $(e_{2u})^1$ each produce a single term, respectively $^2E_{1g}$ and $^2E_{2u}$. These both have $S = \frac{1}{2}$ and so they can be combined to give spin states with $S = \frac{1}{2} + \frac{1}{2} = 1$ or with $S = \frac{1}{2} - \frac{1}{2} = 0$, i.e. either triplet or singlet spin states. The rule (10.4), therefore, shows that this configuration of six electrons contains terms of the type $^3(E_{1g} \times E_{2u})$ and of the type $^1(E_{1g} \times E_{2u})$.

Now the direct product of E_{1g} and E_{2u} is, for $\mathscr{D}_{6h}$,

$$E_{1g} \times E_{2u} = B_{1u} + B_{2u} + E_{1u}.$$

We conclude that $(a_{2u})^2(e_{1g})^3(e_{2u})^1$ produces altogether six different terms, namely

$$^3B_{1u}, \; ^3B_{2u}, \; ^3E_{1u}, \; ^1B_{1u}, \; ^1B_{2u}, \; ^1E_{1u}.$$

Because these terms belong to different IRs and/or have different S values, they will have different energies and this is as much as our qualitative considerations, based on the symmetry of the molecule and the general properties of spin angular momentum, can tell us. The determination of the energies of the different terms of the excited configuration, relative to each other and to the ground state, would require a detailed quantitative calculation involving explicit expressions for the wave functions of the various terms and the MOs from which they are constructed. We shall not enter into this matter except to say that the results of such a calculation are illustrated in the term diagram shown in Fig. 10.1 which shows the relative ordering of the terms that is to be expected. Our next task is to show how such a term diagram can be used to explain the electronic spectrum of a molecule.

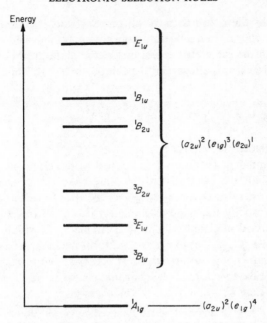

10.1 The terms of the lowest excited configuration of benzene.

10.4 Electronic Selection Rules

A molecule in its ground electronic state may absorb a photon from a beam of incident radiation and make a transition to an excited electronic state. Such a transition can only occur with appreciable intensity when the energy of the photon is equal to the energy difference between the ground state and the excited state and it is these transitions, occurring at definite energies, which give rise to the absorption spectrum of the molecule. One might, therefore, expect each excited term to give rise to a band in the absorption spectrum of the molecule. This is not in fact the case and not every excited term is accessible from the ground state; there are certain *selection rules* which operate to 'allow' or 'forbid' any particular transition.

In benzene with the term diagram of Fig. 10.1, for example, one might expect to find six absorption bands associated with transitions from the ground state $^1A_{1g}$ term to the six terms of the excited configuration. In fact, benzene shows only four bands; there is a strong band at a wavelength of 1800 Å, two comparatively weak bands at 2000 and 2600 Å respectively, and one very weak band at 3500 Å. One of our tasks is, therefore, to explain why the benzene spectrum shows four rather than six bands and why there is a qualitative difference between their intensities.

The quantity which determines the selection rules is the electric dipole moment of the electrons. This is a vector with components μ_x μ_y, μ_z, which are functions of the coordinates of all the electrons. If electron k has coordinates $x^{(k)}$, $y^{(k)}$, $z^{(k)}$ relative to a coordinate system whose origin is left unmoved by all the symmetry operations of the point group of the molecule and there are n electrons altogether, the components of the dipole moment are the functions

$$\mu_x = e \sum_{k=1}^{n} x^{(k)}, \quad \mu_y = e \sum_{k=1}^{n} y^{(k)}, \quad \mu_z = e \sum_{k=1}^{n} z^{(k)}$$

where e is the electronic charge.

When a symmetry operation R is applied to the electrons it changes the coordinates of all the electrons in the same way. Hence the effect of the corresponding operator O_R on μ_x, μ_y, μ_z regarded as functions of the electron coordinates is exactly the same as the effect of O_R on the p AOs p_x, p_y, p_z that were discussed in Chapter 9 and in Example 1 of Section 4.7. It follows that the functions μ_x, μ_y, μ_z, like p_x, p_y, p_z, form the basis for a representation of the molecular point group which is identical with the representation afforded by the base vectors of the coordinate system. The characters of this representation may be found from the matrices given in Section 4.2 and one can use these to find the IRs to which μ_x, μ_y and μ_z belong. This information is given in the character tables: the xyz axes for each point group are chosen in the manner explained in the introduction to Appendix H and μ_x, μ_y, μ_z correspond respectively to the symbols T_x, T_y, T_z that appear in the column to the right of the character table proper. In $\mathscr{D}_{6h}$, for example, μ_z forms a basis for A_{2u} and μ_x and μ_y are a pair of base functions for E_{1u} while in $\mathscr{O}_h$ the three components of the dipole moment stay together and form a basis for T_{1u}.

Let us now consider a transition from the ground state to an excited state of the electrons. The ground state wave functions will belong to a term specified by a total spin S_i and an IR Γ_i and the wave functions of the excited term will have a total spin S_f and will generate an IR Γ_f. We denote one of the ground term wave functions by Ψ_i and one of the excited term wave functions by Ψ_f and we suppose that these wave functions have been chosen to be real.

The theory of the interaction between electromagnetic radiation and electrons shows that the probability of a transition from a state with wave function Ψ_i to a state with wave function Ψ_f depends on the values of the quantities

$$\int \Psi_f \mu_x \Psi_i \, d\tau, \quad \int \Psi_f \mu_y \Psi_i \, d\tau, \quad \int \Psi_f \mu_z \Psi_i \, d\tau \qquad (10.5)$$

where, since the wave functions contain the spin as well as the space coordinates of the electrons, $\int \cdots d\tau$ represents a summation over the spin coordinates as well as an integration over the space coordinates of all the electrons. In particular the transition between the ground term and the excited term is forbidden and cannot occur if all these integrals vanish for any pair of wave functions Ψ_i and Ψ_f from the two terms.

Now μ_x, μ_y, μ_z do not depend at all on the spins of the electrons and so, as far as the summation over the spin variables is concerned, the integrals of (10.5) are like the scalar product of two spin wave functions with definite S and M_S values. Such spin wave functions have the properties, which we state without proof, that two functions with different S values are orthogonal to each other and that two functions with the same value of S but different M_S values are orthogonal to each other. Hence the integrals of (10.5) must vanish if $S_f \neq S_i$. This gives us the *spin selection rule*: transitions between terms with different values of S are forbidden.

If $S_f = S_i$ the transition between the two terms may be allowed. In this case the only possibly non-vanishing integrals are those in which Ψ_i and Ψ_f both refer to the same M_S value. The various functions Ψ_i and Ψ_f which belong to a given M_S value form bases for Γ_i and Γ_f respectively. Consequently, the integrals in (10.5) are like the integrals discussed in Section 7.7 with Ψ_i and Ψ_f playing the parts of Ψ_ρ and Ψ_σ in (7.25) and μ_x, μ_y, μ_z taking the place of F_λ. We may, therefore, apply the conclusions of Section 7.7 to the integrals (10.5). This gives us the *symmetry selection rule*: the transition between two terms characterized by the IRs Γ_i and Γ_f is forbidden if $\Gamma_{(\mu)} \times \Gamma_i$ does not contain Γ_f, where $\Gamma_{(\mu)}$ is the representation which has μ_x, μ_y, μ_z as its basis.

Putting these results in another way, we can say that the transition between the terms $^{2S_i+1}\Gamma_i$ and $^{2S_f+1}\Gamma_f$ is allowed only

$$\text{if } S_f = S_i \quad \text{and} \quad \text{if } \Gamma_{(\mu)} \times \Gamma_i \text{ contains } \Gamma_f.$$

It should be pointed out that the selection rules only lay down the conditions under which the integrals (10.5) must vanish; they tell us nothing about the size of any non-vanishing integral. It may happen that, even though a transition is allowed, the wave functions involved are such that the integrals (10.5) are all very small. In this case the transition would occur with small intensity. Generally, however, an allowed transition is a strong transition and any weak bands that are observed in a spectrum must be ascribed to forbidden transitions which become weakly allowed through a breakdown in the selection rules. One important way in which the symmetry selection rule may be modified is discussed in the next Section.

EXAMPLE: *Benzene*

The ground state term of benzene is $^1A_{1g}$. The character table of $\mathscr{D}_{6h}$ shows that for benzene $\Gamma_{(\mu)} = A_{2u} + E_{1u}$. Consequently, our selection rules tell us that the only spin allowed transitions from the ground state are to the singlet excited terms and that the only symmetry allowed transitions from the ground state are to excited terms whose IRs are contained in

$$\Gamma_{(\mu)} \times A_{1g} = (A_{2u} + E_{1u}) \times A_{1g} = A_{2u} + E_{1u}.$$

The excited terms of benzene are given in Fig. 10.1 and the application of the selection rules to these terms is set out below.

	symmetry allowed	symmetry forbidden
spin allowed	$^1E_{1u}$	$^1B_{1u}$, $^1B_{2u}$
spin forbidden	$^3E_{1u}$	$^3B_{1u}$, $^3B_{2u}$

The selection rules show that there is only one allowed transition for benzene, namely $^1A_{1g} \to {}^1E_{1u}$. This transition must correspond to the strong band observed in the absorption spectrum and the three weaker bands must result from a breakdown of the strict selection rules.

10.5 Vibronic States and Selection Rules

We have so far treated the electronic states of a molecule as if the nuclei were fixed. The nuclei will in fact vibrate about their equilibrium positions and a full description of the internal state of a molecule (apart, that is, from the rotations and translations of the molecule as a whole) requires a specification of its vibrational state as well as its electronic state. As we saw in Chapter 8, the vibrational states can be described by introducing normal coordinates to specify the departures of the nuclei from their equilibrium positions. We denote the set of normal coordinates of a molecule by Q and the set of its electronic coordinates by q. Then an internal state of the molecule will be described by a *vibronic wave function* (vibronic = vibrational + electronic) $\Phi(q, Q)$ which depends on both sets of coordinates.

The molecule will possess a number of vibronic energy levels which can be discussed in much the same way as the electronic terms we have been considering. If we ignore the spins of the nuclei, the vibronic wave functions that belong to a definite vibronic energy level will describe a definite spin state of the electrons and they can be characterized by a vibronic term symbol $^{2S+1}\Gamma^{(v)}$, where $\Gamma^{(v)}$ is the IR of the molecular point group that is associated with the vibronic energy level. A transition between two different vibronic levels with wave functions $\Phi'(q, Q)$ and $\Phi''(q, Q)$ belonging respectively to the IRs $\Gamma'^{(v)}$ and $\Gamma''^{(v)}$ is allowed only if at least one of the integrals of the form

$$\int \Phi'' \, \mu \, \Phi' \, d\tau_q \, d\tau_Q \qquad (10.6)$$

is non-zero, where μ is any one of the components of the electronic dipole moment and $d\tau_q \, d\tau_Q$ indicates an integration over all the variables, the normal coordinates as well as the electronic coordinates. Just as in the discussion of the electronic selection rules based on the integrals (10.5), we see that the transition is allowed only if both the vibronic levels have the same spin and if $\Gamma_{(\mu)} \times \Gamma'^{(v)}$ contains $\Gamma''^{(v)}$ or, putting the symmetry selection rule in another way, if $\Gamma''^{(v)} \times \Gamma_{(\mu)} \times \Gamma'^{(v)}$ contains the identical representation.

In order to make use of this rather general selection rule we must have some way of discovering what the IRs of the various vibronic energy levels will be. We can do this by invoking the Born–Oppenheimer approximation which states that the electronic and vibrational motions of a molecule can be separated from each other so that a vibronic wave function can be written approximately as a product of the form

$$\Phi(q, Q) = \Psi(q)\psi(Q) \tag{10.7}$$

where $\Psi(q)$ is an electronic wave function and $\psi(Q)$ is a vibrational wave function. The electronic and vibrational wave functions in the product are precisely the wave functions we have discussed in isolation from each other in this chapter and in Chapter 8.

The vibrational levels of importance are the vibrational ground state, with a wave function $\psi_0(Q)$ that forms a basis for the identical representation Γ_1 of the point group of the molecule, and the fundamental levels. The fundamental levels are associated with a definite set of IRs (symmetry species) of the molecular point group that can be found by the methods described in Chapter 8. We denote these IRs by $\Gamma_a, \Gamma_b, \ldots, \Gamma_p, \ldots$ and the corresponding vibrational wave functions by $\psi_a, \psi_b, \ldots, \psi_p, \ldots$.

A set of vibronic wave functions is obtained by combining the vibrational wave functions that belong to a definite vibrational level with the electronic wave functions $\Psi_k(q)$ that belong to a definite electronic term with IR Γ_k; this gives a set of wave functions that belong to a single vibronic energy level and these wave functions form a basis for a representation $\Gamma^{(v)}$ which is the direct product of Γ_k with the IR of the vibrational wave functions. Since the energy differences between the vibrational levels are generally much smaller than the differences in energy between the various electronic terms, each electronic term gives rise to a number of relatively closely spaced vibronic energy levels with wave functions and representations of the form

$$\Phi_{k,0}(q, Q) = \Psi_k(q)\psi_0(Q): \quad \Gamma^{(v)} = \Gamma_k \times \Gamma_1 = \Gamma_k,$$

$$\Phi_{k,a}(q, Q) = \Psi_k(q)\psi_a(Q): \quad \Gamma^{(v)} = \Gamma_k \times \Gamma_a,$$

$$\cdots \qquad \cdots \qquad \qquad \cdots \tag{10.8}$$

$$\Phi_{k,p}(q, Q) = \Psi_k(q)\psi_p(Q): \quad \Gamma^{(v)} = \Gamma_k \times \Gamma_p,$$

$$\cdots \qquad \cdots \qquad \qquad \cdots$$

The ground electronic term with wave functions Ψ_i and IR Γ_i produces the ground vibronic level with wave functions $\Phi_{i,0} = \Psi_i \psi_0$ in which the nuclei are in their vibrationless ground state. We consider transitions from this level to the vibronic levels arising from an excited electronic term with electronic wave functions Ψ_f and IR Γ_f. One of the vibronic levels arising from this term also has the nuclei in their vibrationless ground state and its vibronic wave functions are $\Phi_{f,0} = \Psi_f \psi_0$. A transition from the ground state to this level is allowed if integrals of the form

$$\int \Phi_{f,0} \mu \Phi_{i,0} \, d\tau_q \, d\tau_Q = \int \Psi_f \mu \Psi_i \, d\tau_q \int \psi_0^2 \, d\tau_Q$$

are non-zero. Since $\int \psi_0^2 \, d\tau_Q \neq 0$, we recover the symmetry selection rule that was found in the last Section: a vibrationless transition from Ψ_i to Ψ_f is allowed only if $\Gamma_f \times \Gamma_{(\mu)} \times \Gamma_i$ contains the identical representation.

One may ask whether a transition from the ground state to one of the vibronic levels $\Phi_{f,p} = \Psi_f \psi_p$ in which the nuclei are in an excited vibrational state would be allowed. Such a transition has a probability which depends upon integrals of the form

$$\int \Phi_{f,p} \mu \Phi_{i,0} \, d\tau_q \, d\tau_Q = \int \Psi_f \mu \Psi_i \, d\tau_q \int \psi_p \psi_0 \, d\tau_Q. \tag{10.9}$$

Since the excited vibrational wave functions ψ_p are orthogonal to the ground state wave function ψ_0, the integrals (10.9) must necessarily vanish irrespective of Ψ_f and Ψ_i, so that if the Born–Oppenheimer approximation were strictly correct the only possible transitions from the ground state would be vibrationless transitions governed by the symmetry selection rule we have previously found.

It must be remembered, however, that the separation of the electronic and vibrational motions is only an approximation; the motions of the electrons and the nuclei must influence each other to some extent and the simple representation of a vibronic wave function as a product like those in (10.8) is only valid if we neglect the interaction between the motions of the electrons and the nuclei. Since the Born–Oppenheimer approximation is a good approximation and the electron-vibration interaction has only a small effect, the discussion of perturbations in Section 7.4 allows us to say that the energies of the actual vibronic levels will not be very different from the energies of the approximate levels whose wave functions are given in (10.8) and that the actual vibronic wave functions, although they cannot be written as simple products of the form given in (10.8), will nevertheless form bases for the same representations. This means that we can still legitimately speak of the vibrationless ground state with wave functions $\Phi_{i,0}$ forming a basis for Γ_i and of a vibrationless excited state with wave functions $\Phi_{f,0}$ forming a basis for Γ_f as well as other excited states, involving vibrations of the nuclei, with wave functions $\Phi_{f,a}, \ldots, \Phi_{f,p}, \ldots$ forming bases for $\Gamma_f \times \Gamma_a, \ldots, \Gamma_f \times \Gamma_p, \ldots$ respectively.

The selection rule that governs transitions from the ground state to these excited vibronic levels is the general rule mentioned in the discussion of (10.6). A vibrationless transition from $\Phi_{i,0}$ to $\Phi_{f,0}$ is allowed, and will usually give rise to a strong band in the absorption spectrum, if $\Gamma_f \times \Gamma_{(\mu)} \times \Gamma_i$ contains the identical representation. If this condition is not satisfied and the vibrationless transition is forbidden, a transition from $\Phi_{i,0}$ to $\Phi_{f,p}$ may be vibronically allowed; this will be the case if $(\Gamma_f \times \Gamma_p) \times \Gamma_{(\mu)} \times \Gamma_i$ contains the identical representation or, putting the condition in another way, if $\Gamma_f \times \Gamma_{(\mu)} \times \Gamma_i$ contains Γ_p. As we saw in the discussion of (10.9), a vibronic transition of this kind would not in fact occur if the product wave functions of (10.8) were the correct wave functions; but now, when the exact vibronic wave functions are involved, the integrals of (10.9) cannot be split into the product of two separate factors and they do not automatically vanish. Since (10.8) is a good approximation to the wave functions, the integrals, even if they do not vanish, will not be very large and a vibronically allowed transition will normally give rise to a rather weak band in the absorption spectrum.

It is, therefore, possible to distinguish two kinds of transitions between the electronic terms Ψ_i and Ψ_f:

(a) A symmetry allowed vibrationless transition which produces a strong band in the absorption spectrum; this will occur if $\Gamma_{(\mu)} \times \Gamma_i$ contains Γ_f.

(b) Symmetry forbidden but vibronically allowed transitions which produce weak bands in the absorption spectrum; these will occur if $\Gamma_f \times \Gamma_{(\mu)} \times \Gamma_i$ contains at least one of the symmetry species Γ_p of the fundamental vibrational levels of the molecule.

EXAMPLE: *Benzene*

As we saw at the end of the last section, the transitions from the $^1A_{1g}$ ground term to the $^1B_{1u}$ and $^1B_{2u}$ excited terms are spin allowed but symmetry forbidden. These transitions will, however, be vibronically allowed if $B_{1u} \times \Gamma_{(\mu)} \times A_{1g}$ and $B_{2u} \times \Gamma_{(\mu)} \times A_{1g}$ contain at least one of the symmetry species of the benzene fundamentals that are listed in Problem 8.6. Now $\Gamma_{(\mu)}$ for benzene is $A_{2u} + E_{1u}$. Thus

$$B_{1u} \times \Gamma_{(\mu)} \times A_{1g} = B_{1u} \times (A_{2u} + E_{1u}) = B_{2g} + E_{2g},$$

$$B_{2u} \times \Gamma_{(\mu)} \times A_{1g} = B_{2u} \times (A_{2u} + E_{1u}) = B_{1g} + E_{2g}.$$

Since B_{2g} and E_{2g} both appear among the symmetry species listed in Problem 8.6 it follows that both these spin allowed but symmetry forbidden transitions are, in fact, vibronically allowed and these transitions must be responsible for two of the three weak bands observed in the benzene spectrum.

We have still to explain the presence of the third weak band in benzene. Of the three weak bands, one is much weaker than the other two and this can be ascribed to the spin forbidden but symmetry allowed $^1A_{1g} \rightarrow {}^3E_{1u}$ transition. The spin selection rule can be broken down to some extent by external causes such as collisions between molecules, as indeed can the symmetry selection rule.

But it can also be weakened by the perturbation caused by the existence of spin-orbit coupling between the spin and orbital angular momenta of the electrons. We shall not discuss this effect except to observe that it only becomes of major importance when heavy atoms are present in a molecule. Then the spin-orbit coupling may become so strong that the whole idea of classifying the total spin of the electrons independently of their orbital motions becomes untenable and the spin selection rule breaks down completely.

10.6 Ground Terms of Transition-metal Complexes

This section and the next are concerned with some consequences of the energy level diagram, shown in Fig. 9.13, for the MX_6 complexes that were discussed in Section 9.9.

The considerations of Section 9.9 showed that in an MX_6 complex the σ bonding levels and the levels that arise from the ligand π orbitals are occupied by 36 electrons to give a closed shell configuration indicated by $(\sigma)^{12}(\pi)^{24}$ and that the complex is characterized by a number of electrons in the levels labelled $2t_{2g}$ and $2e_g$ in Fig. 9.13. Thus in $MoCl_6^{3-}$, for example, there are three electrons to be placed in these levels; they will go into t_{2g} to give the ground state configuration $(\sigma)^{12}(\pi)^{24}(t_{2g})^3$. Since the closed shells have no effect on the terms of a configuration, we shall ignore them and speak simply of a $(t_{2g})^3$ configuration. Table 10.1 shows that this configuration gives rise to the terms $^4A_{2g}$, ^2E_g, $^2T_{1g}$, $^2T_{2g}$. These terms describe states of the three electrons that differ from each other in respect of their spin and orbital properties. They will have different energies and our first task is to decide which of them has the lowest energy; the spectrum of the complex will be caused by transitions from this ground term to various excited terms of higher energy.

The MOs of the t_{2g} level are predominantly the d_{xy}, d_{xz} and d_{yz} orbitals of the central atom with a small admixture of ligand π orbitals. If the ligand orbitals are neglected and the t_{2g} MOs are treated as pure d AOs it is possible to use well developed methods of atomic spectroscopy to calculate the energies of the terms relative to each other [24], [25]. The calculation, which we shall not attempt to describe, shows that the ground term is $^4A_{2g}$, that the next terms in order of energy are ^2E_g and $^2T_{1g}$ approximately degenerate with each other, and that the term of highest energy is $^2T_{2g}$. This ordering of the terms of $(t_{2g})^3$ will hold for more general types of t_{2g} MOs.

The fact that the spin quartet term with $S = 3/2$ lies below the spin doublet terms with $S = 1/2$ is an example of what is known as *Hund's rule*: the ground term of a configuration is the term with the maximum value of the total spin S. In a quartet spin state, the spins of the three electrons combine to give the maximum possible value of S, namely $S = 3/2$, that can be obtained from three electrons; one says that the electrons are unpaired and have parallel spins. The doublet states with $S = \frac{1}{2}$ can be regarded as the result of pairing the spins of two of the electrons to give a zero resultant spin; this effectively leaves one unpaired electron with spin $\frac{1}{2}$. The fact that the state in which the three electrons have parallel spins is more stable than the states in which two of the electrons are paired with opposite spins is a direct consequence of the Pauli principle and its demand that the total wave function including spin should be anti-symmetric in the electron coordinates. This can be shown to give rise to an effective 'exchange interaction' between the electrons which tends to stabilize the arrangement in which as many as possible of the electrons in a configuration have parallel spins relative to the arrangements in which some of the electrons have their spins paired. Thus in a $(t_{2g})^2$ configuration, for example, with the terms $^3T_{1g}$, $^1A_{1g}$, ^1E_g, $^1T_{2g}$ the terms for which the two electrons have paired spins with $S=0$, namely the $^1A_{1g}$, ^1E_g and $^1T_{2g}$ terms, have higher energy than the $^3T_{1g}$ term in which the two electrons have parallel spins with $S=1$.

The situation becomes more interesting when the number of electrons exceeds three. On the one hand, the fact that the e_g level has higher energy than the t_{2g} level will tend to stabilize the arrangement in which as many electrons as possible go into the t_{2g} level; on the other hand, the exchange interaction will tend to stabilize the arrangement in which as many electrons as possible have parallel spins. These two tendencies conflict with each other. Thus with four electrons one could have the configuration $(t_{2g})^4$ in which all the electrons are in t_{2g} but in which two of them necessarily have their spins paired or one could have the configuration $(t_{2g})^3(e_g)^1$ in which all four electrons can have parallel spins but in which the higher energy of the e_g level acts as a destabilizing factor. Which of these configurations will in fact give rise to the ground term of the complex depends upon whether the energy difference Δ between the e_g and t_{2g} levels is large enough to counteract the exchange energy which opposes spin pairing. If Δ is large enough, the ground term will be the $S=1$ term of $(t_{2g})^4$; if Δ is small enough for the exchange interaction to dominate, the ground term will be the $S=2$ term of $(t_{2g})^3(e_g)^1$. Thus an MX_6 complex with four electrons outside the filled MO levels might exist in either a high-spin or a low-spin form; which form would actually occur depends critically on the splitting between the t_{2g} and e_g levels and this splitting is determined, for a given central atom, by the nature of the ligands.

There are similar possibilities of either high-spin or low-spin ground terms when there are five, six or seven electrons to be placed in the t_{2g} and e_g levels. For eight or nine electrons, the t_{2g} level must hold its full complement of six electrons and there is only one possibility for the ground term.

The ground terms that are obtained for $n=1, 2, \ldots, 9$ electrons in the t_{2g} and e_g levels are set out in Table 10.2. Many of these can be identified from Table 10.1 and for those involving mixed t_{2g} and e_g configurations the rule (10.4) applies. Thus in $(t_{2g})^3(e_g)^2$, for example, we want the term with maximum S, namely $S=5/2$. This can only arise from a combination of the

$S=3/2$ term $^4A_{2g}$ of $(t_{2g})^3$ with the $S=1$ term $^3A_{2g}$ of $(e_g)^2$: the resultant term is $^6(A_{2g} \times A_{2g}) = {}^6A_{1g}$.

TABLE 10.2. *Ground terms for* MX_6 *complexes*

$n=1$	$(t_{2g})^1 : {}^2T_{2g}$
2	$(t_{2g})^2 : {}^3T_{1g}$
3	$(t_{2g})^3 : {}^4A_{2g}$
4	$(t_{2g})^4 : {}^3T_{1g}$ or $(t_{2g})^3(e_g)^1 : {}^5E_g$
5	$(t_{2g})^5 : {}^2T_{2g}$ or $(t_{2g})^3(e_g)^2 : {}^6A_{1g}$
6	$(t_{2g})^6 : {}^1A_{1g}$ or $(t_{2g})^4(e_g)^2 : {}^5T_{2g}$
7	$(t_{2g})^6(e_g)^1 : {}^2E_g$ or $(t_{2g})^5(e_g)^2 : {}^4T_{1g}$
8	$(t_{2g})^6(e_g)^2 : {}^3A_{2g}$
9	$(t_{2g})^6(e_g)^3 : {}^2E_g$

This explanation of the occurrence in nature of both high-spin and low-spin octahedral complexes of the transition-metals is due to Van Vleck [22].

10.7 Spectra of Transition-metal Complexes

The spectrum of an MX_6 complex is caused by transitions from its ground term to terms of higher energy. There are various kinds of transition that can occur and these give rise to various characteristic features of the absorption spectrum.

First, the ground state configuration itself will, in most cases, give rise to a number of distinct terms, and transitions from the ground term to these other terms of the same configuration will be possible. Since the ground term is the term of maximum spin, these transitions, which involve a re-arrangement of electrons within the same configuration, are all spin forbidden; they may, however, occur with weak intensity because of the breakdown in the strict spin selection rule caused by spin-orbit coupling.

Second, there are transitions from the ground term to the excited terms that arise when an electron is promoted from the t_{2g} level to the e_g level. Many of these transitions will again be spin forbidden, but there will, in general, be some excited terms with the same spin as the ground term. Transitions to these terms will be spin allowed and stronger than any spin forbidden transitions. All these transitions are, however, symmetry forbidden; they can only show up in the spectrum as vibronically allowed bands with not very large intensities.

The fact that these transitions are symmetry forbidden but vibronically allowed is easily demonstrated. Every term arising from a configuration of the form $(t_{2g})^a(e_g)^b$ must belong to one of the Γ_g IRs of $\mathcal{O}_h$; this is true both of the ground term and of any excited term. Now the electric dipole moment belongs to the representation $\Gamma_{(\mu)} = T_{1u}$ of $\mathcal{O}_h$ and the only symmetry allowed transitions from a Γ_g ground term will be to excited terms whose IRs are contained in $\Gamma_{(\mu)} \times \Gamma_g = T_{1u} \times \Gamma_g$. All the IRs in this product representation must be Γ_u representations and so a direct consequence of the symmetry selection rule is that for molecules with point group $\mathcal{O}_h$ only $g \rightarrow u$ transitions are allowed; $g \rightarrow g$ and, similarly, $u \rightarrow u$ transitions are symmetry forbidden. In our case, since all our terms are Γ_g terms, all transitions between them are symmetry forbidden.

We now look to see whether the transitions are vibronically allowed. To do this we must find the symmetry species of the fundamentals of an MX_6 molecule. The methods of doing this are described in Chapter 8 and the results for MX_6, given in Problem 8.7, show that the fundamentals of MX_6 have symmetry species

$$A_{1g}, E_g, T_{2g}, T_{1u}, T_{2u}. \tag{10.10}$$

The vibronic selection rule given at the end of Section 10.5 shows that a transition between two terms belonging to the IRs Γ_g and Γ'_g of $\mathcal{O}_h$ will be vibronically allowed if $\Gamma'_g \times \Gamma_{(\mu)} \times \Gamma_g = \Gamma'_g \times T_{1u} \times \Gamma_g$ contains one of the IRs listed in (10.10). Now the representations of $\mathcal{O}_h$ are such that the direct product of T_{1u} with any Γ_g contains either or both of T_{1u} and T_{2u}; since both these IRs are contained in (10.10), it follows that all transitions between the terms of different $(t_{2g})^a(e_g)^b$ configurations are vibronically allowed.

Thus the various terms of an MX_6 complex arising from configurations of the general form $(\sigma)^{12}(\pi)^{24}(t_{2g})^a(e_g)^b$ with different values of a and b are responsible for a series of vibronically allowed bands; some of these are spin forbidden and very weak, others are spin allowed and comparatively strong. The transitions causing these bands are often referred to as 'forbidden d-d transitions' since they involve rearrangements of the electrons in MOs that consist mainly of central atom d AOs.

The bands due to these transitions occur at energies that are comparable with the energy difference between the t_{2g} and e_g levels. There is a third kind of transition which can give rise to absorption bands at rather higher energies; these are the transitions that are caused by the excitation of one of the electrons from the filled π or σ levels into the t_{2g} or the e_g level. One can speak, for example, of a $\pi \rightarrow t_{2g}$ transition that changes the configuration from $(\sigma)^{12}(\pi)^{24}(t_{2g})^a(e_g)^b$ to $(\sigma)^{12}(\pi)^{23}(t_{2g})^{a+1}(e_g)^b$. Such a transition moves the electron from an MO which consists mainly of a combination of ligand π AOs into an MO which consists mainly of a central atom d AO; it is, accordingly, called a charge transfer transition. If the π level involved is the t_{1g} level or the $1t_{2g}$ level shown in Fig. 9.13, the transition will be symmetry forbidden but vibronically allowed and it will not show up at all strongly in the absorption spectrum. If, on the other hand, the transition takes place from the t_{2u} or the $2t_{1u}$ levels it may be both spin and symmetry allowed; it will then produce a strong 'allowed' band in the absorption spectrum.

The energy level diagram of Fig. 9.13, therefore, predicts that a typical MX_6 complex will have an absorption spectrum that contains a number of weak or very weak bands due to 'forbidden d–d transitions' followed at higher energies by a number of strong 'allowed' charge transfer bands. This is, indeed, the characteristic form of the spectrum of an octahedrally co-ordinated transition-metal complex and the theory we have outlined has been extraordinarily successful in explaining the often very complicated details of these spectra [23], [25]. We illustrate the results that are obtained by a consideration of a $(t_{2g})^3$ complex like $MoCl_6^{3-}$.

EXAMPLE: *A $(t_{2g})^3$ complex*

The ground state configuration $(\sigma)^{12}(\pi)^{24}(t_{2g})^3$ produces the terms $^4A_{2g}$, ^2E_g, $^2T_{1g}$, $^2T_{2g}$. The ground term with spin $S = 3/2$ is $^4A_{2g}$ and the quantitative theory shows that the ^2E_g and $^2T_{1g}$ terms are approximately degenerate with each other and that they have lower energy than the $^2T_{2g}$ term. There will, therefore, be two spin forbidden transitions between the ground term and the other terms of the ground state configuration which may show up as very weak bands in the absorption spectrum. Transitions such as these which involve a rearrangement of the electrons within the ground state configuration generally give rise to narrow well-defined bands.

The other 'forbidden d–d transitions' are determined by the terms of the excited configurations $(t_{2g})^2(e_g)^1$, $(t_{2g})^1(e_g)^2$ and $(e_g)^3$. Some of these terms will have the same spin as the ground term and will give rise to spin allowed transitions; there will also be many possible spin forbidden transitions. It is generally true, however, that a transition which involves the excitation of an electron from one MO level to another produces a rather broad absorption band. Consequently, the very weak spin forbidden bands do not show up in the spectrum; a typical spectrum shows the broad and comparatively strong bands due to spin allowed transitions and the two weak but well-defined spin forbidden bands mentioned in the paragraph above.

The terms of the excited configurations can be found by using the rule (10.4) for combining the terms that arise from pure t_{2g} or e_g configurations.

(i) $(t_{2g})^2(e_g)^1$: Here we must combine the ^2E_g $(S = \tfrac{1}{2})$ term of $(e_g)^1$ with the terms of $(t_{2g})^2$; these are given by Table 10.1 to be $^3T_{1g}$, $^1A_{1g}$, ^1E_g, $^1T_{2g}$. The combination of ^2E_g with $^3T_{1g}$ can give terms with $S = 1 + \tfrac{1}{2}$ or with $S = 1 - \tfrac{1}{2}$. These terms are

$$^4(T_{1g} \times E_g) = {}^4T_{1g} + {}^4T_{2g} \quad \text{and} \quad {}^2(T_{1g} \times E_g) = {}^2T_{1g} + {}^2T_{2g}.$$

The combination of ^2E_g with any spin singlet term must give a spin doublet. Thus the singlet terms of $(t_{2g})^2$ produce the terms

$$^2(A_{1g} \times E_g) = {}^2E_g, \quad {}^2(E_g \times E_g) = {}^2A_{1g} + {}^2A_{2g} + {}^2E_g, \quad {}^2(T_{2g} \times E_g) = {}^2T_{1g} + {}^2T_{2g}.$$

A complete list of the terms of $(t_{2g})^2(e_g)^1$ is, therefore,

$$^4T_{1g}, \quad {}^4T_{2g}, \quad {}^2A_{1g}, \quad {}^2A_{2g}, \quad {}^2E_g \text{ (twice)}, \quad {}^2T_{1g} \text{ (twice)}, \quad {}^2T_{2g} \text{ (twice)}.$$

(ii) $(t_{2g})^1(e_g)^2$: The terms of this configuration arise from combining $^2T_{2g}$ of $(t_{2g})^1$ with $^3A_{2g} + {}^1A_{1g} + {}^1E_g$ of $(e_g)^2$. They are

$$^4T_{1g}, \quad {}^2T_{1g} \text{ (twice)}, \quad {}^2T_{2g} \text{ (twice)}.$$

(iii) $(e_g)^3$ has the single term ^2E_g.

The only spin allowed transitions from the $^4A_{2g}$ ground term are to the $^4T_{1g}$ and $^4T_{2g}$ terms of $(t_{2g})^2(e_g)^1$ and, at higher energy, to the $^4T_{1g}$ term of $(t_{2g})^1(e_g)^2$. Here, one should bear the approximate nature of the MO description in mind. The t_{2g} and e_g MOs are, in principle, wave functions for the self-consistent field Hamiltonian in which the inter-electronic repulsions are treated only approximately. If we wish to represent wave functions for the correct Hamiltonian by means of products of self-consistent field MOs we must take the difference between the actual inter-electronic potential energy and its representation by means of a self-consistent field into account as a perturbation. This perturbation will have the effect of mixing the wave functions of terms that are described by the same term symbol. Thus whereas there is only one $^4T_{2g}$ term, which must be described by the pure configuration $(t_{2g})^2(e_g)^1$, the wave functions for the $^4T_{1g}$ terms will be combinations of wave functions arising from the $(t_{2g})^2(e_g)^1$ and $(t_{2g})^1(e_g)^2$ configurations; this 'configuration interaction' may have a considerable effect on the energies of the terms and on the probability of a transition to them from the ground term.

These considerations are important for quantitative calculations. Qualitatively, however, it remains true to say that a $(t_{2g})^3$ complex should show three spin allowed but symmetry forbidden bands. The actual positions of these bands relative to each other and to the spin forbidden bands mentioned above depend critically on the value of the energy difference between the t_{2g} and e_g levels and its relation to certain parameters describing the effects of the inter-electronic repulsions; hence the spectra of different $(t_{2g})^3$ complexes may look rather different from each other. It is one of the triumphs of the quantitative theory of these forbidden d–d transitions that the theory can be used to fit all these spectra into a single coherent pattern.

The bands due to the forbidden transitions occur in the visible and near ultra-violet regions of the spectrum. At shorter wavelengths one comes across the strong, allowed charge transfer bands caused by transitions from the π levels designated by t_{2u} and $2t_{1u}$ in Fig. 9.13. These transitions produce the excited configurations $(t_{2u})^5(t_{2g})^4$ and $(2t_{1u})^5(t_{2g})^4$, where we have omitted the closed shells from the description of the configurations.

The first configuration has terms that are obtained by combining the terms $^3T_{1g}, {}^1A_{1g}, {}^1E_g, {}^1T_{2g}$ of $(t_{2g})^4$ with the single term, $^2T_{2u}$, of $(t_{2u})^5$. The only spin allowed transitions from the ground term are to the terms with $S = 1 + \frac{1}{2}$ obtained by combining $^2T_{2u}$ of $(t_{2u})^5$ with $^3T_{1g}$ of $(t_{2g})^4$. These terms are

$$^4(T_{2u} \times T_{1g}) = {}^4A_{2u}, {}^4E_u, {}^4T_{1u}, {}^4T_{2u}.$$

The symmetry selection rule tells us that, since $\Gamma_{(\mu)} = T_{1u}$, the only symmetry allowed transitions from the $^4A_{2g}$ ground term are to terms whose IRs belong to $\Gamma_{(\mu)} \times A_{2g} = T_{1u} \times A_{2g} = T_{2u}$. Hence the configuration $(t_{2u})^5(t_{2g})^4$ gives rise to a single $^4A_{2g} \rightarrow {}^4T_{2u}$ allowed band in the absorption spectrum. Similarly, the quartet terms of $(2t_{1u})^5(t_{2g})^4$ are

$$^4(T_{1u} \times T_{1g}) = {}^4A_{1u}, {}^4E_u, {}^4T_{1u}, {}^4T_{2u}$$

and the transition to this excited configuration also gives rise to just one allowed band.

PROBLEMS

10.1. Show that for any molecule with a centre of symmetry, the IRs contained in $\Gamma_{(\mu)}$ are always of type u and deduce that all $g \to g$ and $u \to u$ transitions are symmetry forbidden. (This is known as the *Laporte selection rule*.)

10.2. The C_5H_5 ring with point group $\mathscr{D}_{5h}$ discussed in Problem 9.1 has π-electron MOs of the type a_2'', e_1'' and e_2'' in order of increasing energy, and the ground state configuration is $(a_2'')^2(e_1'')^3$ with term $^2E_1''$. Possible excited configurations are (i) $(a_2'')^1(e_1'')^4$ and (ii) $(a_2'')^2(e_1'')^2(e_2'')^1$. Use (10.4), Table 10.1 and the results for direct products in $\mathscr{D}_{5h}$ that are collected in Appendix I to show that the terms of these excited configurations are:

(i) $^2A_2''$ and (ii) $^4E_2''$, $^2A_1''$, $^2A_2''$, $^2E_1''$, $^2E_2''$, $^2E_2''$. Show that the spin and symmetry allowed transitions from the ground term are those to the $^2A_1''$, $^2A_2''$ and $^2E_2''$ excited terms.

10.3. Show that the following configurations in an $\mathscr{O}_h$ complex have the indicated terms. (Since all terms are of type g, this suffix has been omitted. A bracketed number after a term symbol indicates the number of different terms of that type that occur.)

$(t_2)^2(e)^2$: $^5T_2$; $^3A_2$, ^3E, $^3T_1(3)$, $^3T_2(2)$; $^1A_1(2)$, $^1A_2$, $^1E(3)$, $^1T_1$, $^1T_2(3)$.

$(t_2)^3(e)^1$: ^5E; $^3A_1$, $^3A_2$, $^3E(2)$, $^3T_1(2)$, $^3T_2(2)$; $^1A_1$, $^1A_2$, ^1E, $^1T_1(2)$, $^1T_2(2)$.

10.4. A possible level scheme for MnO_4^- (compare Problems 9.3, 9.4) gives the ion a closed shell configuration with the filled level of highest energy a t_1 level and the lowest-lying unoccupied level an e level. Thus the ground state configuration is (closed shells) $(t_1)^6$ with term $^1A_1$ and the first excited configuration is (closed shells) $(t_1)^5(e)$. Show that the terms of this excited configuration are $^3T_1$, $^3T_2$, $^1T_1$, $^1T_2$ and that the only spin and symmetry allowed transition from the ground term is to the excited $^1T_2$ term.

10.5. If an extra electron is added to permanganate to form the manganate ion MnO_4^{2-} it would, on the level scheme postulated in Problem 10.4, go into the e level to give the ground state configuration $(t_1)^6(e)$ with term ^2E. An excited configuration would then be $(t_1)^5(e)^2$. Show that the terms of this configuration are $^4T_2$, $^2T_1(2)$, $^2T_2(2)$ and that the four transitions from the ground term to these excited terms that are spin allowed are also symmetry allowed.

Appendix A

RELATIONS BETWEEN SYMMETRY OPERATIONS

The results we require can be explained by reference to Fig. A.1 in which OB

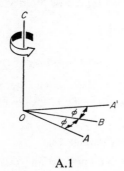

A.1

is the line bisecting the angle between the lines OA and OA' and OC is perpendicular to the plane OAA'.

(i) The product of two reflections

Suppose that OAC, OBC are two symmetry planes with reflection operations σ_a, σ_b, and consider the product $\sigma_b\sigma_a$. This combined operation leaves the line of intersection OC of the two planes unaltered and must evidently be equivalent to a rotation about OC. Since σ_a leaves all the points on OAC unaltered, and σ_b moves each point of this plane into the corresponding point of the plane $OA'C$, the rotation must be through an angle 2ϕ, where ϕ is the angle between the planes OAC and OBC. Hence

$$\sigma_b\sigma_a = C(2\phi), \qquad (A.1)$$

in the sense indicated in the figure. The operation $\sigma_a\sigma_b$ is, similarly, a rotation about OC through an angle 2ϕ in the opposite sense.

Thus the line of intersection of two symmetry planes of a molecule is a symmetry axis. If it is an n-fold axis and σ_a and σ_b are reflections in two immediately adjacent planes which intersect on this axis, we have the result

$$\sigma_b\sigma_a = C_n; \qquad \sigma_a\sigma_b = C_n{}^{-1};$$

or, using the fact that σ_a is its own inverse,

$$\sigma_b = C_n\sigma_a = \sigma_aC_n{}^{-1}. \qquad (A.2)$$

We deduce that if a molecule has an n-fold symmetry axis and a plane of symmetry containing this axis, then it possesses altogether n such symmetry planes and the angle between two adjacent planes is π/n. If σ_v denotes a reflection in one of these planes, it follows from $(A.2)$ that

$$C_n{}^{-1} = \sigma_vC_n\sigma_v,$$

or, more generally, that

$$C_n{}^{-k} = (\sigma_vC_n\sigma_v)(\sigma_vC_n\sigma_v)\ldots(\sigma_vC_n\sigma_v) \quad (k \text{ factors})$$

$$= \sigma_vC_n{}^k\sigma_v. \qquad (A.3)$$

In the special case where there are just two perpendicular planes with reflections σ_v, σ_h, their line of intersection is a two-fold axis. If C_2' is the corresponding rotation, we have

$$\sigma_v\sigma_h = C_2' = \sigma_h\sigma_v, \qquad (A.4)$$

or, equivalently,

$$\sigma_v = C_2'\sigma_h = \sigma_hC_2',$$

so that the two reflections commute with each other and with the rotation. These three operations are mutually dependent, and the presence of any two of them implies the third.

(ii) The product of two rotations through 180°

Suppose that in the figure the lines OA and OB are twofold symmetry axes with rotations C_{2a}, C_{2b}, and consider the product $C_{2b}C_{2a}$. In this combined operation, C_{2a} reverses the direction of OC and then C_{2b} restores this line to its original position; the product must therefore be a rotation about OC. Since C_{2a} leaves OA unaltered and C_{2b} moves each point on OA into the corresponding point on OA', the resultant angle of rotation is 2ϕ in the sense indicated in the figure. The product $C_{2a}C_{2b}$ will, similarly, be a rotation through 2ϕ in the opposite sense.

A similar argument to that used in (i) shows that if the molecule has an n-fold symmetry axis and a perpendicular twofold axis, which intersects the n-fold axis at a point O, then there are altogether n such twofold axes intersecting at O; the angle between two adjacent axes is π/n. If C_2', C_2'' denote rotations through 180° about two adjacent twofold axes, then

$$C_2'' = C_nC_2' = C_2'C_n{}^{-1}.$$

Thus

$$C_n{}^{-1} = C_2'C_nC_2' \quad \text{and} \quad C_n{}^{-k} = C_2'C_n{}^kC_2'. \qquad (A.5)$$

In particular we may note that rotations through 180° about three mutually perpendicular axes commute with each other, and that the product of any two of them is equal to the third.

(iii) A product arising in $\mathcal{D}_{nd}$

In this group one needs to evaluate products of the form $C_2'\sigma_d$ where C_2' is a rotation about a twofold axis which is perpendicular to an n-fold axis and σ_d is a reflection in one of the symmetry planes containing the n-fold axis. The angle between the twofold axis and the symmetry plane may have any one of the values $(k+\frac{1}{2})\pi/n$ where $k = 0, 1, 2, \ldots, n-1$. These products may be evaluated by noting that if σ_v and σ_h denote reflections in planes respectively containing and perpendicular to the n-fold axis and which intersect along the twofold axis (note that neither σ_v nor σ_h are by themselves symmetry operations in $\mathcal{D}_{nd}$) we can use $(A.4)$ to write

$$C_2'\sigma_d = \sigma_h\sigma_v\sigma_d.$$

Now the product $\sigma_v\sigma_d$ is, from $(A.1)$, a rotation about the n-fold axis through an angle $2(k+\frac{1}{2})\pi/n = (2k+1)2\pi/2n$; it is in fact the rotation C_{2n}^{2k+1}. Hence

$$C_2'\sigma_d = \sigma_h C_{2n}^{2k+1} = S_{2n}^{2k+1},$$

and the main axis in $\mathcal{D}_{nd}$ is also a $2n$-fold rotary reflection axis.

(iv) The rules for dividing a point group into classes

Two elements P and Q of a group belong to the same class if the group contains some element R such that $P = R^{-1}QR$. The rules, stated in Section 2.5, which enable us to decide which elements of a group belong to the same class are:

Rule (i): A rotation C_n^k and its inverse C_n^{-k} about an n-fold symmetry axis belong to the same class if there is a plane of symmetry containing the axis or a twofold symmetry axis perpendicular to the n-fold axis. This rule is a direct consequence of $(A.3)$ and $(A.5)$, since a reflection σ_v and a rotation C_2' are their own inverses. The extension to improper rotations is immediate.

Rules (ii) and (iii): These state that two reflections in different symmetry planes (or two rotations through the same angle about different symmetry axes) belong to the same class if the group contains a symmetry operation which moves one of the planes (or axes) of symmetry into the other.

These rules are a consequence of the following considerations. Suppose that P is a reflection (or rotation) related to a plane (or axis) of symmetry p in the same way as the reflection (or rotation) Q is related to the plane (or axis) q. Then under P all the points of p remain unmoved and under Q all the points of q remain unmoved. Now suppose that R is a reflection or rotation that, among its other effects, moves all the points of p into corresponding points of q, and consider the operation $R^{-1}QR$. This operation must be of the same type, rotation or reflection, as Q. The factors in the product are (a) R, which moves the points of p into those of q, (b) Q, which reflects (or rotates) the molecule with respect to q leaving the points occupying positions on q unmoved, and (c) R^{-1}, which returns all points on q to their original positions on p and at the same time undoes the other effects of R. The result of all this will be a reflection (or rotation) related to the plane (or axis) p in the same way as Q is related to q; in other words, it is the operation P and

$$R^{-1}QR = P.$$

This argument can be extended to improper rotations in which p and q would stand for axes of rotation together with perpendicular reflection planes.

Rule (iv) states that, since the inversion i commutes with every other symmetry operation, it is always in a class by itself. The commuting property of i follows because a rotation about an axis and a reflection in a plane perpendicular to the axis are commuting operations and because we can write $i = C_2\sigma_h$, where σ_h is a reflection in *any* plane containing the centre of symmetry and C_2 is a rotation about an axis perpendicular to this plane. Thus, if the group contains an axis of symmetry (which will pass through the centre of symmetry) we can choose this axis as the C_2 axis for the inversion. C_2 and σ_h then both commute with any rotation or improper rotation about the axis of symmetry, and so, therefore, does i. If the group contains a plane of symmetry (which will contain the centre of symmetry) we can choose this plane as the σ_h plane for the inversion, and see that i will commute with a reflection in this plane.

Appendix B

THE SUFFIX NOTATION

The suffix notation allows us to handle general linear relations between different sets of quantities with great ease and economy. Thus the three separate equations of (4.5) expressing the vectors $R\mathbf{e}_1$, $R\mathbf{e}_2$, $R\mathbf{e}_3$ in terms of $\mathbf{e}_1$, $\mathbf{e}_2$, $\mathbf{e}_3$ are summarized in the single equation (4.5′) and the three equations of (4.6) are summarized in the single equation (4.6′), namely

$$x'_k = \sum_{j=1}^{3} r_{kj} x_j, \quad (k = 1, 2, 3). \tag{B.1}$$

An equation such as $(B.1)$ stands for the three separate equations obtained by substituting the three different possible values for k. This suffix appears once on the left-hand side and it also appears once on the right-hand side; it is called a *free suffix* since it is free to take on any particular numerical value. The other suffix, j, that appears on the right-hand side is not free since the summation sign tells us that we must perform a summation over all the different numerical values of j. This suffix, which is twice repeated, is a *dummy suffix* and we could use any other symbol for it, except k, without changing the meaning of the equation:

$$x'_k = \sum_{j=1}^{3} r_{kj} x_j = \sum_{i=1}^{3} r_{ki} x_i = \sum_{p=1}^{3} r_{kp} x_p.$$

Equation $(B.1)$ is typical of equations that describe linear relations between two sets of quantities; the free suffix appears once on each side and the dummy suffix is repeated twice. There is no need to restrict ourselves to three variables. In general, one may consider relations of the form

$$y_k = \sum_{j=1}^{n} r_{kj} x_j, \quad (k = 1, 2, \ldots, m).$$

These equations represent m linear combinations $y_1, y_2, \ldots, y_m$ of n different quantities $x_1, x_2, \ldots, x_n$.

There are very simple rules for manipulating the summations that appear in the development of the theory. The rules are simply

$$\left(\sum_{i=1}^{n} A_i \right) \left(\sum_{j=1}^{m} B_j \right) = \sum_{i=1}^{n} A_i \left(\sum_{j=1}^{m} B_j \right) = \sum_{j=1}^{m} B_j \left(\sum_{i=1}^{n} A_i \right) = \sum_{i=1}^{n} \sum_{j=1}^{m} A_i B_j.$$

If, for instance, $n=3$ and $m=2$, the relations we have written down correspond to the obvious relations

$$(A_1 + A_2 + A_3)(B_1 + B_2) = A_1(B_1 + B_2) + A_2(B_1 + B_2) + A_3(B_1 + B_2)$$

$$= B_1(A_1 + A_2 + A_3) + B_2(A_1 + A_2 + A_3)$$

$$= A_1B_1 + A_1B_2 + A_2B_1 + A_2B_2 + A_3B_1 + A_3B_2.$$

Some care must be taken in the use of suffixes. Suppose, for example, that we had two sets of equations

$$x'_k = \sum_{j=1}^{n} r_{kj}x_j, \qquad y'_k = \sum_{j=1}^{n} s_{kj}y_j,$$

and that we wished to form all the products $x'_k y'_i$ with all the different possible values of k and i. By changing the free suffix in the y equation to i, we can write

$$x'_k y'_i = \left(\sum_{j=1}^{n} r_{kj}x_j \right) \left(\sum_{j=1}^{n} s_{ij}y_j \right).$$

Since the two summations are quite independent of each other, it is essential to distinguish between the two dummy suffixes involved before we can multiply out the expression on the right-hand side. This can be done by changing the second summation suffix from j to, say, p. Then we can write

$$x'_k y'_i = \left(\sum_{j=1}^{n} r_{kj}x_j \right) \left(\sum_{p=1}^{n} s_{ip}y_p \right)$$

and the right-hand side can now be multiplied out to give

$$x'_k y'_i = \sum_{j=1}^{n} \sum_{p=1}^{n} r_{kj}s_{ip}x_j y_p.$$

REPRESENTATIONS OF $\mathscr{G} \times i$ AND $\mathscr{G} \times \sigma_h$

The group $\mathscr{G}$ has a multiplication table which associates a definite element T of $\mathscr{G}$ with the product RS of each pair of elements R and S of $\mathscr{G}$: $RS = T$. The elements of $\mathscr{G} \times i$ are the elements $\ldots, R, \ldots, S, \ldots, T, \ldots$ of $\mathscr{G}$, together with a corresponding set of elements

$$\ldots, \ R' = iR, \ \ldots, \ S' = iS, \ \ldots, \ T' = iT, \ \ldots$$

Since i commutes with all other symmetry operations and since $i^2 = E$, it follows that the multiplication table of $\mathscr{G} \times i$ has entries of the form

$$RS = T, \quad R'S = T' = RS', \quad R'S' = T,$$

and that it is completely determined by the multiplication table of $\mathscr{G}$.

Now suppose that $\varGamma$ is a representation of $\mathscr{G}$ with matrices which satisfy the appropriate multiplication rules:

$$D(R)D(S) = D(RS) = D(T).$$

Then we can use these matrices to construct two independent representations, $\varGamma_g$ and $\varGamma_u$, of $\mathscr{G} \times i$ as follows:

(i) $\varGamma_g$: Associate matrices $D_g(R) = D(R)$ with elements of type R, and matrices $D_g(R') = D(R)$ with elements of type R'.

(ii) $\varGamma_u$: Associate matrices $D_u(R) = D(R)$ with elements of type R, and matrices $D_u(R') = -D(R)$ with elements of type R'.

We verify that these sets of matrices do indeed form representations of $\mathscr{G} \times i$ by checking their multiplication rules.

(i) $\begin{aligned}[t]
D_g(RS) &= D_g(T) = D(T) = D(R)D(S) = D_g(R)D_g(S), \\
D_g(R'S) &= D_g(T') = D(T) = D(R)D(S) = D_g(R')D_g(S), \\
D_g(R'S') &= D_g(T) = D(T) = D(R)D(S) = D_g(R')D_g(S').
\end{aligned}$

(ii) $\begin{aligned}[t]
D_u(RS) &= D_u(T) = D(T) = D(R)D(S) = D_u(R)D_u(S), \\
D_u(R'S) &= D_u(T') = -D(T) = -D(R)D(S) = D_u(R')D_u(S), \\
D_u(R'S') &= D_u(T) = D(T) = D(R)D(S) = D_u(R')D_u(S').
\end{aligned}$

This shows that $\varGamma_g$ and $\varGamma_u$ are both representations of $\mathscr{G} \times i$. Furthermore, any change of basis which reduces $\varGamma_g$ or $\varGamma_u$ must at the same time reduce the representation Γ of $\mathcal{G}$ and, conversely, if Γ is an IR of $\mathcal{G}$, Γ_g and Γ_u will be IRs of $\mathcal{G} \times i$. Also, from their definitions, the characters of Γ_g and Γ_u satisfy the relations:

(i) in Γ_g, $\chi(R') = \chi(R)$;   (ii) in Γ_u, $\chi(R') = -\chi(R)$.

Exactly similar arguments will apply to a group of the form $\mathcal{G} \times \sigma_h$, since σ_h commutes with all the elements of $\mathcal{G}$ and $\sigma_h^2 = E$.

Appendix D

THE PROOF OF EQUATION (8.39)

The proof of (8.39), which is equivalent to the proof that the introduction of normal coordinates reduces the configuration space representation, follows from the invariance property (7.1) of the potential energy and the orthogonality of the matrices $D_n(R)$.

If we express V as a function of the normal coordinates, (7.1) shows that $V(Q') = V(Q)$, where Q and Q' stand for the two configurations whose normal coordinates are related by (8.37) and where R in (8.37) may be any symmetry operation of the molecular point group. Now (8.36) shows that in the Q' configuration

$$V(Q') = \tfrac{1}{2} \sum_{\rho,l} \lambda^{(\rho)} Q'_{\rho l}{}^2$$

where we have indicated the sum $\sum\limits_{\rho=1}^{N} \sum\limits_{l=1}^{n_\rho}$ over all the normal coordinates by the abbreviated notation $\sum\limits_{\rho,l}$. If we use (8.37) to express the $Q'_{\rho l}$ in terms of the unprimed coordinates, we obtain

$$V(Q') = \tfrac{1}{2} \sum_{\rho,l} \lambda^{(\rho)} \Big(\sum_{\sigma,k} [D_n(R)]_{\rho l, \sigma k} Q_{\sigma k} \Big) \Big(\sum_{v,j} [D_n(R)]_{\rho l, vj} Q_{vj} \Big)$$

$$= \tfrac{1}{2} \sum_{v,j} \sum_{\sigma,k} \sum_{\rho,l} \lambda^{(\rho)} [D_n(R)]_{\rho l, vj} [D_n(R)]_{\rho l, \sigma k} Q_{vj} Q_{\sigma k}. \qquad (D.1)$$

The invariance property of V shows that this must be identical with

$$V(Q) = \tfrac{1}{2} \sum_{v,j} \lambda^{(v)} Q_{vj}{}^2,$$

whatever the values of the Q_{vj}. It follows that $D_n(R)$ must be such that the coefficient of $Q_{vj}{}^2$ in $(D.1)$ is $\lambda^{(v)}$, while the coefficient of $Q_{vj} Q_{\sigma k}$ with $\sigma \neq v$ and/or $k \neq j$ must be zero:

$$\sum_{\rho,l} \lambda^{(\rho)} [D_n(R)]_{\rho l, vj} [D_n(R)]_{\rho l, \sigma k} = \lambda^{(v)} \delta_{\sigma v} \delta_{kj}. \qquad (D.2)$$

We now make use of the fact that $D_n(R)$ is orthogonal. This is expressed by the orthogonality relations

$$\sum_{\sigma,k} [D_n(R)]_{\rho l, \sigma k} [D_n(R)]_{\mu l, \sigma k} = \delta_{\rho \mu} \delta_{ll} \qquad (D.3)$$

Multiply $(D.2)$ by $[D_n(R)]_{\mu i, \sigma k}$ and sum over all values of σ, k. The sum over σ, k which appears on the left-hand side is given by $(D.3)$ and we obtain

$$\sum_{\rho, i} \lambda^{(\rho)} [D_n(R)]_{\rho i, \nu j}\, \delta_{\rho \mu}\, \delta_{i i} = \sum_{\sigma, k} \lambda^{(\nu)} [D_n(R)]_{\mu i, \sigma k}\, \delta_{\sigma \nu}\, \delta_{k j},$$

i.e. $$\lambda^{(\mu)} [D_n(R)]_{\mu i, \nu j} = \lambda^{(\nu)} [D_n(R)]_{\mu i, \nu j}. \qquad (D.4)$$

If $\mu \neq \nu$, so that $\lambda^{(\mu)} \neq \lambda^{(\nu)}$, it follows from $(D.4)$ that

$$[D_n(R)]_{\mu i, \nu j} = 0,$$

which is the result (8.39) that we set out to prove.

Appendix E

SYMMETRY PROPERTIES OF THE POLARIZABILITY

The dipole moment induced in a molecule by an external electric field **E** with components E_i is given by (8.67). If a symmetry operation R is applied to the molecule, it will change the molecular configuration from X to X', and it will also rotate or reflect the electric field vector **E** and change its components to

$$E_i' = \sum_{j=1}^{3} r_{ij}E_j,$$

where the r_{ij} are the same coefficients that appear in the equations (4.6') which describe the effect of R on the components x_i of a position vector. The same coefficients also appear in equation (8.66) which describes the effect of R on the components of a dipole moment vector.

In the configuration X', the induced dipole moment will have components

$$M_i(X') = \sum_{l=1}^{3} \alpha_{il}(X')E_l' = \sum_{l=1}^{3} \alpha_{il}(X')\left(\sum_{j=1}^{3} r_{lj}E_j \right). \qquad (E.1)$$

Since we are dealing with a dipole moment, the functions $M_k(X)$ and $M_i(X')$ in the two configurations must be related by an equation of the same form as (8.66):

$$M_k(X) = \sum_{i=1}^{3} r_{ik}M_i(X').$$

If we substitute ($E.1$) into this equation and rearrange the order of the summations, we obtain

$$M_k(X) = \sum_{j=1}^{3} \left\{ \sum_{i=1}^{3} \sum_{l=1}^{3} r_{ik}r_{lj}\alpha_{il}(X') \right\} E_j.$$

On comparing this equation with (8.67), we see that

$$(O_R\alpha_{kj})(X') = \alpha_{kj}(X) = \sum_{i=1}^{3} \sum_{l=1}^{3} r_{ik}r_{lj}\alpha_{il}(X'). \qquad (E.2)$$

Consider now the functions $f_{kj}(x) = x_k x_j$, $k, j = 1, 2, 3$, which can be formed from the coordinates of a point. R changes the coordinates (x_1, x_2, x_3) to (x_1', x_2', x_3')

in accordance with (4.6′). Since the matrix $[r_{ij}]$ is orthogonal, these equations may be written in the form

$$x_q = \sum_{p=1}^{3} r_{pq} x_p',$$

and we see that

$$(O_R f_{kj})(x') = f_{kj}(x) = x_k x_j = \left(\sum_{i=1}^{3} r_{ik} x_i' \right) \left(\sum_{l=1}^{3} r_{lj} x_l' \right)$$

$$= \sum_{i=1}^{3} \sum_{l=1}^{3} r_{ik} r_{lj} f_{il}(x'). \qquad (E.3)$$

Comparison of $(E.2)$ and $(E.3)$ shows that the effect of R on a polarizability coefficient α_{kj} is exactly the same as the effect of R on the corresponding function $f_{kj} = x_k x_j$.

Appendix F

BASE FUNCTIONS FOR $E \times E$

The real orthonormal base functions ϕ_a and ϕ_b of the representation E_{1g} of $\mathscr{D}_{6h}$ that were introduced in Section 10.2 must be such that, for any operation R of $\mathscr{D}_{6h}$,

$$O_R \phi_a = c\phi_a + d\phi_c, \qquad O_R \phi_b = c'\phi_a + d'\phi_b$$

where the coefficients c, d, c', d' are such that $O_R \phi_a$ and $O_R \phi_b$ also form a pair of real orthonormal functions. This means that

$$c^2 + d^2 = 1, \quad c'^2 + d'^2 = 1, \quad cc' + dd' = 0.$$

(These are the orthogonality relations of (4.52) expressed in our current notation.) It is readily seen that these equations admit of only two essentially different kinds of solution, namely

$$c = \cos \theta, \quad d = \sin \theta, \quad c' = -\sin \theta, \quad d' = \cos \theta;$$

$$c = \cos \theta', \quad d = \sin \theta', \quad c' = \sin \theta', \quad d' = -\cos \theta'.$$

Here θ and θ' are angles whose values will depend on the precise relation between R and the base functions ϕ_a and ϕ_b. It follows that the symmetry operations of $\mathscr{D}_{6h}$ can be divided into two kinds. The first kind, which we denote generally by R, has a matrix in E_{1g} of the form

$$\mathsf{D}(R) = \begin{bmatrix} \cos \theta & -\sin \theta \\ \sin \theta & \cos \theta \end{bmatrix} \quad \text{with character} \quad \chi(R) = 2 \cos \theta,$$

and the second kind, which we denote generally by R', has a matrix in E_{1g} of the form

$$\mathsf{D}(R') = \begin{bmatrix} \cos \theta' & \sin \theta' \\ \sin \theta' & -\cos \theta' \end{bmatrix} \quad \text{with character} \quad \chi(R') = 0.$$

If one examines the characters of E_{1g} in $\mathscr{D}_{6h}$ it appears, for instance, that $\chi(C_6) = 1$ so that C_6 must be an operation of type R with $\cos \theta = \frac{1}{2}$. Then $\sin \theta = \sqrt{3}/2$ or $-\sqrt{3}/2$ and these two choices for $\sin \theta$ give the matrices which represent the two operations C_6 and C_6^{-1} in E_{1g}. The other operations of type R in E_{1g} are the rotations C_3 and C_2 and the improper rotations S_3, S_6 and $\sigma_h = S_2$ about the main symmetry axis and also E and i. All the C_2', C_2'', σ_v and σ_d operations have zero character in E_{1g} and they are of type R'.

Consider now the product representation

$$E_{1g} \times E_{1g} = A_{1g} + A_{2g} + E_{2g}.$$

Four orthonormal base functions for this representation, formed from ϕ_a and ϕ_b, are

$$\psi_1 = \phi_a(1)\phi_a(2), \quad \psi_2 = \phi_b(1)\phi_b(2), \quad \psi_3 = \phi_a(1)\phi_b(2), \quad \psi_4 = \phi_b(1)\phi_a(2)$$

and we wish to find linear combinations of these products to act as bases for A_{1g}, A_{2g} and E_{2g}:

The effects of operations of the types R and R' on ψ_1, ψ_2, ψ_3, ψ_4 are easily evaluated. For example,

$$O_R\psi_3 = [O_R\phi_a(1)][O_R\phi_b(2)]$$

$$= [\cos\theta\phi_a(1) + \sin\theta\phi_b(1)][-\sin\theta\phi_a(2) + \cos\theta\phi_b(2)].$$

This product can be multiplied out and expressed as a linear combination of $\psi_1, \ldots, \psi_4$. Doing this in detail for $\psi_1, \ldots, \psi_4$ one finds:

$$O_R\psi_1 = \cos^2\theta\psi_1 + \sin^2\theta\psi_2 + \sin\theta\cos\theta(\psi_3 + \psi_4),$$

$$O_R\psi_2 = \sin^2\theta\psi_1 + \cos^2\theta\psi_2 - \sin\theta\cos\theta(\psi_3 + \psi_4),$$

$$O_R\psi_3 = -\sin\theta\cos\theta(\psi_1 - \psi_2) + \cos^2\theta\psi_3 - \sin^2\theta\psi_4,$$

$$O_R\psi_4 = -\sin\theta\cos\theta(\psi_1 - \psi_2) - \sin^2\theta\psi_3 + \cos^2\theta\psi_4;$$

$$O_{R'}\psi_1 = \cos^2\theta'\psi_1 + \sin^2\theta'\psi_2 + \sin\theta'\cos\theta'(\psi_3 + \psi_4),$$

$$O_{R'}\psi_2 = \sin^2\theta'\psi_1 + \cos^2\theta'\psi_2 - \sin\theta'\cos\theta'(\psi_3 + \psi_4),$$

$$O_{R'}\psi_3 = \sin\theta'\cos\theta'(\psi_1 - \psi_2) - \cos^2\theta'\psi_3 + \sin^2\theta'\psi_4,$$

$$O_{R'}\psi_4 = \sin\theta'\cos\theta'(\psi_1 - \psi_2) + \sin^2\theta'\psi_3 - \cos^2\theta'\psi_4.$$

By inspection of these equations we see that for any θ or θ'

$$O_R(\psi_1 + \psi_2) = O_{R'}(\psi_1 + \psi_2) = \psi_1 + \psi_2;$$

thus $(\psi_1 + \psi_2)$ is invariant under all the symmetry operations of the group. It is the base function for A_{1g}. The equations also show that

$$O_R(\psi_3 - \psi_4) = \psi_3 - \psi_4, \quad O_{R'}(\psi_3 - \psi_4) = -(\psi_3 - \psi_4).$$

Thus $(\psi_3 - \psi_4)$ is left unaltered by any operation of type R but has its sign reversed by any operation of type R'. From the character table of $\mathscr{D}_{6h}$ we see that this is precisely the behaviour required of a base function for A_{2g}. We have, therefore, found the correct base functions for A_{1g} and A_{2g}; they are written out in full in (10.3).

We must now look for two other combinations of $\psi_1, \ldots, \psi_4$ which are orthogonal to each other and to $\psi_1 + \psi_2$ and $\psi_3 - \psi_4$ to serve as a basis for E_{2g}. A suitable pair would be $\psi_1 - \psi_2$ and $\psi_3 + \psi_4$. These combinations are written out explicitly in (10.3) and it is readily verified that they have the correct behaviour for a pair of E functions. From the above equations we find

$$O_R(\psi_1 - \psi_2) = \cos 2\theta(\psi_1 - \psi_2) + \sin 2\theta(\psi_3 + \psi_4),$$

$$O_R(\psi_3 + \psi_4) = -\sin 2\theta(\psi_1 - \psi_2) + \cos 2\theta(\psi_3 + \psi_4);$$

$$O_{R'}(\psi_1 - \psi_2) = \cos 2\theta'(\psi_1 - \psi_2) + \sin 2\theta'(\psi_3 + \psi_4),$$

$$O_{R'}(\psi_3 + \psi_4) = \sin 2\theta'(\psi_1 - \psi_2) - \cos 2\theta'(\psi_3 + \psi_4).$$

(Here we have used $\cos 2\theta = \cos^2 \theta - \sin^2 \theta$, $\sin 2\theta = 2 \sin \theta \cos \theta$.)

This argument has used no specific properties of $\mathscr{D}_{6h}$ except that it has operations of the types R and R'. The same analysis clearly applies to any E representation which is such that $E \times E = A_1 + A_2 + E$, whatever the point group may be. The appropriate base functions are given by (10.3) in all cases; the A_1 and E base functions are always symmetrical in the electron coordinates and the A_2 base function is always anti-symmetrical. The arguments used in Section 10.2, therefore, show that for all E representations of this type the terms of $(e)^2$ are $^1A_1$, $^3A_2$ and ^1E.

There are some point groups, for example $\mathscr{D}_4$, which have E representations such that

$$E \times E = A_1 + A_2 + B_1 + B_2.$$

These are groups whose operations are such that they give rise to the values $\pm \pi/2$, $\pm \pi$ of θ and θ' so that, for all operations R or R', $\cos 2\theta = \pm 1$ and $\sin 2\theta = 0$. In this case it is seen that $\psi_1 - \psi_2$ and $\psi_3 + \psi_4$ no longer combine together; they generate separate one-dimensional representations and must be base functions for B_1 and B_2. They are symmetrical functions of the electron coordinates and must give rise to $^1B_1$ and $^1B_2$ terms in $(e)^2$.

Appendix G

GENERAL METHOD FOR THE TERMS OF $(\gamma)^n$

There is a general method for finding the terms of a $(\gamma)^n$ configuration that is based upon the results of Section 7.4 relating to the perturbation induced by a distortion of the molecule. We illustrate the method by considering a molecule with point group $\mathcal{O}_h = \mathcal{O} \times i$. Suppose that the molecule is slightly distorted so that its symmetry is reduced to $\mathcal{D}_{4h} = \mathcal{D}_4 \times i$. The effect of this distortion on an energy level of the molecule, either an individual MO level or an electronic term, is described by the correlations between the IRs of $\mathcal{O}$ and $\mathcal{D}_4$ that are given in Table 7.1. In order to avoid confusion in referring to representations of these two groups we shall use the normal symbols A_1, A_2, E, T_1, T_2 for the IRs of $\mathcal{O}$ and we shall use the symbols A_1', A_2', B_1', B_2', E', distinguished by a prime, for the IRs of $\mathcal{D}_4$. These are turned into symbols for the IRs of $\mathcal{O}_h$ and $\mathcal{D}_{4h}$ by adding the appropriate g or u suffix; for the present we shall ignore this complication and shall deal with representations of $\mathcal{O}$ and $\mathcal{D}_4$ that may correspond to either g or u representations of $\mathcal{O}_h$ and $\mathcal{D}_{4h}$.

The distortion of the molecule has two effects: firstly, it may split a particular electronic energy level or term of the undistorted molecule, classified by an IR of $\mathcal{O}$, into a number of distinct terms of the distorted molecule, classified by IRs of $\mathcal{D}_4$; secondly, it may split a particular MO level of the undistorted molecule into a number of distinct MO levels of the distorted molecule. Since the terms of an electron configuration depend upon the MO levels involved, these two effects of the distortion are closely related and it is by analysing their relationship that we can obtain the results we require.

Consider first an electronic term, say $^{2S+1}T_2$, of the undistorted molecule. The distortion has no effect on the electron spins but, as Table 7.1 shows, it changes the representation T_2 of $\mathcal{O}$ into the representation $B_2' + E'$ of $\mathcal{D}_4$. This means that the distortion splits $^{2S+1}T_2$ into two distinct terms $^{2S+1}B_2'$ and $^{2S+1}E'$. The effect of the distortion on the other possible terms of the undistorted molecule can, similarly, be read off from Table 7.1: the results are summarized in Table G.1.

TABLE G.1. *The effect of an $\mathcal{O} \rightarrow \mathcal{D}_4$ distortion on the terms of a molecule*

Undistorted terms	A_1	A_2	E	T_1	T_2
Distorted	A_1'	B_1'	A_1', B_1'	A_2', E'	B_2', E'

Closed Shells

Consider an e level of the undistorted molecule. Table 7.1 shows that the distortion splits this into two non-degenerate levels characterized by the $\mathcal{D}_4$ symbols a_1' and b_1'. The terms of an $(e)^n$ configuration must therefore correspond, when the molecule is distorted, to the terms that are obtained by placing n electrons in all possible ways into an a_1' and a b_1' level. In particular, the closed shell configuration $(e)^4$ becomes the configuration $(a_1')^2(b_1')^2$ of the distorted molecule. As we proved in Section 10.3, any $(a)^2$ or $(b)^2$ closed shell configuration gives rise to the term $^1\Gamma_1$, where Γ_1 is the identical representation of the point group concerned; thus, with point group $\mathcal{D}_4$, the term of $(a_1')^2(b_1')^2$ is $^1A_1'$. Now $(e)^4$ produces a non-degenerate term with $S = 0$ and it must be either $^1A_1$ or $^1A_2$ since the only one-dimensional IRs of $\mathcal{O}$ are A_1 and A_2. The effect of the distortion on these terms would be to change them into $^1A_1'$ and $^1B_1'$. Thus, by comparing $(e)^4$ with $(a_1')^2(b_1')^2$, we can see that $(e)^4$ must produce the term $^1A_1$ which is changed by the distortion into $^1A_1'$; $(e)^4$ cannot produce a $^1A_2$ term.

A similar argument may be applied to an e level for any point group: in all cases $(e)^4$ gives rise to $^1\Gamma_1$.

Now consider a t level of the undistorted molecule, say t_2, and the closed shell configuration $(t_2)^6$. This must produce a single non-degenerate term and this must be either $^1A_1$ or $^1A_2$; under the distortion these terms change to $^1A_1'$ and $^1B_1'$ respectively, and we can decide between them by considering the effect of the distortion on the t_2 level. The distortion splits this level into an e' and a b_2' level and so $(t_2)^6$ becomes the closed shell configuration $(b_2')^2(e')^4$ of the distorted molecule. Our results for closed shells of the form $(b)^2$ or $(e)^4$ show that this configuration gives the term $^1A_1'$ and not $^1B_1'$; hence $(t_2)^6$ must give the term $^1A_1$ and not $^1A_2$. Similar considerations can be used to show that $(t_1)^6$ also gives a $^1A_1$ term. The same result holds for $(t)^6$ in a molecule with $\mathcal{T}_d$ symmetry, as we shall show at the end of this appendix.

Hole-electron Equivalence

One electron in an e level gives the configuration $(e)^1$ with term ^2E and this term is split by the distortion into $^2A_1'$ and $^2B_1'$. These terms of the distorted molecule arise from the configurations $(a_1')^1$ and $(b_1')^1$ which are obtained by placing one electron into either component of the split e level. If we began with an $(e)^3$ configuration, with one hole instead of one electron, we should have to consider the configurations $(a_1')^2(b_1')^1$ and $(a_1')^1(b_1')^2$ of the distorted molecule. Since the closed shells make no difference to the term classification, these configurations produce the terms $^2B_1'$ and $^2A_1'$ respectively, the same terms that arise from the distorted $(e)^1$ configuration. Thus $(e)^3$ and $(e)^1$ of the undistorted molecule both have the same ^2E term. The same result can be proved to hold for an e level in any point group.

Consider next the configurations $(t_2)^1$ and $(t_2)^5$ with one electron and one hole respectively. The one-electron configuration produces the term $^2T_2$ which is split by the distortion into $^2B_2'$ and $^2E'$. The one-hole configuration is equivalent, under the distortion, to all the configurations obtained by placing five electrons into a b_2' and an e' level. These are $(b_2')^2(e')^3$ which produces the same term as $(e')^1$, namely $^2E'$, and $(b_2')^1(e')^4$ which produces the same term as $(b_2')^1$, namely $^2B_2'$. Thus the terms of $(t_2)^1$ and $(t_2)^5$ in the distorted molecule are identical and must correspond to the same $^2T_2$ term of the undistorted molecule.

Similarly, $(t_2)^2$ becomes, under the distortion, equivalent to the configurations $(b_2')^2$ with term $^1A_1'$, $(e')^2$ with the terms $^3A_2'$, $^1A_1'$, $^1B_1'$, $^1B_2'$ (as proved in Appendix F and Section 10.2) and $(b_2')^1(e')^1$ with the terms $^3(B_2' \times E') = {}^3E'$ and $^1(B_2' \times E') = {}^1E'$. [Compare (10.4).] Thus the effect of the distortion on the terms of $(t_2)^2$ is to produce the terms

$$^3A_2', \ ^3E', \ ^1A_1', \ ^1A_1', \ ^1B_1', \ ^1B_2', \ ^1E'. \tag{G.1}$$

The equivalent two-hole configuration is $(t_2)^4$; its distorted terms arise from the configurations $(e')^4$ with the same term, $^1A_1'$, as $(b_2')^2$, $(b_2')^2(e')^2$ with the same terms as $(e')^2$ and $(b_2')^1(e')^3$ with the same terms as $(b_2')^1(e')^1$. Thus the terms of $(t_2)^4$ are the same as those of $(t_2)^2$.

Similar results apply to t_1 configurations and also to t_1 and t_2 configurations with $\mathcal{T}_d$ symmetry. In all cases and for every kind of level, one has the result that $(\gamma)^n$ and $(\gamma)^{N-n}$ produce the same terms, where N is the total number of electrons that can be accommodated in the level γ.

$(t)^2$ Configurations of $\mathcal{O}_h$

The terms that arise when a $(t_2)^2$ configuration is distorted are listed in $(G.1)$. A comparison of these terms with the correlations given in Table G.1 shows that the two spin triplet terms $^3A_2'$ and $^3E'$ must come from a $^3T_1$ term of the undistorted molecule. The table also shows that the only way in which a $^1B_2'$ term can arise is from the splitting of $^1T_2$ into $^1B_2'$ and $^1E'$; these two terms in $(G.1)$ must, therefore, originate from a $^1T_2$ term of the undistorted molecule. The remaining terms of $(G.1)$ are $^1A_1'$, $^1A_1'$ and $^1B_1'$ and here there are two possibilities: either $^1B_1'$ remains by itself and arises from a $^1A_2$ term of the undistorted molecule, in which case the two $^1A_1'$ terms must come from separate $^1A_1$ terms of $(t_2)^2$, or $^1B_1'$ combines with one of the $^1A_1'$ terms to give a ^1E term of $(t_2)^2$, in which case the remaining $^1A_1'$ term must arise from $^1A_1$ in $(t_2)^2$. We conclude that the terms of $(t_2)^2$ are

$$^3T_1, \ ^1T_2, \ ^1A_1 \quad \text{and either } {}^1A_1, \ ^1A_2 \text{ or } {}^1E. \tag{G.2}$$

The ambiguity in $(G.2)$ may be resolved by considering another distortion of the molecule. Instead of a distortion which changes $\mathcal{O}_h$ to $\mathcal{D}_{4h}$ we can imagine a distortion which singles out one of the threefold axes of $\mathcal{O}_h$ and the three C_2' axes which are perpendicular to this C_3 axis. This gives the point group $\mathcal{D}_3$ which becomes $\mathcal{D}_{3d}$ on addition of the inversion; we imagine a distortion in which the symmetry is reduced from $\mathcal{O}_h = \mathcal{O} \times i$ to $\mathcal{D}_{3d} = \mathcal{D}_3 \times i$. The correlation between the IRs of $\mathcal{O}$ and $\mathcal{D}_3$ is shown in Table G.2 which is constructed in the same way as Table 7.1. Here we have distinguished the IRs of $\mathcal{D}_3$ by a double prime.

TABLE G.2. *Correlations between $\mathcal{O}$ and $\mathcal{D}_3$*

IRs of $\mathcal{O}$	Classes of $\mathcal{D}_3$			IRs of $\mathcal{D}_3$
	E	$2C_3$	$3C_2'$	
A_1	1	1	1	A_1''
A_2	1	1	-1	A_2''
E	2	-1	0	E''
T_1	3	0	-1	$A_2'' + E''$
T_2	3	0	1	$A_1'' + E''$

Under this distortion, the terms of $(t_2)^2$ become those of $(a_1'')^2$, $(a_1'')^1(e'')^1$ and $(e'')^2$ and these terms are, respectively,

$$^1A_1''; \quad {}^3(A_1'' \times E'') = {}^3E'', \quad {}^1(A_1'' \times E'') = {}^1E''; \quad {}^3A_2'', \, {}^1A_1'', \, {}^1E''. \qquad (G.3)$$

Now we know from $(G.2)$ that some of these terms must arise from the terms $^3T_1$, $^1T_2$ and $^1A_1$ which are certainly terms of $(t_2)^2$. The correlations between $\mathcal{O}$ and $\mathcal{D}_3$ show that these terms split into $^3A_2''$, $^3E''$, $^1A_1''$, $^1E''$, $^1A_1'$. If these terms are removed from the list in $(G.3)$ one is left with $^1E''$. Since this term is by itself, it must originate from a ^1E term of $(t_2)^2$ and so the ambiguity in $(G.2)$ is removed: the terms of $(t_2)^2$ must be $^3T_1$, $^1T_2$, $^1A_1$ and ^1E. A similar argument applied to the terms of $(t_1)^2$ shows that this configuration produces the same terms as $(t_2)^2$.

We have so far ignored the g, u classification that arises in $\mathcal{O}_h$. But since the product of two g functions or of two u functions must give a g function, we can summarize the results we have obtained by saying that for an $\mathcal{O}_h$ molecule the configurations $(t_{1g})^2$, $(t_{1u})^2$, $(t_{2g})^2$, $(t_{2u})^2$ and also the configurations with four electrons in these levels all produce the same set of terms, namely

$$^3T_{1g}, \, {}^1T_{2g}, \, {}^1A_{1g}, \, {}^1E_g.$$

$(t)^3$ Configurations of $\mathcal{O}_h$

The effect of an $\mathcal{O} \to \mathcal{D}_4$ distortion on the terms of $(t_2)^3$ is found by writing down the terms that arise when three electrons are placed in the b_2' and e' levels into which t_2 is split by the distortion. The configurations to be considered are $(b_2')^2(e')^1$ with term $^2E'$, $(e')^3$ with term $^2E'$ and $(b_2')^1(e')^2$. The terms of $(e')^2$ are $^3A_2'$, $^1A_1'$, $^1B_1'$, $^1B_2'$; these combine with the $^2B_2'$ term of $(b_2')^1$, according to the rule (10.4), to give

$$^4(B_2' \times A_2') = {}^4B_1', \quad {}^2(B_2' \times A_2') = {}^2B_1', \quad {}^2(B_2' \times A_1') = {}^2B_2',$$

$$^2(B_2' \times B_1') = {}^2A_2', \quad {}^2(B_2' \times B_2') = {}^2A_1'.$$

A complete list of the terms of the distorted $(t_2)^3$ configuration is, therefore,

$$^4B_1', \, {}^2E', \, {}^2E', \, {}^2B_1', \, {}^2B_2', \, {}^2A_1', \, {}^2A_2'.$$

The single spin quartet term $^4B_1'$ can only come from a $^4A_2$ term of $(t_2)^3$. Table G.1 also shows that $^2A_2'$ and $^2B_2'$ can only come from $^2T_1$ and $^2T_2$ terms of $(t_2)^3$ respectively which are split by the distortion into $^2A_2'$, $^2E'$ and $^2B_2'$, $^2E'$. This leaves us with $^2B_1'$ and $^2A_1'$ to be accounted for, and there are two possibilities:

they either arise from distinct $^2A_2$ and $^2A_1$ terms of $(t_2)^3$ or they originate from a single ^2E term. We conclude that the terms of $(t_2)^3$ are

$$^4A_2, \ ^2T_1, \ ^2T_2, \ \text{and} \ \text{either} \ ^2A_1, \ ^2A_2 \ \text{or} \ ^2E. \qquad (G.4)$$

The ambiguity in $(G.4)$ can be removed by considering an $\mathcal{O} \to \mathcal{D}_3$ distortion. In this case the terms of $(t_2)^3$ become the terms of $(a_1'')^2(e'')^1$, $(e'')^3$ and $(a_1'')^1(e'')^2$. The first two configurations both produce $^2E''$ terms. The terms of the third configuration are obtained by combining the $^2A_1''$ term of $(a_1'')^1$ with the terms $^3A_2''$, $^1A_1''$, $^1E''$ of $(e'')^2$. The complete list of terms for the distorted $(t_2)^3$ configuration is

$$^4A_2'', \ ^2A_2'', \ ^2A_1'', \ ^2E'', \ ^2E'', \ ^2E''. \qquad (G.5)$$

The $^4A_2$, $^2T_1$ and $^2T_2$ terms, which we know from $(G.4)$ to be present in $(t_2)^3$, are split by the $\mathcal{O} \to \mathcal{D}_3$ distortion into $^4A_2''$; $^2A_2''$, $^2E''$; $^2A_1''$, $^2E''$. When these terms are removed from $(G.5)$ one is left with a single $^2E''$ term which can only come from a ^2E term of $(t_2)^3$. This removes the ambiguity from $(G.4)$; the terms of $(t_2)^3$ must be $^4A_2$, ^2E, $^2T_1$, $^2T_2$.

A similar argument shows that the terms of $(t_1)^3$ are $^4A_1$, ^2E, $^2T_1$, $^2T_2$. Since the product of three g functions is a g function and the product of three u functions is a u function, the terms of the $\mathcal{O}_h$ configurations $(t_{1g})^3$ and $(t_{1u})^3$ are obtained from these results by simply adding the appropriate g or u suffix.

Terms of a Molecule with $\mathcal{T}_d$ Symmetry

Since $\mathcal{T}_d$ is a sub-group of $\mathcal{O}_h$ we can use the results for $\mathcal{O}_h$ to deduce the corresponding results for $\mathcal{T}_d$. The correlations between the IRs of these two groups are shown in Table G.3.

TABLE G.3. *Correlations between $\mathcal{O}_h$ and $\mathcal{T}_d$*

IRs of $\mathcal{O}_h$	Classes of $\mathcal{T}_d$					IRs of $\mathcal{T}_d$
	E	$8C_3$	$3C_2$	$6S_4$	$6\sigma_d$	
A_{1g}, A_{2u}	1	1	1	1	1	A_1
A_{2g}, A_{1u}	1	1	1	-1	-1	A_2
E_g, E_u	2	-1	2	0	0	E
T_{1g}, T_{2u}	3	0	-1	1	-1	T_1
T_{2g}, T_{1u}	3	0	-1	-1	1	T_2

This table shows, for example, that if an $\mathcal{O}_h$ molecule is distorted so that its symmetry is reduced to $\mathcal{T}_d$, a t_{2g} and a t_{1u} level of the undistorted molecule both become t_2 levels of the distorted molecule and that undistorted T_{2g} or T_{1u} terms both become T_2 terms of the distorted molecule. Similar results for the other kinds of MO levels and terms can be read off from the table.

Thus, under the distortion, $(t_{2g})^3$ and $(t_{1u})^3$ both become $(t_2)^3$ configurations of $\mathcal{T}_d$. As we have seen, the terms of $(t_{2g})^3$ are $^4A_{2g}$, ^2E_g, $^2T_{1g}$, $^2T_{2g}$ and the terms of $(t_{1u})^3$ are $^4A_{1u}$, ^2E_u, $^2T_{1u}$, $^2T_{2u}$. The table shows that both these sets of terms turn into the terms $^4A_2$, ^2E, $^2T_1$, $^2T_2$ of the distorted configuration.

Since the term classification of a configuration depends solely on the symmetry properties of the MOs involved and not at all on the detailed form of their dependence on the electron coordinates, it follows that a $(t_2)^3$ configuration of a genuine $\mathcal{T}_d$ molecule must produce just the same set of terms as a $(t_{2g})^3$ or $(t_{1u})^3$ configuration of an $\mathcal{O}_h$ molecule which has been distorted to $\mathcal{T}_d$ symmetry. Thus the terms of $(t_2)^3$ in a $\mathcal{T}_d$ molecule must be $^4A_2$, ^2E, $^2T_1$, $^2T_2$.

All the results that we have obtained for $\mathcal{O}_h$ may be translated in this way into the corresponding results for $\mathcal{T}_d$; this gives the term classifications that are listed in Table 10.1 as the reader may easily verify. (It is, of course, possible to obtain the results for $\mathcal{T}_d$ *ab initio* by considering distortions of a $\mathcal{T}_d$ molecule; the reader will find that the arguments given above for $\mathcal{O}_h$ molecules may be applied almost word for word to $\mathcal{T}_d$ molecules which are distorted so that they have $\mathcal{D}_{2d}$ or $\mathcal{C}_{3v}$ symmetry.)

Appendix H

CHARACTER TABLES

The character tables given below are set out in the way described in Sections 6.1 and 6.2; the different point groups and their division into classes are discussed in Sections 2.6 and 2.7. For the groups with one main axis of symmetry, rotations about this axis are denoted by C_n^k and rotations through 180° about axes perpendicular to the main axis are denoted by C_2' and C_2''. Reflections in vertical planes containing the main axis are denoted by σ_v or σ_d and a reflection in the horizontal plane perpendicular to the main axis is denoted by σ_h.

Apart from the character tables proper, the tables contain information about the IRs of the rotational and translational coordinates R_x, R_y, R_z and T_x, T_y, T_z described in Section 8.8(b), and about the IRs generated by p and d atomic orbitals; the (p_x, p_y, p_z) AOs behave like (T_x, T_y, T_z) and the d AOs like the corresponding combinations xy, xz, yz, $x^2 - y^2$, $2z^2 - x^2 - y^2$ of x, y, z. This information is also used for determining the selection rules for infra-red (Section 8.12), Raman (Section 8.13) and electronic (Section 10.4) spectra.

The x, y, z axes referred to in the tables are a set of three mutually perpendicular axes chosen as follows:

(a) $\mathscr{C}_s$: the z axis is perpendicular to the reflection plane.

(b) Groups with one main axis of symmetry:

The z axis points along the main axis of symmetry and, where applicable, the x axis lies in one of the σ_v planes or coincides with one of the C_2' axes. For $\mathscr{D}_2$ and $\mathscr{D}_{2h}$, the x, y, z axes coincide with the three equivalent twofold axes.

(c) Groups $\mathcal{O}_h$, $\mathcal{O}$, $\mathscr{T}_d$:

The x, y, z axes lie along the three mutually perpendicular fourfold ($\mathcal{O}_h$, $\mathcal{O}$) or twofold ($\mathscr{T}_d$) axes.

.

I: Groups $\mathscr{C}_s$, $\mathscr{C}_i$ *and* $\mathscr{C}_n$ $(n=2, 3, 4, 5, 6)$

$\mathscr{C}_s$	E	σ_h		
A'	1	1	$T_x; T_y; R_z$	$x^2; y^2; z^2; xy$
A''	1	-1	$T_z; R_x; R_y$	$xz; yz$

$\mathscr{C}_i$	E	i		
A_g	1	1	$R_x; R_y; R_z$	$x^2; y^2; z^2; xy;$ $xz; yz$
A_u	1	-1	$T_x; T_y; T_z$	

$\mathscr{C}_2$	E	C_2		
A	1	1	$T_z; R_z$	$x^2; y^2; z^2; xy$
B	1	-1	$T_x; T_y; R_x; R_y$	$xz; yz$

$\mathscr{C}_3$	E	C_3	$C_3{}^2$		$\epsilon = \exp{(2\pi i/3)}$
A	1	1	1	$T_z; R_z$	$x^2+y^2; z^2$
E	$\begin{cases}1 \\ 1\end{cases}$	$\begin{matrix}\epsilon \\ \epsilon^*\end{matrix}$	$\begin{matrix}\epsilon^* \\ \epsilon\end{matrix}$	$(T_x, T_y); (R_x, R_y)$	$(x^2-y^2, xy); (xz, yz)$

$\mathscr{C}_4$	E	C_4	C_2	$C_4{}^3$		
A	1	1	1	1	$T_z; R_z$	$x^2+y^2; z^2$
B	1	-1	1	-1		$x^2-y^2; xy$
E	$\begin{cases}1 \\ 1\end{cases}$	$\begin{matrix}i \\ -i\end{matrix}$	$\begin{matrix}-1 \\ -1\end{matrix}$	$\begin{matrix}-i \\ i\end{matrix}$	$(T_x, T_y); (R_x, R_y)$	(xz, yz)

$\mathscr{C}_5$	E	C_5	$C_5{}^2$	$C_5{}^3$	$C_5{}^4$		$\epsilon = \exp{(2\pi i/5)}$
A	1	1	1	1	1	$T_z; R_z$	$x^2+y^2; z^2$
E_1	$\begin{cases}1 \\ 1\end{cases}$	$\begin{matrix}\epsilon \\ \epsilon^*\end{matrix}$	$\begin{matrix}\epsilon^2 \\ \epsilon^{2*}\end{matrix}$	$\begin{matrix}\epsilon^{2*} \\ \epsilon^2\end{matrix}$	$\begin{matrix}\epsilon^* \\ \epsilon\end{matrix}$	$(T_x, T_y); (R_x, R_y)$	(xz, yz)
E_2	$\begin{cases}1 \\ 1\end{cases}$	$\begin{matrix}\epsilon^2 \\ \epsilon^{2*}\end{matrix}$	$\begin{matrix}\epsilon^* \\ \epsilon\end{matrix}$	$\begin{matrix}\epsilon \\ \epsilon^*\end{matrix}$	$\begin{matrix}\epsilon^{2*} \\ \epsilon^2\end{matrix}$		(x^2-y^2, xy)

$\mathscr{C}_6$	E	C_6	C_3	C_2	$C_3{}^2$	$C_6{}^5$		$\epsilon = \exp{(2\pi i/6)}$
A	1	1	1	1	1	1	$T_z; R_z$	$x^2+y^2; z^2$
B	1	-1	1	-1	1	-1		
E_1	$\begin{cases}1 \\ 1\end{cases}$	$\begin{matrix}\epsilon \\ \epsilon^*\end{matrix}$	$\begin{matrix}-\epsilon^* \\ -\epsilon\end{matrix}$	$\begin{matrix}-1 \\ -1\end{matrix}$	$\begin{matrix}-\epsilon \\ -\epsilon^*\end{matrix}$	$\begin{matrix}\epsilon^* \\ \epsilon\end{matrix}$	$(T_x, T_y); (R_x, R_y)$	(xz, yz)
E_2	$\begin{cases}1 \\ 1\end{cases}$	$\begin{matrix}-\epsilon^* \\ -\epsilon\end{matrix}$	$\begin{matrix}-\epsilon \\ -\epsilon^*\end{matrix}$	$\begin{matrix}1 \\ 1\end{matrix}$	$\begin{matrix}-\epsilon^* \\ -\epsilon\end{matrix}$	$\begin{matrix}-\epsilon \\ -\epsilon^*\end{matrix}$		(x^2-y^2, xy)

II: Groups $\mathscr{D}_n$ ($n = 2, 3, 4, 5, 6$)

$\mathscr{D}_2 = \mathscr{V}$	E	$C_2(z)$	$C_2(y)$	$C_2(x)$		
A	1	1	1	1		$x^2; y^2; z^2$
B_1	1	1	-1	-1	$T_z; R_z$	xy
B_2	1	-1	1	-1	$T_y; R_y$	xz
B_3	1	-1	-1	1	$T_x; R_x$	yz

$\mathscr{D}_3$	E	$2C_3$	$3C_2'$		
A_1	1	1	1		$x^2 + y^2; z^2$
A_2	1	1	-1	$T_z; R_z$	
E	2	-1	0	$(T_x, T_y); (R_x, R_y)$	$(x^2 - y^2, xy); (xz, yz)$

$\mathscr{D}_4$	E	$2C_4$	C_2	$2C_2'$	$2C_2''$		
A_1	1	1	1	1	1		$x^2 + y^2; z^2$
A_2	1	1	1	-1	-1	$T_z; R_z$	
B_1	1	-1	1	1	-1		$x^2 - y^2$
B_2	1	-1	1	-1	1		xy
E	2	0	-2	0	0	$(T_x, T_y); (R_x, R_y)$	(xz, yz)

$\mathscr{D}_5$	E	$2C_5$	$2C_5{}^2$	$5C_2'$		$\alpha = 72°$
A_1	1	1	1	1		$x^2 + y^2; z^2$
A_2	1	1	1	-1	$T_z; R_z$	
E_1	2	$2\cos\alpha$	$2\cos 2\alpha$	0	$(T_x, T_y); (R_x, R_y)$	(xz, yz)
E_2	2	$2\cos 2\alpha$	$2\cos\alpha$	0		$(x^2 - y^2, xy)$

$\mathscr{D}_6$	E	$2C_6$	$2C_3$	C_2	$3C_2'$	$3C_2''$		
A_1	1	1	1	1	1	1		$x^2 + y^2; z^2$
A_2	1	1	1	1	-1	-1	$T_z; R_z$	
B_1	1	-1	1	-1	1	-1		
B_2	1	-1	1	-1	-1	1		
E_1	2	1	-1	-2	0	0	$(T_x, T_y); (R_x, R_y)$	(xz, yz)
E_2	2	-1	-1	2	0	0		$(x^2 - y^2, xy)$

III: Groups $\mathscr{C}_{nv}$ ($n = 2, 3, 4, 5, 6$)

$\mathscr{C}_{2v}$	E	C_2	$\sigma_v(xz)$	$\sigma_v(yz)$		
A_1	1	1	1	1	T_z	$x^2; y^2; z^2$
A_2	1	1	-1	-1	R_z	xy
B_1	1	-1	1	-1	$T_x; R_y$	xz
B_2	1	-1	-1	1	$T_y; R_x$	yz

$\mathscr{C}_{3v}$	E	$2C_3$	$3\sigma_v$		
A_1	1	1	1	T_z	$x^2 + y^2; z^2$
A_2	1	1	-1	R_z	
E	2	-1	0	$(T_x, T_y); (R_x, R_y)$	$(x^2 - y^2, xy); (xz, yz)$

$\mathscr{C}_{4v}$	E	$2C_4$	C_2	$2\sigma_v$	$2\sigma_d$		
A_1	1	1	1	1	1	T_z	$x^2 + y^2; z^2$
A_2	1	1	1	-1	-1	R_z	
B_1	1	-1	1	1	-1		$x^2 - y^2$
B_2	1	-1	1	-1	1		xy
E	2	0	-2	0	0	$(T_x, T_y); (R_x, R_y)$	(xz, yz)

$\mathscr{C}_{5v}$	E	$2C_5$	$2C_5^2$	$5\sigma_v$		$\alpha = 72°$
A_1	1	1	1	1	T_z	$x^2 + y^2; z^2$
A_2	1	1	1	-1	R_z	
E_1	2	$2\cos\alpha$	$2\cos 2\alpha$	0	$(T_x, T_y); (R_x, R_y)$	(xz, yz)
E_2	2	$2\cos 2\alpha$	$2\cos\alpha$	0		$(x^2 - y^2, xy)$

$\mathscr{C}_{6v}$	E	$2C_6$	$2C_3$	C_2	$3\sigma_v$	$3\sigma_d$		
A_1	1	1	1	1	1	1	T_z	$x^2 + y^2; z^2$
A_2	1	1	1	1	-1	-1	R_z	
B_1	1	-1	1	-1	1	-1		
B_2	1	-1	1	-1	-1	1		
E_1	2	1	-1	-2	0	0	$(T_x, T_y); (R_x, R_y)$	(xz, yz)
E_2	2	-1	-1	2	0	0		$(x^2 - y^2, xy)$

IV: Groups $\mathscr{C}_{nh}$ $(n=2, 3, 4, 5, 6)$

$\mathscr{C}_{2h}$	E	C_2	i	σ_h		
A_g	1	1	1	1	R_z	$x^2; y^2; z^2; xy$
B_g	1	-1	1	-1	$R_x; R_y$	$xz; yz$
A_u	1	1	-1	-1	T_z	
B_u	1	-1	-1	1	$T_x; T_y$	

$\mathscr{C}_{3h}$	E	C_3	C_3^2	σ_h	S_3	S_3^5		$\epsilon = \exp(2\pi i/3)$
A'	1	1	1	1	1	1	R_z	$x^2+y^2; z^2$
E'	$\begin{cases} 1 \\ 1 \end{cases}$	$\begin{matrix} \epsilon \\ \epsilon^* \end{matrix}$	$\begin{matrix} \epsilon^* \\ \epsilon \end{matrix}$	$\begin{matrix} 1 \\ 1 \end{matrix}$	$\begin{matrix} \epsilon \\ \epsilon^* \end{matrix}$	$\begin{matrix} \epsilon^* \\ \epsilon \end{matrix} \Big\}$	(T_x, T_y)	(x^2-y^2, xy)
A''	1	1	1	-1	-1	-1	T_z	
E''	$\begin{cases} 1 \\ 1 \end{cases}$	$\begin{matrix} \epsilon \\ \epsilon^* \end{matrix}$	$\begin{matrix} \epsilon^* \\ \epsilon \end{matrix}$	$\begin{matrix} -1 \\ -1 \end{matrix}$	$\begin{matrix} -\epsilon \\ -\epsilon^* \end{matrix}$	$\begin{matrix} -\epsilon^* \\ -\epsilon \end{matrix} \Big\}$	(R_x, R_y)	(xz, yz)

$\mathscr{C}_{4h}$	E	C_4	C_2	C_4^3	i	S_4^3	σ_h	S_4		
A_g	1	1	1	1	1	1	1	1	R_z	$x^2+y^2; z^2$
B_g	1	-1	1	-1	1	-1	1	-1		$x^2-y^2; xy$
E_g	$\begin{cases} 1 \\ 1 \end{cases}$	$\begin{matrix} i \\ -i \end{matrix}$	$\begin{matrix} -1 \\ -1 \end{matrix}$	$\begin{matrix} -i \\ i \end{matrix}$	$\begin{matrix} 1 \\ 1 \end{matrix}$	$\begin{matrix} i \\ -i \end{matrix}$	$\begin{matrix} -1 \\ -1 \end{matrix}$	$\begin{matrix} -i \\ i \end{matrix} \Big\}$	(R_x, R_y)	(xz, yz)
A_u	1	1	1	1	-1	-1	-1	-1	T_z	
B_u	1	-1	1	-1	-1	1	-1	1		
E_u	$\begin{cases} 1 \\ 1 \end{cases}$	$\begin{matrix} i \\ -i \end{matrix}$	$\begin{matrix} -1 \\ -1 \end{matrix}$	$\begin{matrix} -i \\ i \end{matrix}$	$\begin{matrix} -1 \\ -1 \end{matrix}$	$\begin{matrix} -i \\ i \end{matrix}$	$\begin{matrix} 1 \\ 1 \end{matrix}$	$\begin{matrix} i \\ -i \end{matrix} \Big\}$	(T_x, T_y)	

$\mathscr{C}_{5h}$	E	C_5	C_5^2	C_5^3	C_5^4	σ_h	S_5	S_5^7	S_5^3	S_5^9		$\epsilon = \exp(2\pi i/5)$
A'	1	1	1	1	1	1	1	1	1	1	R_z	$x^2+y^2; z^2$
E_1'	$\begin{cases} 1 \\ 1 \end{cases}$	$\begin{matrix} \epsilon \\ \epsilon^* \end{matrix}$	$\begin{matrix} \epsilon^2 \\ \epsilon^{2*} \end{matrix}$	$\begin{matrix} \epsilon^{2*} \\ \epsilon^2 \end{matrix}$	$\begin{matrix} \epsilon^* \\ \epsilon \end{matrix}$	$\begin{matrix} 1 \\ 1 \end{matrix}$	$\begin{matrix} \epsilon \\ \epsilon^* \end{matrix}$	$\begin{matrix} \epsilon^2 \\ \epsilon^{2*} \end{matrix}$	$\begin{matrix} \epsilon^{2*} \\ \epsilon^2 \end{matrix}$	$\begin{matrix} \epsilon^* \\ \epsilon \end{matrix} \Big\}$	(T_z, T_y)	
E_2'	$\begin{cases} 1 \\ 1 \end{cases}$	$\begin{matrix} \epsilon^2 \\ \epsilon^{2*} \end{matrix}$	$\begin{matrix} \epsilon^* \\ \epsilon \end{matrix}$	$\begin{matrix} \epsilon \\ \epsilon^* \end{matrix}$	$\begin{matrix} \epsilon^{2*} \\ \epsilon^2 \end{matrix}$	$\begin{matrix} 1 \\ 1 \end{matrix}$	$\begin{matrix} \epsilon^2 \\ \epsilon^{2*} \end{matrix}$	$\begin{matrix} \epsilon^* \\ \epsilon \end{matrix}$	$\begin{matrix} \epsilon \\ \epsilon^* \end{matrix}$	$\begin{matrix} \epsilon^{2*} \\ \epsilon^2 \end{matrix} \Big\}$		(x^2-y^2, xy)
A''	1	1	1	1	1	-1	-1	-1	-1	-1	T_z	
E_1''	$\begin{cases} 1 \\ 1 \end{cases}$	$\begin{matrix} \epsilon \\ \epsilon^* \end{matrix}$	$\begin{matrix} \epsilon^2 \\ \epsilon^{2*} \end{matrix}$	$\begin{matrix} \epsilon^{2*} \\ \epsilon^2 \end{matrix}$	$\begin{matrix} \epsilon^* \\ \epsilon \end{matrix}$	$\begin{matrix} -1 \\ -1 \end{matrix}$	$\begin{matrix} -\epsilon \\ -\epsilon^* \end{matrix}$	$\begin{matrix} -\epsilon^2 \\ -\epsilon^{2*} \end{matrix}$	$\begin{matrix} -\epsilon^{2*} \\ -\epsilon^2 \end{matrix}$	$\begin{matrix} -\epsilon^* \\ -\epsilon \end{matrix} \Big\}$	(R_x, R_y)	(xz, yz)
E_2''	$\begin{cases} 1 \\ 1 \end{cases}$	$\begin{matrix} \epsilon^2 \\ \epsilon^{2*} \end{matrix}$	$\begin{matrix} \epsilon^* \\ \epsilon \end{matrix}$	$\begin{matrix} \epsilon \\ \epsilon^* \end{matrix}$	$\begin{matrix} \epsilon^{2*} \\ \epsilon^2 \end{matrix}$	$\begin{matrix} -1 \\ -1 \end{matrix}$	$\begin{matrix} -\epsilon^2 \\ -\epsilon^{2*} \end{matrix}$	$\begin{matrix} -\epsilon^* \\ -\epsilon \end{matrix}$	$\begin{matrix} -\epsilon \\ -\epsilon^* \end{matrix}$	$\begin{matrix} -\epsilon^{2*} \\ -\epsilon^2 \end{matrix} \Big\}$		

$\mathscr{C}_{6h}$	E	C_6	C_3	C_2	C_3^2	C_6^5	i	S_3^5	S_6^5	σ_h	S_6	S_3		$\epsilon = \exp(2\pi i/6)$
A_g	1	1	1	1	1	1	1	1	1	1	1	1	R_z	$x^2+y^2; z^2$
B_g	1	-1	1	-1	1	-1	1	-1	1	-1	1	-1		
E_{1g}	$\begin{cases} 1 \\ 1 \end{cases}$	$\begin{matrix} \epsilon \\ \epsilon^* \end{matrix}$	$\begin{matrix} -\epsilon^* \\ -\epsilon \end{matrix}$	$\begin{matrix} -1 \\ -1 \end{matrix}$	$\begin{matrix} -\epsilon \\ -\epsilon^* \end{matrix}$	$\begin{matrix} \epsilon^* \\ \epsilon \end{matrix}$	$\begin{matrix} 1 \\ 1 \end{matrix}$	$\begin{matrix} \epsilon \\ \epsilon^* \end{matrix}$	$\begin{matrix} -\epsilon^* \\ -\epsilon \end{matrix}$	$\begin{matrix} -1 \\ -1 \end{matrix}$	$\begin{matrix} -\epsilon \\ -\epsilon^* \end{matrix}$	$\begin{matrix} \epsilon^* \\ \epsilon \end{matrix} \Big\}$	(R_x, R_y)	(xz, yz)
E_{2g}	$\begin{cases} 1 \\ 1 \end{cases}$	$\begin{matrix} -\epsilon^* \\ -\epsilon \end{matrix}$	$\begin{matrix} -\epsilon \\ -\epsilon^* \end{matrix}$	$\begin{matrix} 1 \\ 1 \end{matrix}$	$\begin{matrix} -\epsilon^* \\ -\epsilon \end{matrix}$	$\begin{matrix} -\epsilon \\ -\epsilon^* \end{matrix}$	$\begin{matrix} 1 \\ 1 \end{matrix}$	$\begin{matrix} -\epsilon^* \\ -\epsilon \end{matrix}$	$\begin{matrix} -\epsilon \\ -\epsilon^* \end{matrix}$	$\begin{matrix} 1 \\ 1 \end{matrix}$	$\begin{matrix} -\epsilon^* \\ -\epsilon \end{matrix}$	$\begin{matrix} -\epsilon \\ -\epsilon^* \end{matrix} \Big\}$		(x^2-y^2, xy)
A_u	1	1	1	1	1	1	-1	-1	-1	-1	-1	-1	T_z	
B_u	1	-1	1	-1	1	-1	-1	1	-1	1	-1	1		
E_{1u}	$\begin{cases} 1 \\ 1 \end{cases}$	$\begin{matrix} \epsilon \\ \epsilon^* \end{matrix}$	$\begin{matrix} -\epsilon^* \\ -\epsilon \end{matrix}$	$\begin{matrix} -1 \\ -1 \end{matrix}$	$\begin{matrix} -\epsilon \\ -\epsilon^* \end{matrix}$	$\begin{matrix} \epsilon^* \\ \epsilon \end{matrix}$	$\begin{matrix} -1 \\ -1 \end{matrix}$	$\begin{matrix} -\epsilon \\ -\epsilon^* \end{matrix}$	$\begin{matrix} \epsilon^* \\ \epsilon \end{matrix}$	$\begin{matrix} 1 \\ 1 \end{matrix}$	$\begin{matrix} \epsilon \\ \epsilon^* \end{matrix}$	$\begin{matrix} -\epsilon^* \\ -\epsilon \end{matrix} \Big\}$	(T_x, T_y)	
E_{2u}	$\begin{cases} 1 \\ 1 \end{cases}$	$\begin{matrix} -\epsilon^* \\ -\epsilon \end{matrix}$	$\begin{matrix} -\epsilon \\ -\epsilon^* \end{matrix}$	$\begin{matrix} 1 \\ 1 \end{matrix}$	$\begin{matrix} -\epsilon^* \\ -\epsilon \end{matrix}$	$\begin{matrix} -\epsilon \\ -\epsilon^* \end{matrix}$	$\begin{matrix} -1 \\ -1 \end{matrix}$	$\begin{matrix} \epsilon^* \\ \epsilon \end{matrix}$	$\begin{matrix} \epsilon \\ \epsilon^* \end{matrix}$	$\begin{matrix} -1 \\ -1 \end{matrix}$	$\begin{matrix} \epsilon \\ \epsilon \end{matrix}$	$\begin{matrix} \epsilon^* \\ \epsilon^* \end{matrix} \Big\}$		

V: Groups $\mathscr{D}_{nh}$ ($n = 2, 3, 4, 5, 6$)

$\mathscr{D}_{2h} = \mathscr{V}_h$	E	$C_2(z)$	$C_2(y)$	$C_2(x)$	i	$\sigma(xy)$	$\sigma(xz)$	$\sigma(yz)$		
A_g	1	1	1	1	1	1	1	1		$x^2; y^2; z^2$
B_{1g}	1	1	-1	-1	1	1	-1	-1	R_z	xy
B_{2g}	1	-1	1	-1	1	-1	1	-1	R_y	xz
B_{3g}	1	-1	-1	1	1	-1	-1	1	R_x	yz
A_u	1	1	1	1	-1	-1	-1	-1		
B_{1u}	1	1	-1	-1	-1	-1	1	1	T_z	
B_{2u}	1	-1	1	-1	-1	1	-1	1	T_y	
B_{3u}	1	-1	-1	1	-1	1	1	-1	T_x	

$\mathscr{D}_{3h}$	E	$2C_3$	$3C_2'$	σ_h	$2S_3$	$3\sigma_v$		
A_1'	1	1	1	1	1	1		$x^2 + y^2; z^2$
A_2'	1	1	-1	1	1	-1	R_z	
E'	2	-1	0	2	-1	0	(T_x, T_y)	$(x^2 - y^2, xy)$
A_1''	1	1	1	-1	-1	-1		
A_2''	1	1	-1	-1	-1	1	T_z	
E''	2	-1	0	-2	1	0	(R_x, R_y)	(xz, yz)

$\mathscr{D}_{4h}$	E	$2C_4$	C_2	$2C_2'$	$2C_2''$	i	$2S_4$	σ_h	$2\sigma_v$	$2\sigma_d$		
A_{1g}	1	1	1	1	1	1	1	1	1	1		$x^2 + y^2; z^2$
A_{2g}	1	1	1	-1	-1	1	1	1	-1	-1	R_z	
B_{1g}	1	-1	1	1	-1	1	-1	1	1	-1		$x^2 - y^2$
B_{2g}	1	-1	1	-1	1	1	-1	1	-1	1		xy
E_g	2	0	-2	0	0	2	0	-2	0	0	(R_x, R_y)	(xz, yz)
A_{1u}	1	1	1	1	1	-1	-1	-1	-1	-1		
A_{2u}	1	1	1	-1	-1	-1	-1	-1	1	1	T_z	
B_{1u}	1	-1	1	1	-1	-1	1	-1	-1	1		
B_{2u}	1	-1	1	-1	1	-1	1	-1	1	-1		
E_u	2	0	-2	0	0	-2	0	2	0	0	(T_x, T_y)	

$\mathscr{D}_{5h}$	E	$2C_5$	$2C_5{}^2$	$5C_2'$	σ_h	$2S_5$	$2S_5{}^3$	$5\sigma_v$		$\alpha = 72°$
A_1'	1	1	1	1	1	1	1	1		$x^2 + y^2; z^2$
A_2'	1	1	1	-1	1	1	1	-1	R_z	
E_1'	2	$2\cos\alpha$	$2\cos 2\alpha$	0	2	$2\cos\alpha$	$2\cos 2\alpha$	0	(T_x, T_y)	
E_2'	2	$2\cos 2\alpha$	$2\cos\alpha$	0	2	$2\cos 2\alpha$	$2\cos\alpha$	0		$(x^2 - y^2, xy)$
A_1''	1	1	1	1	-1	-1	-1	-1		
A_2''	1	1	1	-1	-1	-1	-1	1	T_z	
E_1''	2	$2\cos\alpha$	$2\cos 2\alpha$	0	-2	$-2\cos\alpha$	$-2\cos 2\alpha$	0	(R_x, R_y)	(xz, yz)
E_2''	2	$2\cos 2\alpha$	$2\cos\alpha$	0	-2	$-2\cos 2\alpha$	$-2\cos\alpha$	0		

$\mathscr{D}_{6h}$	E	$2C_6$	$2C_3$	C_2	$3C_2'$	$3C_2''$	i	$2S_3$	$2S_6$	σ_h	$3\sigma_d$	$3\sigma_v$		
A_{1g}	1	1	1	1	1	1	1	1	1	1	1	1		x^2+y^2; z^2
A_{2g}	1	1	1	1	-1	-1	1	1	1	1	-1	-1	R_z	
B_{1g}	1	-1	1	-1	1	-1	1	-1	1	-1	1	-1		
B_{2g}	1	-1	1	-1	-1	1	1	-1	1	-1	-1	1		
E_{1g}	2	1	-1	-2	0	0	2	1	-1	-2	0	0	(R_x, R_y)	(xz, yz)
E_{2g}	2	-1	-1	2	0	0	2	-1	-1	2	0	0		(x^2-y^2, xy)
A_{1u}	1	1	1	1	1	1	-1	-1	-1	-1	-1	-1		
A_{2u}	1	1	1	1	-1	-1	-1	-1	-1	-1	1	1	T_z	
B_{1u}	1	-1	1	-1	1	-1	-1	1	-1	1	-1	1		
B_{2u}	1	-1	1	-1	-1	1	-1	1	-1	1	1	-1		
E_{1u}	2	1	-1	-2	0	0	-2	-1	1	2	0	0	(T_x, T_y)	
E_{2u}	2	-1	-1	2	0	0	-2	1	1	-2	0	0		

VI: Groups $\mathscr{D}_{nd}$ $(n=2, 3, 4, 5, 6)$

$\mathscr{D}_{2d}=\mathscr{V}_d$	E	$2S_4$	C_2	$2C_2'$	$2\sigma_d$		
A_1	1	1	1	1	1		x^2+y^2; z^2
A_2	1	1	1	-1	-1	R_z	
B_1	1	-1	1	1	-1		x^2-y^2
B_2	1	-1	1	-1	1	T_z	xy
E	2	0	-2	0	0	(T_x, T_y); (R_x, R_y)	(xz, yz)

$\mathscr{D}_{3d}$	E	$2C_3$	$3C_2'$	i	$2S_6$	$3\sigma_d$		
A_{1g}	1	1	1	1	1	1		x^2+y^2; z^2
A_{2g}	1	1	-1	1	1	-1	R_z	
E_g	2	-1	0	2	-1	0	(R_x, R_y)	(x^2-y^2, xy); (xz, yz)
A_{1u}	1	1	1	-1	-1	-1		
A_{2u}	1	1	-1	-1	-1	1	T_z	
E_u	2	-1	0	-2	1	0	(T_x, T_y)	

$\mathscr{D}_{4d}$	E	$2S_8$	$2C_4$	$2S_8^3$	C_2	$4C_2'$	$4\sigma_d$		
A_1	1	1	1	1	1	1	1		x^2+y^2; z^2
A_2	1	1	1	1	1	-1	-1	R_z	
B_1	1	-1	1	-1	1	1	-1		
B_2	1	-1	1	-1	1	-1	1	T_z	
E_1	2	$\sqrt{2}$	0	$-\sqrt{2}$	-2	0	0	(T_x, T_y)	
E_2	2	0	-2	0	2	0	0		(x^2-y^2, xy)
E_3	2	$-\sqrt{2}$	0	$\sqrt{2}$	-2	0	0	(R_x, R_y)	(xz, yz)

$\mathscr{D}_{5d}$	E	$2C_5$	$2C_5^2$	$5C_2'$	i	$2S_{10}^3$	$2S_{10}$	$5\sigma_d$		$\alpha=72°$
A_{1g}	1	1	1	1	1	1	1	1		x^2+y^2; z^2
A_{2g}	1	1	1	-1	1	1	1	-1	R_z	
E_{1g}	2	$2\cos\alpha$	$2\cos2\alpha$	0	2	$2\cos\alpha$	$2\cos2\alpha$	0	(R_x, R_y)	(xz, yz)
E_{2g}	2	$2\cos2\alpha$	$2\cos\alpha$	0	2	$2\cos2\alpha$	$2\cos\alpha$	0		(x^2-y^2, xy)
A_{1u}	1	1	1	1	-1	-1	-1	-1		
A_{2u}	1	1	1	-1	-1	-1	-1	1	T_z	
E_{1u}	2	$2\cos\alpha$	$2\cos2\alpha$	0	-2	$-2\cos\alpha$	$-2\cos2\alpha$	0	(T_x, T_y)	
E_{2u}	2	$2\cos2\alpha$	$2\cos\alpha$	0	-2	$-2\cos2\alpha$	$-2\cos\alpha$	0		

$\mathscr{D}_{6d}$	E	$2S_{12}$	$2C_6$	$2S_4$	$2C_3$	$2S_{12}^5$	C_2	$6C_2'$	$6\sigma_d$		
A_1	1	1	1	1	1	1	1	1	1		x^2+y^2; z^2
A_2	1	1	1	1	1	1	1	-1	-1	R_z	
B_1	1	-1	1	-1	1	-1	1	1	-1		
B_2	1	-1	1	-1	1	-1	1	-1	1	T_z	
E_1	2	$\sqrt{3}$	1	0	-1	$-\sqrt{3}$	-2	0	0	(T_x, T_y)	
E_2	2	1	-1	-2	-1	1	2	0	0		(x^2-y^2, xy)
E_3	2	0	-2	0	2	0	-2	0	0		
E_4	2	-1	-1	2	-1	-1	2	0	0		
E_5	2	$-\sqrt{3}$	1	0	-1	$\sqrt{3}$	-2	0	0	$(R_x, R)_y$	(xz, yz)

VII: Groups $\mathscr{S}_n$ ($n=4, 6, 8$)

$\mathscr{S}_4$	E	S_4	C_2	$S_4{}^3$		
A	1	1	1	1	R_z	x^2+y^2; z^2
B	1	-1	1	-1	T_z	x^2-y^2; xy
E	$\begin{Bmatrix}1 \\ 1\end{Bmatrix}$	$\begin{matrix}i \\ -i\end{matrix}$	$\begin{matrix}-1 \\ -1\end{matrix}$	$\begin{matrix}-i \\ i\end{matrix}$	(T_x, T_y); (R_x, R_y)	(xz, yz)

$\mathscr{S}_6$	E	C_3	$C_3{}^2$	i	$S_6{}^5$	S_6		$\epsilon = \exp(2\pi i/3)$
A_g	1	1	1	1	1	1	R_z	x^2+y^2; z^2
E_g	$\begin{Bmatrix}1 \\ 1\end{Bmatrix}$	$\begin{matrix}\epsilon \\ \epsilon^*\end{matrix}$	$\begin{matrix}\epsilon^* \\ \epsilon\end{matrix}$	$\begin{matrix}1 \\ 1\end{matrix}$	$\begin{matrix}\epsilon \\ \epsilon^*\end{matrix}$	$\begin{matrix}\epsilon^* \\ \epsilon\end{matrix}$	(R_x, R_y)	(x^2-y^2, xy); (xz, yz)
A_u	1	1	1	-1	-1	-1	T_z	
E_u	$\begin{Bmatrix}1 \\ 1\end{Bmatrix}$	$\begin{matrix}\epsilon \\ \epsilon^*\end{matrix}$	$\begin{matrix}\epsilon^* \\ \epsilon\end{matrix}$	$\begin{matrix}-1 \\ -1\end{matrix}$	$\begin{matrix}-\epsilon \\ -\epsilon^*\end{matrix}$	$\begin{matrix}-\epsilon^* \\ -\epsilon\end{matrix}$	(T_x, T_y)	

$\mathscr{S}_8$	E	S_8	C_4	$S_8{}^3$	C_2	$S_8{}^5$	$C_4{}^3$	$S_8{}^7$		$\epsilon = \exp(2\pi i/8)$
A	1	1	1	1	1	1	1	1	R_z	x^2+y^2; z^2
B	1	-1	1	-1	1	-1	1	-1	T_z	
E_1	$\begin{Bmatrix}1 \\ 1\end{Bmatrix}$	$\begin{matrix}\epsilon \\ \epsilon^*\end{matrix}$	$\begin{matrix}i \\ -i\end{matrix}$	$\begin{matrix}-\epsilon^* \\ -\epsilon\end{matrix}$	$\begin{matrix}-1 \\ -1\end{matrix}$	$\begin{matrix}-\epsilon \\ -\epsilon^*\end{matrix}$	$\begin{matrix}-i \\ i\end{matrix}$	$\begin{matrix}\epsilon^* \\ \epsilon\end{matrix}$	(T_x, T_y)	
E_2	$\begin{Bmatrix}1 \\ 1\end{Bmatrix}$	$\begin{matrix}i \\ -i\end{matrix}$	$\begin{matrix}-1 \\ -1\end{matrix}$	$\begin{matrix}-i \\ i\end{matrix}$	$\begin{matrix}1 \\ 1\end{matrix}$	$\begin{matrix}i \\ -i\end{matrix}$	$\begin{matrix}-1 \\ -1\end{matrix}$	$\begin{matrix}-i \\ i\end{matrix}$		(x^2-y^2, xy)
E_3	$\begin{Bmatrix}1 \\ 1\end{Bmatrix}$	$\begin{matrix}-\epsilon^* \\ -\epsilon\end{matrix}$	$\begin{matrix}-i \\ i\end{matrix}$	$\begin{matrix}\epsilon \\ \epsilon^*\end{matrix}$	$\begin{matrix}-1 \\ -1\end{matrix}$	$\begin{matrix}\epsilon^* \\ \epsilon\end{matrix}$	$\begin{matrix}i \\ -i\end{matrix}$	$\begin{matrix}-\epsilon \\ -\epsilon^*\end{matrix}$	(R_x, R_y)	(xz, yz)

VIII: Groups $\mathscr{T}_d$, $\mathscr{O}$ and $\mathscr{O}_h$

$\mathscr{T}_d$	E	$8C_3$	$3C_2$	$6S_4$	$6\sigma_d$		
A_1	1	1	1	1	1		$x^2+y^2+z^2$
A_2	1	1	1	-1	-1		
E	2	-1	2	0	0		$(2z^2-x^2-y^2, x^2-y^2)$
T_1, F_1	3	0	-1	1	-1	(R_x, R_y, R_z)	
T_2, F_2	3	0	-1	-1	1	(T_x, T_y, T_z)	(xy, xz, yz)

$\mathscr{O}$	E	$8C_3$	$3C_2$	$6C_4$	$6C_2'$		
A_1	1	1	1	1	1		$x^2+y^2+z^2$
A_2	1	1	1	-1	-1		
E	2	-1	2	0	0		$(2z^2-x^2-y^2, x^2-y^2)$
T_1, F_1	3	0	-1	1	-1	(R_x, R_y, R_z); (T_x, T_y, T_z)	
T_2, F_2	3	0	-1	-1	1		(xy, xz, yz)

$\mathscr{O}_h$	E	$8C_3$	$3C_2$	$6C_4$	$6C_2'$	i	$8S_6$	$3\sigma_h$	$6S_4$	$6\sigma_d$		
A_{1g}	1	1	1	1	1	1	1	1	1	1		$x^2+y^2+z^2$
A_{2g}	1	1	1	-1	-1	1	1	1	-1	-1		
E_g	2	-1	2	0	0	2	-1	2	0	0		$(2z^2-x^2-y^2, x^2-y^2)$
T_{1g}, F_{1g}	3	0	-1	1	-1	3	0	-1	1	-1	(R_x, R_y, R_z)	
T_{2g}, F_{2g}	3	0	-1	-1	1	3	0	-1	-1	1		(xy, xz, yz)
A_{1u}	1	1	1	1	1	-1	-1	-1	-1	-1		
A_{2u}	1	1	1	-1	-1	-1	-1	-1	1	1		
E_u	2	-1	2	0	0	-2	1	-2	0	0		
T_{1u}, F_{1u}	3	0	-1	1	-1	-3	0	1	-1	1	(T_x, T_y, T_z)	
T_{2u}, F_{2u}	3	0	-1	-1	1	-3	0	1	1	-1		

IX: Groups $\mathscr{C}_{\infty v}$ and $\mathscr{D}_{\infty h}$

$\mathscr{C}_{\infty v}$	E	$2C(\phi)$	$\ldots$	$\infty\sigma_v$		
$A_1 = \Sigma^+$	1	1	$\ldots$	1	T_z	x^2+y^2; z^2
$A_2 = \Sigma^-$	1	1	$\ldots$	-1	R_z	
$E_1 = \Pi$	2	$2\cos\phi$	$\ldots$	0	(T_x, T_y); (R_x, R_y)	(xz, yz)
$E_2 = \Delta$	2	$2\cos 2\phi$	$\ldots$	0		(x^2-y^2, xy)
$E_3 = \Phi$	2	$2\cos 3\phi$	$\ldots$	0		
$\ldots$	$\ldots$	$\ldots$	$\ldots$	$\ldots$		

$\mathscr{D}_{\infty h}$	E	$2C(\phi)$	$\ldots$	$\infty\sigma_v$	i	$2S(\phi)$	$\ldots$	$\infty C_2'$		
Σ_g^+	1	1	$\ldots$	1	1	1	$\ldots$	1		x^2+y^2; z^2
Σ_g^-	1	1	$\ldots$	-1	1	1	$\ldots$	-1	R_z	
Π_g	2	$2\cos\phi$	$\ldots$	0	2	$-2\cos\phi$	$\ldots$	0	(R_x, R_y)	(xz, yz)
Δ_g	2	$2\cos 2\phi$	$\ldots$	0	2	$2\cos 2\phi$	$\ldots$	0		(x^2-y^2, xy)
$\ldots$	$\ldots$	$\ldots$	$\ldots$	$\ldots$	$\ldots$	$\ldots$	$\ldots$	$\ldots$		
Σ_u^+	1	1	$\ldots$	1	-1	-1	$\ldots$	-1	T_z	
Σ_u^-	1	1	$\ldots$	-1	-1	-1	$\ldots$	1		
Π_u	2	$2\cos\phi$	$\ldots$	0	-2	$2\cos\phi$	$\ldots$	0	(T_x, T_y)	
Δ_u	2	$2\cos 2\phi$	$\ldots$	0	-2	$-2\cos 2\phi$	$\ldots$	0		
$\ldots$	$\ldots$	$\ldots$	$\ldots$	$\ldots$	$\ldots$	$\ldots$	$\ldots$	$\ldots$		

Appendix I

DIRECT PRODUCTS

The definition of the direct product of two representations and the way in which its characters may be found is discussed in Section 7.6. The following 'multiplication rules' apply to the point groups whose character tables are given in Appendix H.

1. *Groups of the form $\mathscr{G} \times i$ or $\mathscr{G} \times \sigma_h$.*
   The g, u or $'$, $''$ additions to the IR symbols in these groups satisfy

$$g \times g = u \times u = g, \quad g \times u = u, \quad ' \times ' = '' \times '' = ', \quad ' \times '' = ''.$$

2. *Products of the form $A \times A$, $B \times B$, $A \times B$.*
   For all groups:

   Letter symbols: $A \times A = A$, $B \times B = A$, $A \times B = B$.

   Subscripts: $1 \times 1 = 1$, $2 \times 2 = 1$, $1 \times 2 = 2$

except for the B representations of $\mathscr{D}_2$ and $\mathscr{D}_{2h}$ where $B \times B = B$ and $1 \times 2 = 3$, $2 \times 3 = 1$, $3 \times 1 = 2$.

3. *Products of the form $A \times E$, $B \times E$.*

   (*a*) For all groups: $A \times E_k = E_k$ irrespective of the suffix on A.

   (*b*) For all groups except $\mathscr{D}_{6d}$, $\mathscr{D}_{4d}$, $\mathscr{S}_8$:

$$B \times E_1 = E_2, \qquad B \times E_2 = E_1$$

irrespective of the suffix on B. (If the group has only one E representation put $E_1 = E_2 = E$.)

   (*c*) For $\mathscr{D}_{6d}$:

$$B \times E_1 = E_5, \quad B \times E_2 = E_4, \quad B \times E_3 = E_3, \quad B \times E_4 = E_2, \quad B \times E_5 = E_1$$

irrespective of the suffix on B.

   (*d*) For $\mathscr{D}_{4d}$, $\mathscr{S}_8$:

$$B \times E_1 = E_3, \quad B \times E_2 = E_2, \quad B \times E_3 = E_1$$

irrespective of the suffix on B.

4. *Products of the form $E \times E$.*

(For groups which have A, B or E symbols without suffixes put $A_1 = A_2 = A$, etc in the equations below.)

    (*a*) For $\mathcal{O}_h$, $\mathcal{O}$, $\mathcal{T}_d$, $\mathcal{D}_{6h}$, $\mathcal{D}_6$, $\mathcal{C}_{6v}$, $\mathcal{C}_{6h}$, $\mathcal{C}_6$, $\mathcal{S}_6$, $\mathcal{D}_{3d}$, $\mathcal{D}_{3h}$, $\mathcal{D}_3$, $\mathcal{C}_{3v}$, $\mathcal{C}_{3h}$, $\mathcal{C}_3$:

$$E_1 \times E_1 = E_2 \times E_2 = A_1 + A_2 + E_2,$$

$$E_1 \times E_2 = B_1 + B_2 + E_1.$$

    (*b*) For $\mathcal{D}_{4h}$, $\mathcal{D}_4$, $\mathcal{C}_{4v}$, $\mathcal{C}_{4h}$, $\mathcal{C}_4$, $\mathcal{S}_4$, $\mathcal{D}_{2d}$:

$$E \times E = A_1 + A_2 + B_1 + B_2.$$

    (*c*) For $\mathcal{D}_{6d}$:

$$E_1 \times E_1 = E_5 \times E_5 = A_1 + A_2 + E_2, \qquad E_2 \times E_2 = E_4 \times E_4 = A_1 + A_2 + E_4,$$

$$E_3 \times E_3 = A_1 + A_2 + B_1 + B_2,$$

$$E_1 \times E_2 = E_4 \times E_5 = E_1 + E_3, \qquad E_1 \times E_3 = E_3 \times E_5 = E_2 + E_4,$$

$$E_1 \times E_4 = E_2 \times E_5 = E_3 + E_5, \qquad E_2 \times E_3 = E_3 \times E_4 = E_1 + E_5,$$

$$E_1 \times E_5 = B_1 + B_2 + E_4, \qquad E_2 \times E_4 = B_1 + B_2 + E_2.$$

    (*d*) For $\mathcal{D}_{5d}$, $\mathcal{D}_{5h}$, $\mathcal{D}_5$, $\mathcal{C}_{5v}$, $\mathcal{C}_{5h}$, $\mathcal{C}_5$:

$$E_1 \times E_1 = A_1 + A_2 + E_2, \quad E_2 \times E_2 = A_1 + A_2 + E_1, \quad E_1 \times E_2 = E_1 + E_2.$$

    (*e*) For $\mathcal{D}_{4d}$, $\mathcal{S}_8$:

$$E_1 \times E_1 = E_3 \times E_3 = A_1 + A_2 + E_2, \quad E_2 \times E_2 = A_1 + A_2 + B_1 + B_2,$$

$$E_1 \times E_2 = E_2 \times E_3 = E_1 + E_3, \qquad E_1 \times E_3 = B_1 + B_2 + E_2.$$

5. *Products involving the T (or F) representations of $\mathcal{O}_h$, $\mathcal{O}$ and $\mathcal{T}_d$.*

$$A_1 \times T_1 = T_1, \quad A_1 \times T_2 = T_2, \quad A_2 \times T_1 = T_2, \quad A_2 \times T_2 = T_1,$$

$$E \times T_1 = E \times T_2 = T_1 + T_2,$$

$$T_1 \times T_1 = T_2 \times T_2 = A_1 + E + T_1 + T_2,$$

$$T_1 \times T_2 = A_2 + E + T_1 + T_2.$$

BIBLIOGRAPHY

Some of the following books and papers are referred to in the text but many are inserted as a guide to further reading. The choice of books for this purpose is, inevitably, a personal one and this bibliography makes no claim to completeness.

Quantum Mechanics

[1] PAULING, L. C. and WILSON, E. B. *Introduction to Quantum Mechanics*, McGraw-Hill, New York (1935).
[2] EYRING, H., WALTER, J. and KIMBALL, G. E. *Quantum Chemistry*, Wiley, New York (1944).

There are many other books on quantum mechanics which give derivations of the results quoted in the text; we have made specific reference to [1] for this purpose. Excellent introductions to the ideas of quantum mechanics as they are applied in chemistry will be found in the first few chapters of [17] and [18].

Chapter 2

[3] LONGUET–HIGGINS, H. C. 'The symmetry groups of non-rigid molecules', *Molecular Phys.* **6**, 445 (1963).
[4] BUERGER, M. J. *Elementary Crystallography: an Introduction to the Fundamental Geometrical Features of Crystals*, Wiley, New York (1956).
[5] BUNN, C. W. *Chemical Crystallography*, Clarendon Press, Oxford (1946).

Chapters 3–7

[6] HAMERMESH, M. *Group Theory and its Application to Physical Problems*, Addison–Wesley, Reading, Mass. (1962).
[7] HEINE, V. *Group Theory in Quantum Mechanics; an Introduction to its Present Usage*, Pergamon Press, Oxford (1964).
[8] McWEENEY, R. *Symmetry: an Introduction to Group Theory and its Applications*, Pergamon Press, Oxford (1964).
[9] WIGNER, E. P. *Group Theory and its Applications to the Quantum Mechanics of Atomic Spectra*, Academic Press, New York (1959).

[10] BETHE, H. A. *Ann. Phys.* **3**, 133 (1929). English translation: Consultants Bureau, New York (1958).

[11] MULLIKEN, R. S. *Phys. Rev.* **43**, 279 (1933).

Readers wishing to go more deeply into group theory should consult [6]–[9]. The papers by Bethe [10] and Mulliken [11] are of great historical importance and are well worth reading for the insight they give into the connections between quantum mechanics and group theory.

Chapter 8

[12] HERZBERG, G. *Infrared and Raman Spectra of Polyatomic Molecules*, Van Nostrand, New York (1946).

[13] MATOSSI, F. *Gruppentheorie der Eigenschwingungen von Punktsystemen*, Springer, Berlin (1961).

[14] ROSENTHAL, J. E. and MURPHY, G. M. 'Group theory and the vibrations of polyatomic molecules', *Rev. Mod. Phys.* **8**, 317 (1936).

[15] WILSON, E. B., DECIUS, J. C. and CROSS, P. C. *Molecular Vibrations: the Theory of Infrared and Raman Vibrational Spectra*, McGraw-Hill, New York (1955).

[16] WIGNER, E. P. *Göttinger Nachr., Math.-Phys. Klasse*, p. 133 (1930).

The original application of group theory to molecular vibrations was made by Wigner [16]. The book by Herzberg [12] is a magisterial survey of the subject which does not, however, make explicit use of group theory. The quantitative use of group theory in the study of molecular vibrations is dealt with in [13], [14] and [15].

Chapters 9 and 10

[17] CARTMELL, E. and FOWLES, G. W. A. *Valency and Molecular Structure*, 2nd Edn., Butterworths, London (1961).

[18] COULSON, C. A. *Valence*, 2nd Edn., Clarendon Press, Oxford (1961).

[19] COTTON, F. A. *Chemical Applications of Group Theory*, Wiley-Interscience, New York (1963).

[20] ROBERTS, J. D. *Notes on Molecular Orbital Calculations*, Benjamin, New York (1961).

[21] SREITWIESER, A. *Molecular Orbital Theory for Organic Chemists*, Wiley, New York (1961).

Good introductions to the ideas underlying the description of the electronic structure of molecules are given in [17] and [18], while [19] contains many applications of group theory to this problem. Molecular orbital calculations for organic molecules are described in [20] and [21].

[22] VAN VLECK, J. H. *J. Chem. Phys.* **3**, 803 and 807 (1935).

[23] JORGENSEN, C. K. *Orbitals in Atoms and Molecules*, Academic Press, New York (1962).

[24] ORGEL, L. E. *An Introduction to Transition-metal Chemistry: Ligand-field Theory*, Methuen, London (1960).

[25] BALLHAUSEN, C. J. *Introduction to Ligand-field Theory*, McGraw-Hill, New York (1962).

[26] GRIFFITH, J. S. *The Theory of Transition-metal Ions*, Cambridge University Press (1961).

Modern ligand-field theory stems from the papers by Van Vleck [22] which contain the original application of group theory to the problem of transition-metal complexes. Ligand-field theory and its relation to molecular orbitals are described qualitatively in [23] and [24]; detailed quantitative methods of calculation which make full use of group theory are discussed in [25] and [26].

[27] HERZBERG, G. *Electronic Spectra and Electronic Structure of Polyatomic Molecules*, Van Nostrand, Princeton, N. J. (1967)

[28] ALBASINY, E. L. and COOPER, J. R. A. *Molecular Phys.* **4**, 353 (1961).

This paper is referred to in the text as an example of a detailed self-consistent field molecular orbital calculation.

INDEX